ORGANOPHOSPHORUS MONOMERS AND POLYMERS

by

Ye. L. GEFTER

Institute of Element-Organic Compounds,
Academy of Sciences of the U. S. S. R.

Translated from the Russian

by

J. BURDON, Ph. D.

Authorised Edition

PERGAMON PRESS

THE MACMILLAN COMPANY
NEW YORK

PERGAMON PRESS INC.
122 East 55th Street, New York 22, N. Y.
1404 New York Avenue N.W., Washington 5, D.C.

PERGAMON PRESS LTD.
Headington Hill Hall, Oxford
4 and 5 Fitzroy Square, London W. 1

PERGAMON PRESS S. A. R. L.
24 Rue des Écoles, Paris Vᵉ

PERGAMON PRESS G. m. b. H.
Kaiserstrasse 75, Frankfurt am Main

PRINTED IN HUNGARY
by the Printing House of the Hungarian Academy of Sciences

CONTENTS

v

SECTION 2

HIGH MOLECULAR WEIGHT ORGANOPHOSPHORUS COMPOUNDS

PREFACE

In the last ten years the chemistry of high molecular weight compounds has stood out as one of the most important branches of organic chemistry. These compounds are of great theoretical interest and have an important practical significance.

Various types of rubbers, plastics, artificial glass and synthetic fibres have found wide application in industry and everyday life.

Everyday demands are being made of industry for new synthetic materials with improved mechanical strength, chemical resistance, thermal stability, etc. Already, many of these requirements cannot be met by compounds whose molecules consist only of carbon, hydrogen and oxygen, and it is hence necessary to produce polymers from monomers of more complex structure. Therefore, alongside the development of methods of synthesis and manipulation of purely organic high molecular weight compounds — made from unsaturated hydrocarbons, unsaturated ethers and esters, polyesters etc. — chemical science and industry have also turned to substances containing nitrogen, the halogens, silicon, phosphorus, titanium, boron and other elements. Polyamides, polyvinyl chloride, fluorine-containing plastics, polysiloxanes, etc., have found particularly wide application. Rapid growth of the branches of chemistry concerned with such high molecular weight compounds is urgently required so that the multiplicity of experimental results and theoretical investigations can be generalized.

The solution of these problems is essential today, especially in view of the statement of the May meeting (1958) of the Central Committee of the Communist Party of the U.S.S.R. and of the twenty-first meeting of the Communist Party of the U.S.S.R. about the necessity for the widespread development of chemical science and industry based on high molecular weight compounds.

The general methods of synthesizing and manipulating purely organic nitrogen- and silicon-containing resins have been described in detail in monographs by Korshak, Ellis, Losev and Petrov, Shorygin, Andrianov and Sobolevski, Barg and other authors; however, so far there have been no similar books on other organo-element high molecular weight compounds.

An important place among such substances is occupied by phosphorus-containing high molecular weight compounds, the chemistry of which has developed rapidly in recent years. It has been shown that many phosphorus-containing resins possess a range of useful properties (high temperature stability, non-inflammability, sometimes even non-combustibility, inertness to many chemical reagents, etc.); it is hardly surprising, therefore, that these

1

compounds have been extensively investigated. In the last few years a great deal of experimental material on the synthesis of high molecular weight organophosphorus compounds has accumulated. Studies of the properties of these polymers have shown the basic ways in which they can be used in various branches of industry and technology. The increased interest in such compounds has led to a number of reports on them in conferences on high molecular weight compounds in England (1955), East Germany (1956), the U.S.S.R. (1957), and in other countries.

The books by Pletz [1] and Kosolopoff [2] (up till now there have been no other books on organosphosphorus compounds) are mainly concerned with the formation of low molecular weight compounds.

This book is the first attempt at a generalization and systemization of existent knowledge of the methods of synthesis and the basic properties of monomers and polymers of organophosphorus compounds, and also of their fields of application.

This book contains valuable reference material, collated in tables (physical constants of the monomers, properties of the polymers and copolymers, etc.). The literature used by the author has covered journals, patents and books up to 1958, and in some cases more recent results are included.

The book is intended for scientists, research workers, engineers and technologists working on the preparation, manipulation and investigation of monomers and high molecular weight compounds, and also for students studying related branches of chemistry. Because of the newness and occasional inconsistency of the literature results, this monograph may well contain an insufficiently critical approach to some questions, as well as other faults. Any comments will be gratefully received by the author.

The author thanks Academician M. I. Kabachnik and corresponding member of the Academy of Science of the U.S.S.R. V.V. Korshak for the valuable advice and information given to him during the preparation of this book.

YE. GEFTER

INTRODUCTION

THE nomenclature of phosphorus-containing compounds, and in particular of the acids of phosphorus and their derivatives, is very complex. Many compounds have two, and sometimes even more, names. For example: $C_2H_5PCl_2$ with $\|$ O below

can be called the "di-acid chloride of ethylphosphonic acid", the "acid chloride of ethylphosphonic acid", or "ethylphosphonic dichloride". For the convenience of readers we have listed the structures of the main classes of organophosphorus compounds with their names (see pp. 4–6), and below we describe the rules for the use of the tables.

In this book, the monomers and polymers are tabulated according to the particular class of phosphorus-containing compounds to which they belong: acids of phosphorus, their derivatives, phosphines, polymers and co-polymers of unsaturated esters of acids of phosphorus, etc.

Groups of monofunctional unsaturated phosphorus-containing compounds (acids, acid chlorides, amides, etc.) are listed in the order of: *(a)* the distance of the multiple bonds from the phosphorus atom, and *(b)* the number of multiple bonds.

Within each group, the unsaturated substances are listed from simple to complex according to the rules laid down in *The Chemist's Handbook* [3].

Phosphorus-containing compounds having sulphur in their structures are listed after their oxygen analogues, except in certain cases where the thio-compounds are allotted separate tables.

With these rules and the List of Tables (see p. 288) it is easy to find any monomer or polymer which is included in the various tables. For example, suppose we wish to know the physical constants of the 2,2-dichlorovinyl ester of diethyl phosphoric acid (2,2-dichlorovinyl diethyl phosphate). It is clear from the list of structures that the formula of this compound is that of an ester of an inorganic acid of phosphorus, namely phosphoric acid:

$$C_2H_5O \diagdown \atop C_2H_5O \diagup \underset{\underset{O}{\|}}{P}-OCH=CCl_2.$$

In the List of Tables we find successively:

(1) esters of acids of phosphorus and unsaturated alcohols;

(2) unsaturated esters – acid-chlorides and esters of inorganic acids of phosphorus;

Structures of Certain Classes of Phosphorus-containing Compounds

	Acids	Acid chlorides and ester-acid-chlorides	Amides, amido-acid chlorides and amidoesters	Esters
Inorganic Acids of Phosphorus and their Derivatives	$H-P\underset{=O}{\overset{OH}{\diagdown}}OH$ phosphorous acid	$P\overset{Cl}{\underset{Cl}{\diagdown}}Cl$ phosphorus trichloride	$(RNH)_3P$ N,N',N''-trialkyl-(triaryl)phosphorous triamide	$P\overset{OR}{\underset{OR''}{\diagdown}}OR'$ trialkyl(dialkylaryl, alkyl-diaryl, triaryl) phosphite
		$ROP\overset{Cl}{\underset{Cl}{\diagdown}}$ di-acid chloride of alkyl-(aryl) phosphorous acid; al-kyl (aryl) phosphorodichlo-ridite	$R\overset{\diagup}{\underset{R'}{\diagdown}}NPCl_2$ di-acid chloride of dialkyl-(alkylaryl, diaryl)phosphor-amidous acid; dialkyl(alkyl-aryl, diaryl)phosphoramid-ous dichloride	
	$H-P\underset{=O}{\overset{OR'}{\diagdown}}OR$ dialkyl phosphorous acid (see also the heading "Esters")	$RO\overset{\diagup}{\underset{R'O}{\diagdown}}P-Cl$ acid chloride of dialkyl-(alkylaryl, diaryl)phosphor-ous acid; dialkyl(alkylaryl, diaryl) phosphorochloridite	$\left(R\overset{\diagup}{\underset{R'}{\diagdown}}N\right)_2PCl$ acid chloride of tetra-alkyl-(dialkyldiaryl, tetra-aryl)-phosphorodiamidous acid; tetra-alkyl (dialkyldiaryl, tetra-aryl)phosphorodiami-dous chloride	$HP\overset{OR}{\underset{=O}{\diagdown}}OR'$ dialkyl(alkylaryl, diaryl) phosphorous acid; dialkyl-(alkylaryl, diaryl) hydro-gen phosphite (see also the heading "Acids")

$$O = P \begin{cases} OR \\ OR' \\ OR'' \end{cases}$$

trialkyl(dialkylaryl, alkyldiaryl, triaryl)phosphate

$$O = P \begin{cases} NHR \\ NHR' \\ NHR'' \end{cases}$$

N,N',N''-trialkyl(dialkylaryl, alkyldiaryl, triaryl)phosphoric triamide

$$P \begin{cases} Cl \\ Cl \\ Cl \end{cases} = O$$

phosphoryl chloride

$$(HO)_2P — OR, \quad = O$$

Alkyl(aryl)phosphoric acid; alkyl(aryl)dihydrogen phosphate

$$RO — P \begin{cases} NHR' \\ NHR'' \end{cases}, \quad = O$$

alkyl-(aryl)N,N'-dialkyl-(alkylaryl, diaryl)phosphorodiamidate

$$R_2NPOCl_2$$

di-acid chloride of dialkyl(alkylaryl, diaryl)phosphoramidic acid; dialkyl(alkylaryl, diaryl)-phosphoramidic dichloride

$$ROP \begin{cases} Cl \\ Cl \end{cases} = O$$

di-acid chloride of alkyl(aryl) phosphoric acid; alkyl(aryl)phosphorodichloridate

$$HOP \begin{cases} OR \\ OR' \end{cases}, \quad = O$$

Dialkyl(alkylaryl, diaryl) phosphoric acid; dialkyl (alkylaryl, diaryl)-hydrogen phosphate

$$\begin{matrix} RO \\ R'O \end{matrix} \Big\rangle P — NHR'' , \quad = O$$

dialkyl(alkylaryl, diaryl)phosphor- N-alkyl(aryl)phosphor-amidate

$$\left(\begin{matrix} R \\ R' \end{matrix} \right\rangle N \right)_2 POCl$$

Acid chloride of tetra-alkyl(dialkyldi-aryl, tetra-aryl)phosphorodiamidic acid; tetra-alkyl(dialkyl-diaryl, tetra-aryl)phos-phorodiamidochloridate

$$\begin{matrix} RO \\ RO \end{matrix} \Big\rangle P — Cl , \quad = O$$

acid chloride of dialkyl (alkylaryl, diaryl) phosphoric acid; dialkyl(alkylaryl, diaryl)-phosphorochloridate

$$O = P \begin{cases} OH \\ OH \\ OH \end{cases}$$

phosphoric acid, orthophosphoric acid

Inorganic Acids of Phosphorus and their Derivatives

Organophosphorus Acids and their Derivatives

Acids	Acid chlorides	Amides	Esters
$RP\begin{smallmatrix}OH\\OH\end{smallmatrix} \rightleftharpoons R\text{—}P\begin{smallmatrix}OH\\H\end{smallmatrix}=O$ alkyl(aryl)phosphonous acid / alkyl(aryl)phosphinic acid	$R\cdot P\begin{smallmatrix}Cl\\Cl\end{smallmatrix}$ di-acid chloride of alkyl(aryl)phosphonous acid; alkyl(aryl)phosphonous dichloride		$R\text{—}P\begin{smallmatrix}OR'\\OR''\end{smallmatrix}$ dialkyl(alkylaryl, diaryl) alkyl(aryl)phosphonite
$R\!\!>\!\!P\text{—}OH$ R' dialkyl(alkylaryl, diaryl)phosphinous acid	$R\!\!>\!\!P\text{—}Cl$ R' acid chloride of dialkyl(alkylaryl, diaryl)phosphinous acid; dialkyl(alkylaryl, diaryl)phosphinous chloride		$R\!\!>\!\!P\text{—}OR''$ R' alkyl(aryl) dialkyl(alkylaryl, diaryl)phosphinite
$R\text{—}P\begin{smallmatrix}OH\\OH\end{smallmatrix}=O$ alkyl(aryl) phosphonic acid	$RPCl_4$ alkyl(aryl)tetrachlorophosphorane; alkyl(aryl)phosphoranetetrachloride tetrachloride $R\text{—}P\begin{smallmatrix}Cl\\Cl\end{smallmatrix}=O$ di-acid chloride of alkyl(aryl)phosphonic acid; alkyl(aryl)phosphonic dichloride	$R\text{—}P\begin{smallmatrix}NHR'\\NHR''\end{smallmatrix}=O$ N,N'-dialkyl(alkylaryl, diaryl)alkyl(aryl)phosphonic diamide	$R\text{—}P\begin{smallmatrix}OR'\\OR'\end{smallmatrix}=O$ dialkyl(alkylaryl, diaryl) alkyl(aryl)phosphonate
$R\!\!>\!\!P\text{—}OH=O$ R' dialkyl(alkylaryl, diaryl)phosphinic acid	$R\!\!>\!\!P\text{—}Cl=O$ R' acid chloride of dialkyl(alkylaryl, diaryl)phosphinic acid; dialkyl(alkylaryl, diaryl)phosphinic chloride	$R'\!\!>\!\!P\text{—}NHR=O$ R'' N-alkyl(aryl)dialkyl(alkylaryl, diaryl)phosphinic amide	$R\!\!>\!\!P\text{—}OR''=O$ R' alkyl(aryl) dialkyl(alkylaryl, diaryl)phosphinate
$HOOC\text{—}R\text{—}PO(OR')_2$ dialkyl(alkylaryl, diaryl) (carboxyalkyl)phosphonate			$ROOC\cdot R'PO(OR'')_2$ dialkyl(alkylaryl, diaryl) [alkoxy(aryloxy)carbonyl]-alkylphosphonate
$P\begin{smallmatrix}R\\R'\\R''\end{smallmatrix}$ triallyl(dialkylaryl, aryl, diarylalkyl, triaryl)phosphine	$X{=}P\begin{smallmatrix}R\\R'\\R''\end{smallmatrix}$ trialkyl(dialkylaryl, alkyl, triaryl)phosphine oxide (sulphide) where X = O or S		$X^-\left[\begin{smallmatrix}R\\R'\\R''\\R'''\end{smallmatrix}P\right]^+$ tetra-alkyl(trialkylaryl, dialkyldiaryl, alkyltriaryl, tetra-aryl) phosphonium salt

(3) α, β-unsaturated esters of acids of phosphorus; and

(4) esters of the type $XCH = CHOPO(OR)_2$, where $X = H$ or Cl;

$$CX_2 = CHOP(OR)_2 \dots \text{etc. (Table 30, p. 54).}$$
$$\underset{O}{\overset{\|}{}}$$

Alternatively, suppose we wish to find the properties of the polyesters based on the acid chloride of phenyl phosphoric acid. From the list of structures it is clear that the formula of this acid chloride is: $C_6H_5OPOCl_2$. Consequently, polyesters based on this will have the following grouping in their structures:

$$\begin{array}{c} O \\ \| \\ -P- \\ | \\ O \\ | \\ C_6H_5 \end{array}$$

In the List of Tables we find:

(1) heterochain high molecular weight compounds containing phosphorus in the main chain;

(2) high molecular weight compounds containing phosphorus, carbon and oxygen in the main chain (phosphorus-containing polyesters);

(3) polyesters with side chains linked to phosphorus by C—O—P or C—N—P;

(4) polyesters obtained by the reaction of di-acid chlorides of aryl phosphoric acids with dihydroxy phenols (Table 110, p. 225).

PART ONE

STARTING MATERIALS FOR THE PREPARATION OF HIGH MOLECULAR WEIGHT ORGANO-PHOSPHORUS COMPOUNDS

Chapter 1

UNSATURATED ORGANOPHOSPHORUS COMPOUNDS

UNSATURATED ORGANOPHOSPHORUS ACIDS (PHOSPHONOUS, PHOSPHONIC AND PHOSPHONOTHIONIC) AND THEIR DERIVATIVES

The free acids

Few unsaturated phosphonous acids are known.

Allylphosphonous acid was synthesized by Pletz [4] by the reaction of allyl phosphorodichloridite and allyl magnesium iodide, followed by decomposition of the initially formed complex with water.

A few a, β-unsaturated phosphonous acids have been obtained by hydrolysis of the corresponding acid chlorides [5] or from the products of the reaction of acetic acid, phosphorus trichloride and olefins [6].

The simplest unsaturated phosphonic acid — vinylphosphonic acid (the phosphorus analogue of acrylic acid) — has been prepared recently by Kabachnik and Medved' [7] and independently by Schimmelschmidt and Denk [8] by hydrolysis of its acid chloride.

$$CH_2 = CH \cdot POCl_2 \xrightarrow{H_2O} CH_2 = CH \cdot PO(OH)_2$$

Many a, β-unsaturated phosphonic acids have been synthesized by Marsh and Gardner [9], Harnist [10], Bulle [11], Bergmann and Bondi [12–15] and later by Kosolopoff and Huber [16]. These authors investigated the reaction of phosphorus pentachloride with a variety of unsymmetrical hydrocarbons of the ethylene and acetylene series. The products of these reactions — colourless crystalline or yellowish substances — were hydrolysed to give, besides hydrogen chloride, vinyl- and β-chlorovinyl-phosphonic acids. The latter substances, on treatment with alkali, gave acetylenic-phosphonic acids in some cases and acetylenic hydrocarbons in others [17]. The general outline of these reactions can be illustrated as follows:

$$R \cdot CH = CH_2 + 2PCl_5 \longrightarrow R \cdot CHCl - CH_2 \cdot PCl_4 \cdot PCl_5 \xrightarrow{7H_2O}$$
$$\longrightarrow R \cdot CH = CH \cdot PO(OH)_2 + H_3PO_4 + 10HCl$$

$$R \cdot C \equiv CH + 2PCl_5 \longrightarrow R \cdot CCl = CH \cdot PCl_4 \cdot PCl_5 \xrightarrow{7H_2O}$$
$$\longrightarrow R \cdot CCl = CHPO(OH)_2 + H_3PO_4 + 9HCl$$

$$\swarrow \text{KOH} \searrow$$

$$R \cdot C \equiv C \cdot PO(OH)_2 \quad \text{or} \quad R \cdot C \equiv CH + H_3PO_4 + KCl$$

Another method of obtaining unsaturated phosphonic acids has been discovered by Conant and his co-workers in their studies on the addition of phosphorus trichloride to aldehydes and ketones. Hydrolysis of the addition products led in the aldehyde case to α-hydroxyphosphonic acids and in the ketone to the same acids and also to unsaturated acids [17, 18], whose formation was explained by Conant by the following reaction scheme:

$$C_6H_5COCH_3 + PCl_3 \longrightarrow \text{[addition product]} \xrightarrow{3H_2O}$$

$$\longrightarrow 3HCl + \underset{CH_3}{\overset{C_6H_5}{\diagup}}C\underset{OH}{\overset{PO(OH)_2}{\diagdown}} \quad \underset{H_2O}{\overset{HCl}{\rightleftarrows}} \quad \underset{CH_3}{\overset{C_6H_5}{\diagup}}C\underset{Cl}{\overset{PO(OH)_2}{\diagdown}}$$

$$\underset{CH_2}{\overset{C_6H_5}{\diagup}}C\overset{PO(OH)_2}{\diagdown} \quad + HCl$$

(Conant's proposals for the mechanism of the reaction of carbonyl compounds with phosphorus trichloride are, in the main, in accordance with those of Kabachnik and his co-workers [19–24], to whose work we refer those interested in this subject.)

By the halogenation of certain unsaturated ketophosphonic acids [25], dihalogeno-compounds can be isolated, and with alcoholic alkali these compounds give unsaturated phosphonic acids containing a halogen atom in the α-position relative to the keto-group [26]:

$$C_6H_5CH\text{—}CH_2COCH = CHC_6H_5 + Br_2 \longrightarrow$$
$$\underset{PO(OH)_2}{|}$$

$$\longrightarrow C_6H_5CH[PO(OH)_2]\text{—}CH_2COCHBr\text{—}CHBrC_6H_5 \xrightarrow{KOH}$$
$$\longrightarrow C_6H_5CH[PO(OH)_2]CH_2COCBr = CH \cdot C_6H_5 + KBr + H_2O$$

Substituted vinylphosphonic acids have been obtained by the thermal dehydrohalogenation *(in vacuo)* of the corresponding halogenated phosphonic acids [17], by the dehydration of α-hydroxyphosphonic acids [27], and also by the hydrolysis of the acid chlorides of unsaturated phosphonic acids [28].

Allylphosphonic acid has been made (as an impure potassium salt) by Parfent'ev and Shafiyev by the dehydrobromination of γ-bromopropylphosphonic acid [29].

By the reaction of phosphorus trichloride with acetone in the presence of aluminium chloride, Michaelis [30] obtained an interesting ester-acid chloride, for which he proposed the structure:

$$(CH_3)_2C\text{—}O\text{—}PCl$$
$$\diagdown\diagup$$
$$CH\text{—}CO\text{—}CH_3$$

However, Drake and Marvel [31] later synthesized the same compound by another route and showed that it had a different formula, and was a cyclic unsaturated acid chloride; it gave the corresponding unsaturated acid on hydrolysis:

$$(CH_3)_2C—CH = C—CH_3$$
$$O = P————O$$
$$\underset{Cl}{|}$$

In this acid chloride the phosphorus atom is pentavalent and not trivalent, as proposed by Michaelis. (The structure proposed by Drake and Marvel was subsequently confirmed by Anschutz and his co-workers [32].) Other compounds of this type have been made by Drake and Marvel by the reaction of unsaturated ketones with phosphorus trichloride or alkylphosphonous dichlorides [31].

Some unsaturated organophosphorus acids are crystalline substances while others are syrups or oils. Usually they have not been independently characterized, but they can be converted into esters for identification purposes.

Vinylphosphonic acid and its anhydride

$$\left[CH_2 = CHPO(OH)_2 \ \text{and} \ \left(CH_2 = CH\underset{\underset{O}{\|}}{\overset{OH}{\underset{|}{P}}}—O \right)_2 \right] \quad [7]$$

$$2CH_2 = CHPOCl_2 + 4H_2O \longrightarrow 2CH_2 = CHPO(OH)_2 \xrightarrow{-H_2O} \left(CH_2 = CH\underset{\underset{O}{\|}}{\overset{OH}{\underset{|}{P}}}—O \right)_2$$

Vinylphosphonic dichloride (4·35 g, 0.03 mole) was added gradually, with cooling, to water (9 ml). Water and hydrochloric acid were distilled from the resulting solution and the residue was dried to constant weight over phosphorus pentoxide and alkali to leave vinylphosphonic acid (3 g, about 93%) as a syrupy liquid, n_D^{20} 1·4737, d_4^{20} 1·3888.

The distillation of vinylphosphonic acid in high vacuum easily gives the anhydride, b.p. 235–240°/6 × 10⁻⁴ mm, n_D^{20} 1·4851, d_4^{20} 1·4022.

β-Styrylphosphonic acid $[C_6H_5CH = CHPO(OH)_2]$ [16]

$$C_6H_5CH = CH_2 + 2PCl_5 \longrightarrow C_6H_5CHCl—CH_2PCl_4 \cdot PCl_5 \xrightarrow{7H_2O}$$
$$C_6H_5CH = CHPO(OH)_2 + 10HCl + H_3PO_4$$

A solution of styrene (52·1 g, 0·5 mole) in dry benzene (500 ml) was treated with phosphorus trichloride (68·7 g, 0·5 mole). This mixture was stirred and cooled in ice and dry chlorine gas was passed into it. After 5 hr the solution had become distinctly yellow, owing to the presence of free chlorine, and a suspension (reminiscent of cream) of the phosphorus pentachloride addition product of styrene had formed. The reaction product was then hydrolysed with ice (200 g), after which evaporation of the benzene layer gave β-styrylphosphonic acid (32·9 g, 35·7%), m.p. 140–144 °C.

The filtrate from the acid residue contained dichlorostyrene (4·34 g, 49·6%) [a heavy oil, b.p. 105–120°/10·5 mm, n_D^{25} 1·5553].

The β-styrylphosphonic acid was purified by adding a solution of it in dilute caustic soda, slowly, with stirring, to a warm dilute solution of hydrochloric acid. Recrystallization from hot water gave a product, as colourless shining plates, with m.p. 154·5–155°.

Some properties of the unsaturated organophosphorus acids are given in Tables 1–6.

TABLE 1. UNSATURATED PHOSPHONOUS ACIDS [RP(OH)$_2$ OR RPHOH]
$$\overset{\|}{O}$$

R	m.p. (°C)	Reference
$CH_2 = CH \cdot CH_2—$	Decomposes at 120°	[4]
$C_8H_{15}—$ (structure not known)	Oil	[5]
$C_6H_5CH = CH—$	Oil 74–75°	[5]

TABLE 2. α, β-UNSATURATED ALKYL- AND CYCLO-ALKYL-PHOSPHONIC ACIDS
RPO(OH)$_2$

R	m. p. (°C)	Reference
$CH_2 = CH—$	Liquid*	[7]
$CH_2 = CH—$ (anhydride)	Liquid+	[7]
$ClCH = CH—$ (aniline salt)	192–193	[33]
$CH_2 = C(CH_3)—$	White hydroscopic mass	[28]
$C_4H_9CCl = CH—$ (aniline salt)	163–164	[33]
$C_5H_{11}CCl = CH—$	Oil	[14]
$(CH_3)_3CCH_2C(CH_3) = CH—$	104–105	[16]
$\begin{matrix}C_{16}H_{33}\\C_{17}H_{35}\end{matrix}\!\!\!\searrow\!\!\!C = CH—$	35–40	[28]
$CH_3—C—CH_3$ (aniline salt) [cyclohexanone structure with CH—]	195–196	[27]
$C_{10}H_{15}—$ (camphene); both isomers	184 (polyhydrate); decomposes at 167°	[9]
$C_{10}H_{14}Cl—$ (chlorofenchene)	196	[34]

* n_D^{20} 14737: d_4^{20} 13888.
+ b.p. 235–240°.

TABLE 3. α, β-UNSATURATED PHOSPHONIC ACIDS
CONTAINING AN AROMATIC RADICAL

Formula	m.p. (°C)	Reference
$RPO(OH)_2$		
R		
$CH_2 = C(C_6H_5)-$	112–113	[17]
$BrCH = C(C_6H_5)-$	133–135	[17]
$C_6H_5CH = CH-$	146; 154·5–155	[16]
$C_6H_5CCl = CH-$ (aniline salt)	191	[33]
$2\text{-}ClC_6H_4CH = CH-$	187	[14]
$3\text{-}ClC_6H_4CH = CH-$	168	[13]
$2\text{-}CH_3OC_6H_4CCl = CH-$	125–127	[14]
$4\text{-}CH_3OC_6H_4CCl = CH-$	105	[14]
$C_6H_5C(CH_3) = CH-$	95	[12]
$C_6H_5CH_2CCl = CH-$	mixed with isomer 154	[14]
$2,4\text{-}(CH_3)_2C_6H_3CH = CH-$	142–143	[16]
$4\text{-}C_2H_5C_6H_4CH = CH-$	138–140	[16]
$2,4,6\text{-}(CH_3)_3C_6H_2CH = CH-$	176–178	[16]
$2\text{-}(CH_3)_3CC_6H_4CH = CH-$	188–189	[16]
$4\text{-}(CH_3)_3CC_6H_4CH = CH-$	150·5–151·5	[16]
$(C_6H_5)_2C = CH-$	167	[12]
$2\text{-}C_6H_5C_6H_4CH = CH-$	186–188	[16]
$3\text{-}C_6H_5C_6H_4CH = CH-$	156–157·5	[16]
$4\text{-}C_6H_5C_6H_4CH = CH-$	193–193·5	[16]
$(4\text{-}ClC_6H_4)_2C = CH-$	158–159	[13]
$\begin{matrix} C_6H_5 \\ ^{}\diagdown C = CH- \\ 2\text{-}FC_6H_4 \diagup \end{matrix}$	180	[13]
$\begin{matrix} C_6H_5 \\ ^{}\diagdown C = CH- \\ 4\text{-}ClC_6H_4 \diagup \end{matrix}$	181	[13]
$\begin{matrix} C_6H_5 \\ ^{}\diagdown C = CH- \\ 4\text{-}CH_3OC_6H_4 \diagup \end{matrix}$	145	[13]
$\begin{matrix} 4\text{-}ClC_6H_4 \\ ^{}\diagdown C = CH- \\ 4\text{-}CH_3OC_6H_4 \diagup \end{matrix}$	132–133	[13]
$\begin{matrix} C_6H_5 \\ ^{}\diagdown C = CH- \\ 2\text{-}CH_3C_6H_4 \diagup \end{matrix}$	154	[15]
$\begin{matrix} C_6H_4 \\ ^{}\diagdown C = CH- \\ 4\text{-}C_6H_5C_6H_4 \diagup \end{matrix}$	201	[13]
$\begin{matrix} 4\text{-}CH_3C_6H_4 \\ ^{}\diagdown C = CH- \\ 4\text{-}C_6H_5C_6H_4 \diagup \end{matrix}$	Amorphous mass	[13]

TABLE 3 — *(contd.)*

Formula	m.p. (°C)	Reference
$(HO)_2OP-CH=C$ (—C$_6$H$_5$, —C$_6$H$_5$ substituents on central ring) $-C=CH-PO(OH)_2$	210	(13)
$RPO(OH)_2$ R (indene structure)	184	[12]
$2-C_{10}H_7CH = CH-$	181·5–182	[16]
$\begin{array}{c} C_6H_5 \\ \diagdown \\ 1-C_{10}H_7 \end{array} C = CH-$	188	[15]
$\begin{array}{c} C_6H_5 \\ \diagdown \\ 2-C_{10}H_7 \end{array} C = CH-$	220	[15]
(fluorene structure)$-CH = CH-$	Decomposes at 200–205	[16]

TABLE 4. β, γ-UNSATURATED PHOSPHONIC ACIDS

Formula	m.p. (°C)	Reference
$CH_2 = CHCH_2PO(OH)_2$	Oil	[29]
$CH_3C = CHC(CH_3)_2P(O)OH$ (suggested structure) $\lfloor\_\_\_O\_\_\_\rfloor$	143–144	[31]
$\begin{array}{c} \lceil\_\_O\_\_\rceil \\ C_6H_5C = CHCHP(O)OH \\ \ \ \ \ \ C_6H_5CO \end{array}$	197–198	[31]
$\begin{array}{c} C_6H_5CO \\ \ \ \ \mid \\ C_6H_5C = CHCHP(O)OH \\ \ \ \ \ \ \mid\_\_\_O \ \ (oxime) \end{array}$	169–170	[30]
$\begin{array}{c} C_6H_5CH = CH \\ \ \ \ \ \ \ \ \ \ \ \diagdown CHPO(OH)_2 \\ C_6H_5COCH_2 \diagup \end{array}$	159–161	[26]
$\begin{array}{c} C_6H_5CH = CH \\ \ \ \ \ \ \ \ \ \ \mid \\ C_6H_5COCH_2CHP(O)OH \\ \ \ \ \ \ \ \ \ \ \ \mid \\ \ \ \ \ \ \ \ \ \ \ C_6H_5 \end{array}$	200	[26]

Table 5. Other unsaturated phosphonic acids with one double bond

Formula	m. p. (°C)	Reference
$C_6H_5CH = CHCOCH_2CH(C_6H_5)PO(OH)_2$	108	[25]
$C_6H_5CH = CBrCOCH_2CH(C_6H_5)PO(OH)_2$	130–132	[26]
$C_6H_5CH = CHCOCH_2CH(C_6H_5)P(O)OH$ $\quad\quad\quad\quad\quad\quad\quad\quad\quad\quad\quad\quad C_6H_5$	235–236	[26]
$C_6H_5CH = CBrCOCH_2CH(C_6H_5)P(O)OH$ $\quad\quad\quad\quad\quad\quad\quad\quad\quad\quad\quad\quad C_6H_5$	200	[26]

Table 6. Unsaturated phosphonic acids with two double bonds or one triple bond $RPO(OH)_2$

R	m.p. (°C)	Reference
$CH_2 = CHCCl = CH—$ (aniline salt)	186	[33]
$C_6H_5CH = CHCH = CH—$	192	[13]
$C_6H_5—CH$	188–189	[12]
O——— CH_2O—〈　〉—CH	194	[12]
$CH_3OC_6H_4—CH$	192	[12]
$C_6H_5C \equiv C—$	142	[14]
$2\text{-}ClC_6H_4C \equiv C—$	134	[14]

Acid chlorides of unsaturated organophosphorus acids

These acid chlorides, which have a labile chlorine atom in the molecule, are important intermediates since they can easily be converted into the acids themselves, their esters, amides, etc.

There are many diverse methods of synthesizing the acid chlorides of unsaturated phosphonic and phosphonothionic acids.

Vinylphosphonic dichloride was obtained by Kabachnik and Medved' by the catalytic dehydrochlorination of the acid chloride of β-chloroethylphosphonic acid over barium chloride at 330–340° [7]:

$$\text{ClCH}_2\text{CH}_2 \cdot \text{POCl}_2 \xrightarrow{\;-\text{HCl}\;} \text{CH}_2 = \text{CH} \cdot \text{POCl}_2$$

and also by Schimmelschmidt and Denk by the treatment of diethyl vinylphosphonate with phosphorus pentachloride [35]:

$$\text{CH}_2 = \text{CH} \cdot \text{PO(OR)}_2 + 2\text{PCl}_5 \longrightarrow \text{CH}_2 = \text{CH} \cdot \text{POCl}_2 + 2\text{POCl}_3 + 2\text{RCl}$$

Vinylphosphonothionic dichloride was synthesized by Kabachnik and Medved' by the treatment of β-chloroethylphosphonothionic dichloride with triethylamine [36].

One of the main methods of obtaining acid chlorides of unsaturated organophosphorus acids is the addition of phosphorus pentachloride to various unsaturated compounds, followed by treatment of the adducts with sulphur dioxide, phosphorus pentoxide, phosphorus pentasulphide, hydrogen sulphide, or phosphorus and sulphur, according to the following scheme:

$$\text{RCH} = \text{CH}_2 + 2\text{PCl}_5 \longrightarrow \text{RCHClCH}_2\text{PCl}_4 \cdot \text{PCl}_5$$

$$3\text{RCHClCH}_2\text{PCl}_4 \cdot \text{PCl}_5 -
\begin{cases}
\xrightarrow{6\text{SO}_2} 3\text{RCH} = \text{CHPOCl}_2 + 3\text{POCl}_3 + 6\text{SOCl}_2 + 3\text{HCl} \\
\xrightarrow{2\text{P}_2\text{O}_5} 3\text{RCH} = \text{CHPOCl}_2 + 7\text{POCl}_3 + 3\text{HCl} \\
\xrightarrow{2\text{P}_2\text{S}_5} 3\text{RCH} = \text{CHPSCl}_2 + 7\text{PSCl}_3 + 3\text{HCl} \\
\xrightarrow{6\text{H}_2\text{S}} 3\text{RCH} = \text{CHPSCl}_2 + 3\text{PSCl}_3 + 15\text{HCl} \\
\xrightarrow{4\text{P}} 3\text{RCH} = \text{CHPCl}_2 + 7\text{PCl}_3 + 3\text{HCl} \\
\qquad\qquad\quad \downarrow \text{S(orP}_2\text{S}_5) \\
\qquad\quad 3\text{RCH} = \text{CHPSCl}_2
\end{cases}$$

These acid chlorides are usually colourless, transparent liquids which are slowly hydrolysed in the air, and which are soluble in many organic solvents. They are purified by distillation *in vacuo*. Several such acid chlorides have been described in patents by Woodstock [37].

A detailed investigation of the above reactions with unsaturated aliphatic and aromatic hydrocarbons and simple vinylic esters has been carried out by Anisimov, Kolobova and Nesmeyanov. They synthesized many acid chlorides of alkyl-, aryl-, alkoxy- and aryloxy-vinyl-phosphonic and -phosphonothionic acids [38—44], mainly of the form $\text{RCH} = \text{CHPXCl}_2$ and $\text{ROCH} = \text{CHPXCl}_2$, where R = alkyl or aryl, and X = O or S.

Under these conditions, diene hydrocarbons form acid chlorides of γ, δ-unsaturated chlorine-containing phosphonic acids [43, 44]. For example:

$$\text{CH}_2 = \text{CH} \cdot \text{CH} = \text{CH}_2 + 2\text{PCl}_5 \longrightarrow \text{CH}_2 = \text{CH}-\text{CHCl}-\text{CH}_2\text{PCl}_4 \cdot \text{PCl}_5 \xrightarrow{2\text{SO}_2}$$
$$\longrightarrow \text{CH}_2 = \text{CH}-\text{CHCl}-\text{CH}_2\text{POCl}_2 + \text{POCl}_3 + 2\text{SOCl}_2$$

A method of obtaining alkenyl-phosphonic and -phosphonothionic dichlorides has recently been published by Walsh and his co-workers. They treated the addition products of phosphorus pentachloride and olefins with phosphorus (under the catalytic influence of iodine). In this way the di-acid chlorides of alkenylphosphonous acids were obtained [5, 45] (see the diagram on p. 18). Sulphur easily added to these compounds which in this way were converted into alkenylphosphonothionic dichlorides [5, 46].

Several years ago a method was published for obtaining acid chlorides of alkylphosphonic acids by the reaction of alkyl chlorides and phosphorus trichloride in the presence of aluminium chloride. The complex which formed was carefully decomposed by water: [47, 48]

$$PCl_3 + RCl + AlCl_3 \longrightarrow [RPCl_3]^+ [AlCl_4]^- \xrightarrow{H_2O} [HAlCl_4 + RPCl_3OH]$$

$$AlCl_3 + HCl \quad RPOCl_2 + HCl$$

In this way allylphosphonic dichloride was obtained from allyl chloride.

Soborovskii, Zinov'ev and Englin [49, 50] in the U. S. S. R., and Clayton and Jensen [51] in the U. S. A., have, independently of each other, worked out a new method of synthesis of alkylphosphonic dichlorides; this involves the reaction of oxygen with a mixture of a hydrocarbon and phosphorus trichloride:

$$RH + 2PCl_3 + O_2 \longrightarrow RPOCl_2 + POCl_3 + HCl$$

By using acetylenic hydrocarbons, Zinov'ev, Muler and Soborovskii [33] obtained a range of unsaturated acid chlorides which contained chlorine in the hydrocarbon part of the molecule:

$$RC \equiv CH + 2PCl_3 + O_2 \longrightarrow RCCl = CHPOCl_2 + POCl_3$$

and

$$CH_2 = CH-C \equiv CH + 2PCl_3 + O_2 \longrightarrow CH_2 = CHCCl = CHPOCl_2 + POCl_3$$

Finally, it is possible to obtain acid chlorides of α, β-unsaturated phosphonic acids by treating the acids themselves with phosphorus pentachloride [28].

Iso-octenylphosphonous dichloride $C_8H_{15}PCl_2$ [5]

$$3C_8H_{16} + 6PCl_5 \longrightarrow 3HCl + 3C_8H_{15}PCl_4 \cdot PCl_5 \xrightarrow{4P} 3C_8H_{15}PCl_2 + 7PCl_3$$

Di-isobutylene (428 g, 3·2 mole) was added dropwise over 3 hr to a well-stirred suspension of phosphorus pentachloride (417 g, 2 moles) in benzene (750 ml) at 0°. An exothermic reaction took place with the evolution of hydrochloric acid. The flask was then purged with carbon dioxide and a solution of white phosphorus (41·3 g, 1·33 moles) and iodine (0·2 g) in carbon disulphide (8 ml) was added with stirring. The mixture was gradually warmed to 20° and the reaction was allowed to continue until a hard mass had formed. The product (281 g, 66%) was distilled, b. p. 70–72°/3 mm, n_D^{25} 1·5035.

2*

Vinylphosphonic dichloride $CH_2 = CHPOCl_2$ [7]

$$ClCH_2CH_2POCl_2 \xrightarrow{-HCl} CH_2 = CHPOCl_2$$

β-Chloroethylphosphonic dichloride (45·4 g, 0.25 mole) was passed in a gas stream, over 4 hr, into a quartz tube packed with dry barium chloride (small pieces about 1–2 mm in size) heated to 330–340°. The reaction product was condensed and twice fractionated *in vacuo*. There was obtained vinyl-phosphonic dichloride (30·8 g, 85%), b. p. 69–71°/21 mm, n_D^{20} 1·4808, d_4^{20} 1·4092. Dehydrochlorination at a lower temperature lead to a reduction in yield.

Allylphosphonic dichloride $CH_2 = CHCH_2POCl_2$ [48]

$$CH_2 = CHCH_2Cl + PCl_3 + AlCl_3 \longrightarrow [CH_2 = CHCH_2PCl_3]^+ [AlCl_4]^- \xrightarrow{-4H_2O}$$
$$\longrightarrow CH_2 = CHCH_2POCl_2 + Al(OH)_3 \neq 5HCl$$

Allyl chloride was added to a previously prepared suspension of aluminium chloride in phosphorus trichloride (molar ratios: $CH_2 = CHCH_2Cl$: : PCl_3 : $AlCl_3 = 0·25 : 1·0 : 0·5$), and the mixture was stirred for 30 min at 40–50°. After this, the complex which had formed was diluted with 5–10 times its volume of methylene dichloride, and the mixture obtained was cooled to $-20°$ by the addition of solid carbon dioxide. Water (4·5 moles) was then added gradually, with stirring, at such a rate that the milky suspension which formed did not coagulate. The solution was filtered quickly, the solvent was evaporated and the acid chloride (53%, based on PCl_3) was distilled *in vacuo*, b. p. 55°/13 mm.

2-Chlorobut-3-enylphosphonic dichloride $CH_2 = CHCHClCH_2POCl_2$ [43]

$$CH_2 = CH\text{---}CH = CH_2 + 2PCl_5 \longrightarrow CH_2 = CH\text{---}CHCl \cdot CH_2PCl_4 \cdot PCl_5 \xrightarrow{2SO_2}$$
$$\longrightarrow CH_2 = CH\text{---}CHCl \cdot CH_2POCl_2 + POCl_3 + 2SOCl_2$$

Phosphorus pentachloride (208 g) and dry benzene (250 ml) were placed in a three-necked flask fitted with a mechanical stirrer, a condenser and a gas-inlet tube. Butadiene (85–90 g) was passed into the stirred and ice-cooled mixture. After the passage of the butadiene a pale yellow crystalline mass formed and the reaction mixture was kept overnight. On the following day it was treated with sulphur dioxide gas until the crystalline mass dissolved. After the evaporation of solvent, thionyl chloride and phosphoryl chloride, the residue was distilled *in vacuo* to give the acid chloride (114 g, 90%), b. p. 103–105°/2 mm, n_D^{20} 1·5200, d_4^{20} 1·4452.

2-Chlorobuta-1,3-dienylphosphonic dichloride $CH_2 = CH \cdot CCl = CHPOCl_2$ [33]

$$CH_2 = CH \cdot CH \equiv CH + 2PCl_3 + O_2 \longrightarrow CH_2 = CHCCl = CHPOCl_2 + POCl_3$$

Oxygen was passed into a mixture of vinylacetylene (26 g, 0·5 mole) and phosphorus trichloride (137·5 g, 1 mole) at a rate of 4 l/hr at $-20°$. In all

36 l. of oxygen were passed. After evaporation of phosphoryl chloride, the residue was distilled to give the product (15·5 g, 15·8%), b. p. 70–75°/2·5 mm. This was redistilled to give the pure acid chloride, b. p. 71–73°/4 mm, n_D^{20} 1·5291, d_4^{20} 1·4686.

Vinylphosphonothionic dichloride $CH_2 = CHPSCl_2$ [36]

$$ClCH_2CH_2PSCl_2 + N(C_2H_5)_3 \longrightarrow CH_2 = CHPSCl_2 + N(C_2H_5)_3 \cdot HCl$$

Triethylamine (10·1 g, 0·1 mole) was added dropwise to a cooled (0°) solution of β-chloroethylphosphonothionic dichloride (19·8 g, 0·1 mole) in ether (70 ml). After this the mixture was stirred for 30 min at 0°, for 1 hr as the temperature was allowed to rise from 0° to 20°, and for 1 hr at 40°. The triethylamine salt was filtered off and washed with the solvent, and the combined filtrate and washings were washed with a cold 1% solution of hydrochloric acid and with cold water. After this, the solvent was evaporated and the residue was distilled in vacuo to give vinylphosphonothionic dichloride (9·5 g, 59%), b. p. 54—55°/12 mm, n_D^{20} 1·5623, d_4^{20} 1·3954.

Iso-octenylphosphonothionic dichloride $C_8H_{15}PSCl_2$ [5]

$$C_8H_{15}PCl_2 + S \longrightarrow C_8H_{15}PSCl_2$$

A mixture of iso-octenylphosphonous dichloride and sulphur (equimolecular proportions) was stirred and heated at 175° until an exothermic reaction commenced, when the reaction maintained itself at 175°. After the reaction had subsided the mixture was again heated (to 175°) for 10 min, and then cooled and the reaction product (87%) was distilled, b. p. 95–100°/2 mm, n_D^{25} 1·5534.

The properties of the acid chlorides of unsaturated phosphonic acids are recorded in Tables 7–10.

TABLE 7. ACID CHLORIDES OF UNSATURATED PHOSPHONOUS ACIDS $RPCl_2$

R	b. p. °C(mm)	n_D^{25}	Yield (%)	Reference
$CH_3C(CH_3) = CH-$ (mixture of products)	98–104 (100)	1·5087		[5]
$C_3H_7CH = CH-$	100–102 (100)	1·5028		[45]
$C_8H_{15}-$ (structure not known)	70–72 (3)	1·5035	66	[5]
$C_6H_5CH = CH-$	135–138 (8)	1·6350	53·6	[5]
	104–105 (1)		27·6	[5]

TABLE 8. ACID CHLORIDES OF α,β-UNSATURATED PHOSPHONIC ACIDS RPOCl$_2$

R	b. p., °C (mm)	n_D^{20}	d_4^{20}	Yield (%)	Reference
$CH_2 = CH-$	67–69 (21)	1·4808	1·4092	85·6	[7]
$ClCH = CH-$	60–61 (1)	1·5065	1·5605		[33]
$CH_3OCH = CH-$	76 (1·5)	1·5052	1·4186	11	[38]
$C_2H_5OCH = CH-$	84 (2)	1·4969	1·3221	87	[38]
$C_2H_5SCH = CH-$	117 (2)	1·5720	1·3938	68	[42]
$CH_3OC_2H_4OCH = CH-$	115 (2)	1·4991	1·3200	95	[40]
$C_2H_5OC_2H_4OCH = CH-$	123 (2)	1·4920	1·2881	97	[40]
$C_4H_9OC_2H_4OCH = CH-$	142 (2)	1·4869	1·2133	90	[40]
$C_3H_7OCH = CH-$	101 (3)	1·4945	1·2823	78	[38]
iso-$C_3H_7OCH = CH-$	52—53*			76	[38]
$C_4H_9OCH = CH-$	107·5 (2)	1·4926	1·2384	81	[38]
$C_4H_7SCH = CH-$	120–122 (1)	1·5505	1·2845	82	[42]
iso-$C_4H_9OCH = CH-$	96 (1)	1·4900	1·2318	78	[38]
iso-$C_5H_{11}OCH = CH-$	112 (1)	1·4876	1·2058	95	[38]
$C_6H_{13}OCH = CH-$	126 (2)	1·4890	1·2083	92	[38]
$C_6H_5OCH = CH-$	131 (2)	1·5708	1·3710	75	[38]
$CH_2 = C(CH_3)-$	82·5–86 (32); 83 (30)			55	[28]
$(CH_3)_2C = CH-$	99–101 (17)		1·302	80	[37]
$C_4H_9CCl = CH-$	96–97 (2·5)	1·4981	1·3283		[33]
$(CH_3)_3CCH_2C(CH_3) = CH-$	128–129 (13)		1·129 (25°)	75	[37]
$C_6H_5CH = CH-$	182–184 (18); 71–72*			81 96	[37] [41]
$C_6H_5CCl = CH-$	142·5–143·5 (1) 121–123 (25); 58–59*	1·6175	1·4675	80	[41] [33]
	73–74*			62	[41]

* Melting point.

TABLE 9. ACID CHLORIDES OF OTHER UNSATURATED PHOSPHONIC ACIDS

Formula	b. p., °C (mm)	n_D^{20}	d_4^{20}	Yield (%)	Reference
$CH_2 = CHCH_2POCl_2$	55 (3)			53	[48]
$CH_3—C = CHC(CH_3)_2PCl$ (with O bridge)	235; 154 (100); 35–36*				[30]
$CH_2 = CHCHClCH_2POCl_2$	103–105 (2)	1·5200	1·4452	90	[43]
$CH_2 = C(CH_3)CHClCH_2POCl_2$	107–108 (2)	1·5230	1·3918	90	[44]
$CH_2 = CHCCl = CHPOCl_2$	71–73 (4)	1·5291	1·4686		[33]
$CH_2 = CClCCl = CHPOCl_2$ and $CHCl = CHCCl = = CHPOCl_2$ (a mixture)	106 (1); 153–154 (10)	1·5400	1·5673		[52]
$CH_2 = C(CH_2Cl)CCl = CHPOCl_2$ and $CHCl = C(CH_3)CCl = = CHPOCl_2$ (a mixture)	133 (1)	1·5405	1·4975		[52]

TABLE 10. ACID CHLORIDES OF α,β-UNSATURATED PHOSPHONOTHIONIC ACIDS RPSCl$_2$

R	b.p., °C (mm)	n_D^{20}	d_ψ^{20}	Yield (%)	Reference
$CH_2 = CH—$	54–55 (12)	1·5623	1·3954	68	[36]
$C_2H_5OCH = CH—$	84 (2)	1·5422	1·3334	74	[39]
$CH_3OC_2H_4OCH = CH—$	113 (2)	1·5413	1·3364	76	[40]
$C_2H_5OC_2H_4OCH = CH—$	120 (2)	1·5330	1·2887	85	[40]
$C_4H_9OC_2H_4OCH = CH—$	137 (2)	1·5100	1·2210	86	[40]
iso-$C_3H_7OCH = CH—$	92 (2)	1·5224	1·2684	75	[39]
$C_4H_9OCH = CH—$	105 (2)	1·5234	1·2471	77	[39]
$C_6H_{13}OCH = CH—$	128 (2)	1·5255	1·1841	60	[39]
$C_6H_5OCH = CH—$	130 (1)	1·6086	1·1670	80	[39]
$CH_3C(CH_3) = CH—$	115–125 (30)	1·5558		79	[5]
$C_8H_{15}—$ (structure not established)	95–100 (2)	1·5334 (25°)		87	[5]
$C_6H_5CH = CH—$	130 (2)	1·6439	1·3533	91	[39]

Amides of unsaturated organophosphorus acids

Substituted amides of alkenylphosphonic acids with the general formula $RPO(NR'R'')_2$, where R = unsaturated radical and R' and R'' = saturated radical or hydrogen, have been obtained by the reaction of the corresponding alkenylphosphonic dichlorides with ammonia, amines, amine hydrochlorides [7, 28, 53–58] or ethylenimine in the presence of triethylamine.

Substituted alkylamides of alkenylphosphonic acids are thick liquids, distillable *in vacuo*. They are stable and soluble in many organic solvents; the majority of them are insoluble in water (except compounds with ethylenimine groups).

N,N,N',N'-Tetramethylvinylphosphonic diamide $CH_2 = CHPO[N(CH_3)_2]_2$ [7]

$$CH_2 = CHPOCl_2 + 4(CH_3)_2NH \longrightarrow CH_2 = CHPO[N(CH_3)_2]_2 + 2(CH_3)_2NH \cdot HCl$$

A solution of dimethylamine ($7 \cdot 7$ g, $0 \cdot 172$ mole) in ether (50 ml) was added gradually, with stirring, to vinylphosphonic dichloride (6 g, $0 \cdot 043$ mole): the temperature of the reaction was maintained at about $-12°$. The precipitate was filtered off and the solvent was evaporated from the filtrate to leave a residue which was fractionated to give N,N,N',N'-tetramethylvinylphosphonic dichloride ($4 \cdot 2$ g, 52%), b. p. $82°/3$ mm, n_D^{20} $1 \cdot 4732$, d_4^{20} $1 \cdot 0257$.

N,N,N',N'-Tetramethylstyrylphosphonic diamide $C_6H_5CH = CHPO[NCH_3)_2]_2$ [58]

$$C_6H_5CH = CHPOCl_2 + 4(CH_3)_2NH \longrightarrow C_6H_5CH = CHPO[N(CH_3)_2]_2 + 2(CH_3)_2NH \cdot HCl_0$$

To a cooled mixture of petroleum ether (70 ml) and benzene (30 ml) was added dimethylamine (9 g), followed by the gradual addition, with stirring, of styrylphosphonic dichloride ($11 \cdot 05$ g). After all the acid chloride had been added the stirring was continued for 2 hr. On the following day the reaction mixture was heated on a water bath at $30-35°$ for 2 hr. The residue was filtered off and twice washed with petroleum ether. The combined filtrate and washings were treated with portions of a saturated solution of alkali to remove traces of dimethylamine hydrochloride, dried over caustic soda, and distilled to give the product (6 g, $50 \cdot 8$%), b. p. $180°/2$ mm, n_D^{20} $1 \cdot 5665$, d_4^{20} $1 \cdot 0818$.

The properties of amides of unsaturated phosphonic acids are recorded in Tables 11–12.

TABLE 11. AMIDES OF α,β-UNSATURATED PHOSPHONIC ACIDS

Formula		b. p., °C (mm)	n_D^{20}	d_ψ^{20}	Yield (%)	Reference
$CH_2 = CHPO[N(CH_3)_2]_2$		82 (3)	1·4732	1·0257	52	[7]
$ROCH = CHP(O)R_2'$						
R	**R'**					
C_2H_5-	$-N(CH_3)_2$	108 (1)	1·4780	1·0401	57	[54]
C_2H_5-	$-N(C_2H_5)_2$	126·5 (2)	1·4755	1·0950	59	[54]
C_2H_5-	$-NC_5H_{10}$	60–61*				[54]
C_2H_5-	$-N(C_4H_9)_2$	172 (2)	1·4680	0·9399		[54]
$C_2H_5SCH = CHPO[NC_5H_{10}]_2$		62·5*			80–82	[42]
$ROCH = CHP(O)R_2'$						
R	**R'**					
$CH_3OC_2H_4--$	$-N(CH_3)_2$	144 (2)	1·4808	1·0879	56	[55]
$CH_3OC_2H_4-$	$-N(C_2H_5)_2$	153 (2)	1·4765	1·0191	59	[55]
$CH_3OC_2H_4-$	$-NC_5H_{10}$	187 (1)	1·5101	1·1026	84	[55]
$CH_3OC_2H_4-$	$-N(C_3H_7)_2$	160 (1)	1·4733	0·9932	65	[55]
$CH_3OC_2H_4-$	$-N(C_4H_9)_2$	183 (1)	1·4710	0·9741	75	[55]
$C_2H_5OC_2H_4-$	$-N(CH_3)_2$	143 (2)	1·4770	1·0545	72	[55]
$C_2H_5OC_2H_4-$	$-N(C_2H_5)_2$	146 (1)	1·4749	1·0108	78	[55]
$C_2H_5OC_2H_4-$	$-NC_5H_{10}$	185 (2)	1·5062	1·0851	96	[55]
$C_2H_5OC_2H_4-$	$-N(C_3H_7)_2$	163 (2)	1·4721	0·9822	83	[55]
$C_2H_5OC_2H_4-$	$-N(C_4H_9)_2$	180 (1)	1·4705	0·9579	93	[55]
$C_4H_9OC_2H_4-$	$-N(CH_3)_2$	175 (2)	1·4758	1·0274	71	[55]
$C_4H_9OC_2H_4-$	$-N(C_2H_5)_2$	179 (2)	1·4730	0·9948	87	[55]
C_3H_7-	$-N(CH_3)_2$	105·5 (2)	1·4742	1·0182	73	[54]
C_3H_7-	$-N(C_2H_5)_2$	132 (2)	1·4709	0·9962	55	[54]
C_3H_7-	$-N(C_3H_7)_2$	172 (2)	1·4678	0·9301		[54]
C_4H_9-	$-N(CH_3)_2$	116 (1)	1·4755	1·0090	50	[54]
C_4H_9-	$-N(C_2H_5)_2$	130 (2)	1·4729	0·9745	55	[54]
$C_5H_{11}-$	$-N(C_4H_9)_2$	192–193 (2)	1·4691	0·9249		[54]
C_6H_5-	$-N(CH_3)_2$	145 (2)	1·4858	1·1199	50	[54]
C_6H_5-	$-N(C_2H_5)_2$	161 (2)	1·5200	1·0402	58	[54]
R	**R'**					
C_6H_5-	$-NC_5H_{10}$	202 (1)	1·5528	1·1193		[54]
C_6H_5-	$-N(C_4H_9)_2$	212 (0·5)	1·5060	0·9886		[54]
$CH_2 = C(CH_3)PO[N(CH_3)_2]_2$		76–80 (2–3)	1·4735			[28, 53] [59]
$(CH_3)_2C = CHPO\left[N{<}^{CH_2}_{CH_2}\right]_2$		96 (0·7)			35	
$C_6H_5CH = CHPO[N(CH_3)_2]_2$		180 (2)	1·5665	1·0818	50·8	[58]
$C_6H_5CH = CHPO[N(C_2H_5)_2]_2$		103·5*			78·4	[58]
$C_6H_5CH = CHPO[NC_5H_{10}]_2$		135–136*				[58]
$C_6H_5CH = CHPO[N(C_3H_7)_2]_2$		192 (2)	1·5290	1·0050		[58]
$C_6H_5CH = CHPO[N(C_4H_9)_2]_2$		39 –40*				[58]

* Melting point.

TABLE 12. AMIDES AND AMIDO-ESTERS OF β, γ-UNSATURATED PHOSPHONIC ACIDS

Formula	b. p., °C (mm)	Reference
$CH_2 = C(CN)CH_2P \Big\langle \begin{matrix} R' \\ R'' \end{matrix}$ $\|$ O		
R' R''	171–174 (0·7)	[60]
—NHCH₃ —NHCH₃	151–154 (0·7)	[60]
—NHCH₃ —OC₂H₅	165–168 (1)	[60]
—N(C₂H₅)₂ —OC₄H₉	164–168 (0·7)	[60]
—N(C₂H₅)₂ —OC₆H₅	162–165 (0·7)	[60]
—N(C₂H₅)₂ —N(C₂H₅)₂	189–193 (0·7)	[60]
—N(C₃H₇)₂ —N(C₃H₇)₂	167–169 (0·7)	[61]

$CH_2 = C-CH_2PO[NHCH_3]_2$
      |
    COOCH₃		

$CH_2 = C-CH_2PO[N(C_2H_5)_2]_2$
      |
    COOCH₃
	167–169 (0·7)	[61]

$CH_3C = CHC(CH_3)_2\overset{O}{\overset{\|}{P}}NHC_7H_5^+$ |———— O ————|	122–125*	[32]
$CH_2 = CHCH = CHPO[N(CH_3)_2]_2^+$	102–120 (1·25–2·5)	[62]
$CH_2 = CHCH = CHPO[N(CH_2CH = CH_2)_2]_2^+$	157–170 (1)	[62]

* Melting point.

⁺ Structure of the acidic part of the molecule uncertain.

Esters of unsaturated organophosphorus acids and saturated alcohols

Any of these compounds can be synthesized via the previously described methods for acid chlorides of unsaturated acids of phosphorus, followed by treatment of the acid chlorides with saturated alcohols, mercaptans (sometimes in the presence of organic bases), alkoxides or mercaptides, when the esters or thioesters of the corresponding acids are produced [7, 28, 43, 44, 58–72].

This type of ester is also produced as a result of the reaction of alkenyltetrachlorophosphoranes with alcohols [73]:

$$R'PCl_4 + 3ROH \longrightarrow R'PO(OR)_2 + RCl + 3HCl$$

where R' is an unsaturated, and R a saturated radical (this is analogous to the preparation of the unsaturated acid by the hydrolysis of the alkenyltetrachlorophosphorane) [12, 14].

They are also produced as a result of the addition of dialkyl hydrogen phosphites or dialkyl hydrogen phosphorothioites to esters of phenylpropiolic acid [74]:

$$ROOC-C \equiv C-C_6H_5 + HPX(OR)_2 \longrightarrow ROOC-CH = C(C_6H_5)PX(OR)_2$$

where X = oxygen or sulphur.

Esters of unsaturated phosphonic acids are again produced by the removal of the elements of hydrogen halide, two atoms of halogen or the elements of water from (respectively) esters of β-halogenoalkyl- and β-halogenoalkenyl-, [71, 73, 75–82] dihalogenoalkyl- [83–84] and α-hydroxyalkylphosphonic acids [85] according to the following general scheme:

$$R'CHX{-}CR''R'''PO(OR)_2 \xrightarrow{-HX(R''X \text{ or } H_2O)} R'CH = CR'''PO(OR)_2$$

where X = halogen or hydrogen and R″ = halogen, hydroxyl or hydrogen

Diethyl vinylphosphonate $CH_2 = CHPO(OC_2H_5)_2$ [7]

$$CH_2 = CHPOCl_2 + 2C_2H_5OH + 2C_5H_5N \longrightarrow CH_2 = CHPO(OC_2H_5)_2 + 2C_5H_5N \cdot HCl$$

A solution of vinylphosphonic dichloride ($7 \cdot 25$ g, $0 \cdot 05$ mole) in ether (10 ml) was added, with stirring, to a cooled (between $-4°$ and $+2°$) mixture of ethanol ($4 \cdot 6$ g, $0 \cdot 1$ mole), pyridine ($7 \cdot 9$ g, $0 \cdot 1$ mole) and ether (50 ml); more ether (50 ml) was then added. On the following day, the pyridine hydrochloride was filtered off, the solvent was evaporated from the filtrate and the residue was fractionally distilled to give diethyl vinylphosphonate ($3 \cdot 7$ g, 45%), b.p. $62°/3$ mm, n_D^{20} $1 \cdot 4338$, d_4^{20} $1 \cdot 0550$.

Diethyl vinylphosphonate $CH_2 = CHPO(OC_2H_5)_2$ [75]

$$ClCH_2CH_2PO(OC_2H_5)_2 + KOH \longrightarrow CH_2 = CHPO(OC_2H_5)_2 + KCl + H_2O$$

Diethyl β-chloroethylphosphonate ($17 \cdot 6$ g) was added to a solution of caustic potash ($4 \cdot 9$ g) in alcohol. An exothermic reaction took place and potassium chloride was precipitated. The reaction mixture was heated for 1 hr on a water bath, then the precipitate was filtered off, the alcohol was evaporated from the filtrate and the residue was distilled *in vacuo*. Two main fractions were obtained, b.p. 70–75°/3 mm, and b.p. 96–105°/3 mm.

Redistillation of the first fraction gave diethyl vinylphosphonate ($6 \cdot 1$ g, $42 \cdot 5\%$), b.p. 68–70°/3 mm, n_D^{20} $1 \cdot 4300$, d_4^{20} $1 \cdot 0526$. If diethyl β-bromoethylphosphonate is used instead as the starting ester, then by an analogous method diethyl vinylphosphonate can be obtained in 95% yield [77].

Dimethyl α-ethoxyvinylphosphonate $CH_2 = C(OC_2H_5)PO(OC_2H_5)_2$ [80]

$$BrCH_2CH(OC_2H_5)PO(OC_2H_5)_2 + KOH \longrightarrow CH_2 = C(OC_2H_5)PO(OC_2H_5)_2 + KBr + H_2O$$

A flask, fitted with a mechanical stirrer, reflux condenser and dropping funnel, was charged with a 2% solution of caustic potash in dry ethanol (100 ml). Dimethyl β-bromo-α-ethoxyethylphosphonate (9 g) was added slowly, with stirring, to the ice-cooled solution. At the end of the addition the reaction mixture was heated to boiling. The precipitated potassium bromide was filtered off and washed with small portions of dry ethanol. Ethanol was evaporated from the combined filtrate and washings and the residue was distilled *in vacuo.* After two distillations, pure dimethyl *a*-ethoxyvinylphosphonate (4·7 g, 75·3%) was obtained as a colourless, mobile liquid with a characteristic smell, b.p. 122–123°/10 mm, n_D^{20} 1·4462, d_4^{20} 1·1702.

Of immense importance for the synthesis of esters of organophosphorus acids is the rearrangement — it is confined to organophosphorus compounds — discovered by A. Ye. Arbusov [86]. The essential feature of this rearrangement (it is considered in detail below) is the conversion of esters of acids of trivalent phosphorus into esters of pentavalent phosphorus under the influence of halogen-containing compounds as follows:

$$R'X + P(OR)_3 \longrightarrow \overset{R'}{\underset{X\quad OR}{\diagdown P(OR)_2}} \longrightarrow R'PO(OR)_2 + RX$$

where X = halogen.

In recent years it has been shown that the Arbusov rearrangement also takes place between aldehydes, sulphides and certain other compounds and esters of acids of trivalent phosphorus. Hundreds of different esters of phosphonic acids, a number of then unsaturated, have been obtained by means of the Arbusov rearrangement.

At the end of the last century, Michaelis and Becker [87] discovered, and later on Nylen [88], in particular, worked on, a method of obtaining esters of alkylphosphonic acids which involved the reaction of alkyl halides with sodium dialkyl phosphites:

$$R'X + NaPO(OR)_2 \longrightarrow R'PO(OR)_2 + NaX$$

This method of Michaelis and Becker may be used for the synthesis of compounds which can be obtained by the Arbusov rearrangement, but it is not so generally applicable because of the side reactions which occur in many cases. The yields of the esters of alkylphosphonic acids are also usually lower by the Michaelis and Becker method than by the Arbusov. By utilizing these methods, Soviet and foreign chemists have synthesized many esters of allyl- [89–93], butenyl- [94–95], methoxypentenyl- [96–97], butoxypentenyl- [98] and acryloyl- [99–101] phosphonic acids, and other unsaturated organophosphorus acids [102, 103].

A special case of the Arbusov rearrangement, which gives a method for obtaining esters of carboxyalkyl-phosphonic acids, has been carried out by Arbusov and Dunin [104] as follows:

$$R'OOC{-}R''{-}X + P(OR)_3 \longrightarrow R'OOC{-}R''{-}PO(OR)_2 + RX$$

By means of this reaction and also that of Michaelis and Becker, a range of esters of carboxyalkyl-phosphonic acids of general formula $R'OOC{-}R''{-}{-}PO(OR)_2$, where R and R'' are saturated radicals and R' is vinyl, allyl or other unsaturated radical, has been synthesized [101, 105–107].

Dimethyl allylphosphonate $CH_2 = CHCH_2PO(OCH_3)_2$ [90]

$$CH_2 = CHCH_2Br \neq P(OCH_3)_3 \longrightarrow CH_2 = CHCH_2PO(OCH_3)_2 + CH_3Br$$

(1) Trimethyl phosphite (35 g) and double the quantity of allyl bromide (66–68 g) were heated together in a sealed tube at 60–65° for 3 hr. Distillation of the product gave unchanged allyl bromide (about 40 g), dimethyl methylphosphonate (about 5 g), an intermediate fraction and pure dimethyl allylphosphonate (10 g, about 25%).

(2) Trimethyl phosphite (35 g) and allyl bromide (100 g) were heated together in a flask fitted with a reflux condenser. The top of the condenser was connected to a trap, cooled in ice-salt, for the methyl bromide evolved. The mixture was heated for 5 hr at 76–78° (thermometer in the liquid) and methyl bromide (21 g, about theoretical) was collected. The reaction mixture was then distilled to give allyl bromide (55 g) and then, *in vacuo*, the product, dimethyl allylphosphonate (32 g, 76%), b. p. 90–92°/13 mm, d_0^0 1·1378, d_0^{20} 1·1160, n_D^{20} 1·4320.

Dibutyl allylphosphonate $CH_2 = CHCH_2PO(OC_4H_9)_2$ [92]

$$CH_2 = CHCH_2Cl + NaPO(OC_4H_9)_2 \longrightarrow CH_2 = CHCH_2PO(OC_4H_9)_2 + NaCl$$

To the sodium dibutyl phosphite obtained from dibutyl hydrogen phosphite (98 g) and sodium (11 g) in hexane (500 ml), was added allyl chloride (39 g) over 30 min. This mixture was refluxed for 30 min and then treated, with exterior cooling, with iced water (100 ml). The lower layer thus produced was extracted with hexane, the extract was combined with the upper layer, and this mixture was thrice washed with water (about 50 ml). Distillation gave the crude product (16·5 g), b. p. 151°/5 mm. From another reaction [refluxing the mixture for 6 hr and washing the product in hexane with water (500 ml)] a further amount of crude product (15 g) was obtained. In both cases some of the much higher boiling diphosphonate ester was obtained.

Fractional distillation of the crude product (from both experiments) gave pure dibutyl allylphosphonate (17 g), b. p. 110°/0·4 mm, n_D^{25} 1·4336; d_{25}^{25} 0·9548.

If allyl bromide is substituted for allyl chloride and the process carried out in xylene (400 ml) for 3 hr then the yield of product is increased to 39 g.

A simple and general method for obtaining esters of various unsaturated phosphonic acids containing hydroxy- and carbonyl-groups has been discovered by Pudovik. The method involves the addition of dialkyl hydrogen phosphites and phosphorothioites to unsaturated aldehydes [108, 109] and to β,β-dimethyldivinyl ketone [110] in the presence of alkali metal alkoxides. For example:

$$CH_2 = CHCHO + HPO(OR)_2 \longrightarrow CH_2 = CHCHOHPO(OR)_2$$

This reaction usually gives good yields.

The properties of esters of unsaturated organophosphorus acids and saturated alcohols are recorded in Tables 13–27 (cf. pp. 30–45).

TABLE 13. ESTERS OF THE TYPE $CH_2=CXPO(OR)_2$, WHERE $X = H$, Br, RO, CH_3CO_2

Formula	b. p., °C (mm)	n_D^{20}	d_4^{20}	Yield (%)	Reference
$CH_2 = CHPO(OCH_3)_2$	72·5 (10)	1·4330	1·1405	44	[7]
	82–84 (3·5)	1·4305	1·1696	80	[227]
$CH_2 = CHPO(OC_2H_5)_2$	68–70 (3)	1·4300	1·0526	42	[75]
	50 (1)	1·4260 (25°)		95	[77]
$CH_2 = CHPO(OCH_2CH_2Cl)_2$	137–139 (4)	1·4772	1·3182		[75]
	135–137 (4)	1·4787	1·3233	70	[228]
$CH_2{=}CHP{\big\langle}{\overset{O-CH_2}{\underset{O-CH_2}{}}}{\big\rangle}CH_2$ (‖O)	129–130(2)	1·4775	1.2570	53	[7]
$CH_2 = CHPO(OR)_2$ R					
—C_3H_7	83–85 (3)	1·4350	1·0057	45	[229]
—C_3H_7-iso	58–60 (5)	1·4268	0·9908	16	[7]
—C_4H_9	101–102 (1·2)	1·4300	0·9757		[84]
	115–116 (5)	1·4372	0·9810	63·6	[219]
—C_4H_9-iso	78–78·5 (3)	1·4356	0·9730	50	[230]
—C_5H_{11}-iso	129 (13)	1·4400	0·9619	50	[229]
—C_6H_{13}	62 ($<1\times10^{-3}$)	1·4450	0·9515	54	[229]
—C_7H_{15}	64 ($<1\times10^{-3}$)	1·4478	0·9412	46	[229]
—$C_6H_5CH_2$	62 ($<1\times10^{-3}$)	1·5519	1·1647	35	[230]
—sec C_8H_{17}	66 ($<1\times10^{-3}$)	1·4454	0·9234	14	[229]
—C_6H_5	142 (2)	1·5555	1·1947	70–80	[231]
—C_6H_4Cl-4	186–189 (3)	1·5681	1·3422	70–80	[231]
—$C_6H_3(CH_3)_2$-3,4	180–183 (2)	1·5520	1·1448	70–80	[231]
—$C_6H_3(CH_3)_2$-3,5	190–192 (2–3)	1·5512	1·1439	70–80	[231]
$CH_2 = CBrPO(OC_2H_5)_2$	88–90 (3)	1·4681	1·4051		[7]
$CH_2 = C(OC_2H_5)PO(OCH_3)_2$	122–123 (10)	1·4462	1·1702	75·3	[80]
$CH_2 = C(OC_2H_5)PO(OC_2H_5)_2$	128–129 (13)	1·4420	1·0802	61·8	[79]
	128 (10)	1·4408	1·0930	76·6	[80]
$CH_2 = C(OC_2H_5)PO(OC_4H_9)_2$	164–166 (13)	1·4426	1·0182	79·1	[80]
$CH_2 = C(OC_2H_5)PO(OC_4H_9$-iso$)_2$	148–149 (10)	1·4378	0·9954	77·2	[80]
$CH_2 = C(OC_3H_7$-iso$)PO(OC_2H_5)_2$	115–117 (4)	1·4379	1·0462	66·5	[81]
$CH_2 = C(OC_3H_7$-iso$)PO(OC_4H_9)_2$	162–165 (5)	1·4432	1·0157		[81]
$CH_2 = C(OC_4H_9)PO(OC_2H_5)_2$	131·5 (6)	1·4400	1·0263	68	[79]
	134–135 (5)	1·4430	1·0485	37·8	[81]
$CH_2 = C(OCOCH_3)PO(OC_2H_5)_2$*	78 (0·5)	1·436		85–90	[232]
$CH_2 = C(OCOCH_3)PO(OC_3H_7)_2$*	98 (0·5)	1·437		85–90	[232]
$CH_2 = C(OCOCH_3)PO(OC_3H_7$-iso$)_2$*	88 (0·5)	1·433		85–90	[232]

TABLE 14. ESTERS OF THE TYPE $XCH=CHPO(OR)_2$, WHERE $X = Cl$, RO, ROC_2H_4O, RS

Formula		b. p., °C (mm)	n_D^{20}	d_4^{20}	Yield (%)	Reference
$ClCH = CHPO(OC_4H_9)_2$		119–120 (4)	1·4502	1·0712		[84]
$ROCH = CH—PO(OR')_2$						
R	R'					
$C_2H_5—$	$—CH_3$	87 (2)	1·4508	1·1451	56	[63]
$C_2H_5—$	$—C_2H_5$	99·5 (2)	1·4476	1·0710	45	[63]
$C_2H_5—$	$—C_2H_4OCH_3$	155 (2)	1·4568	1·1267	76	[63]
$C_2H_5—$	$—C_2H_4OC_2H_5$	158 (1)	1·4545	1·0842	70	[63]
$C_2H_5—$	$—C_3H_7$	103 (1·5)	1·4475	1·0335	70	[63]
$C_2H_5—$	$—iso-C_3H_7$	91 (2)	1·4402	1·0171	50	[63]
$C_2H_5—$	$—C_4H_9$	127 (2)	1·4492	1·0069	75	[63]
$C_2H_5—$	$—iso-C_4H_9$	107 (0·5)	1·4453	1·0004	75	[63]
$C_2H_5—$	$—C_6H_{13}$	157–158 (2)	1·4511	0·9710		[63]
$CH_3OC_2H_4—$	$—CH_3$	124 (1)	1·4590	1·1747	77·9	[68]
$CH_3OC_2H_4—$	$—C_2H_5$	134 (1)	1·4525	1·1067	76	[68]
$CH_3OC_2H_4—$	$—C_2H_4OCH_3$	171 (1)	1·4620	1·1467	70	[68]
$CH_3OC_2H_4—$	$—C_2H_4OC_2H_5$	175 (1)	1·4570	1·1088	76	[68]
$CH_3OC_2H_4—$	$—C_3H_7$	143 (1)	1·4510	1·0585	88	[68]
$CH_3OC_2H_4—$	$—iso-C_3H_7$	134 (2)	1·4469	1·0529	77	[68]
$CH_3OC_2H_4—$	$—C_4H_9$	153 (1)	1·4518	1·0354	75	[68]
$CH_3OC_2H_4—$	$—iso-C_4H_9$	148 (1)	1·4500	1·0341	77	[68]
$CH_3OC_2H_4—$	$—C_6H_{13}$	180 (1)	1·4540	1·0004	80	[68]
$CH_3OC_2H_4—$	$—C_7H_{15}$	190 (1)	1·4562	0·9845	62	[68]
$C_2H_5OC_2H_4—$	$—CH_3$	126 (2)	1·4528	1·1429	76	[68]
$C_2H_5OC_2H_4—$	$—C_2H_5$	133 (2)	1·4512	1·0812	78	[68]
$C_2H_5OC_2H_4—$	$—C_2H_4OCH_3$	163 (1)	1·4602	1·1279	84	[68]
$C_2H_5OC_2H_4—$	$—C_2H_4OC_2H_5$	180 (1)	1·4546	1·0917	86	[68]
$C_2H_5OC_2H_4—$	$—C_3H_7$	140 (2)	1·4510	1·0470	80	[68]
$C_2H_5OC_2H_4—$	$—iso-C_3H_7$	125 (2)	1·4452	1·0341	72	[68]
$C_2H_5OC_2H_4—$	$—iso-C_4H_9$	143 (2)	1·4492	1·0159	82	[68]
$C_2H_5OC_2H_4—$	$—C_7H_{15}$	200 (1)	1·4546	0·9745	88	[68]
$C_4H_9OC_2H_4—$	$—CH_3$	132 (1)	1·4565	1·1100	77	[68]
$C_4H_9OC_2H_4—$	$—C_2H_5$	155 (2)	1·4519	1·0815	79	[68]
$C_4H_9OC_2H_4—$	$—C_2H_4OC_2H_5$	193 (2)	1·4561	1·0643	87	[68]
$C_4H_9OC_2H_4—$	$—C_3H_7$	163 (2)	1·4529	1·0199	83	[68]
$C_4H_9OC_2H_4—$	$—C_4H_9$	180 (2)	1·4532	1·0008	88	[68]
$C_4H_9OC_2H_4—$	$—iso-C_4H_9$	172 (2)	1·4512	1·0002	83	[68]

TABLE 14 — *(contd.)*

Formula		b.p., °C (mm)	n_D^{20}	d_4^{20}	Yield (%)	Reference
R	R′					
$C_4H_9OC_2H_4$—	—C_6H_{13}	202 (2)	1·4550	0·9794	85	[68]
$C_4H_9OC_2H_4$—	—C_7H_{15}	207 (1)	1·4553	0·9644	89	[68]
C_3H_7—	—CH_3	95 (1)	1·4500	1·1095		[63]
C_3H_7—	—C_2H_5	106 (1)	1·4455	1·0523		[63]
C_3H_7—	—$C_2H_4OCH_3$	158 (1)	1·4565	1·1089		[63]
C_3H_7—	—$C_2H_4OC_2H_5$	156 (2)	1·4580	1·0694		[63]
C_3H_7—	—C_3H_7	128 (2)	1·4471	1·0201	60	[63]
C_3H_7—	iso-C_3H_7	110 (2)	1·4402	1·0042		[63]
C_3H_7—	—C_4H_9	139 (2)	1·4485	0·9969	64	[63]
C_3H_7—	iso-C_4H_9	121 (2)	1·4449	0·9906		[63]
C_3H_7—	—C_6H_{13}	157 (1)	1·4509	0·9664		[63]
iso-C_3H_7—	—CH_3	94–95 (2)	1·4438	1·1042	62	[64]
iso-C_3H_7—	—C_2H_5	103 (1)	1·4428	1·0450		[64]
iso-C_3H_7—	—$C_2H_4OCH_3$	155 (3)	1·4555	1·1002	57	[64]
iso-C_3H_7—	—$C_2H_4OC_2H_5$	155 (1)	1·4520	1·0652		[64]
iso-C_3H_7—	—C_3H_7	113 (1)	1·4439	1·0141	72	[64]
iso-C_3H_7—	iso-C_3H_7	99 (2)	1·4360	0·9973		[64]
iso-C_3H_7—	—C_4H_9	132–133 (2)	1·4460	0·9910		[64]
iso-C_3H_7—	iso-C_4H_9	116 (1)	1·4440	0·9847		[64]
iso-C_3H_7—	—C_6H_{13}	149 (2)	1·4498	0·9628		[64]
C_4H_9—	—CH_3	111 (2)	1·4515	1·0867	51	[63]
C_4H_9—	—C_2H_5	116 (2)	1·4460	1·0360		[63]
C_4H_9—	—$C_2H_4OCH_3$	161 (2)	1·4558	1·0873	55	[63]
C_4H_9—	—$C_2H_4OC_2H_5$	164 (2)	1·4532	1·0584	50	[63]
C_4H_9—	—C_3H_7	123 (2)	1·4478	1·0060	68	[63]
C_4H_9—	iso-C_3H_7	105 (2)	1·4401	0·9916		[63]
C_4H_9—	—C_4H_9	144 (2)	1·4491	0·9879	67	[63]
C_4H_9—	iso-C_4H_9	131·5 (2)	1·4460	0·9810	63	[63]
C_4H_9—	—C_6H_{13}	164–165 (2)	1·4518	0·9635	57	[63]
iso-C_4H_9—	—CH_3	105 (2)	1·4487	1·0831	75	[64]
iso-C_4H_9—	—C_2H_5	110 (2)	1·4435	1·0310	73	[64]
iso-C_4H_9—	—$C_2H_4OCH_3$	163 (2)	1·4543	1·0900		[64]
iso-C_4H_9—	—$C_2H_4OC_2H_5$	170 (2)	1·4509	1·0533		[64]
iso-C_4H_9—	—C_3H_7	124 (2)	1·4442	1·0014		[64]
iso-C_4H_9—	iso-C_3H_7	120 (2)	1·4405	0·9948		[64]
iso-C_4H_9—	—C_4H_9	144 (1)	1·4470	0·9849	70	[64]
iso-C_4H_9—	iso-C_4H_9	135 (2)	1·4440	0·9804		[64]

TABLE 14 — *(contd.)*

Formula		b.p., °C (mm)	n_D^{29}	d_4^{20}	Yield (%)	Reference
R	R′					
iso-C_4H_9—	—C_6H_{13}	165 (1)	1·4498	0·9597		[64]
iso-C_5H_{11}—	—CH_3	109·5 (1)	1·4508	1·0667		[64]
iso-C_5H_{11}—	—C_2H_5	119 (1)	1·4464	1·0928		[64]
iso-C_5H_{11}—	—$C_2H_4OCH_3$	173 (1)	1·4550	1·0758		[64]
iso-C_5H_{11}—	—$C_2H_4OC_2H_5$	179 (1)	1·4527	1·0453		[64]
iso-C_5H_{11}—	—C_3H_7	132 (1)	1·4482	0·9960		[64]
iso-C_5H_{11}—	—iso-C_3H_7	120 (2)	1·4418	0·9866		[64]
iso-C_5H_{11}—	—C_4H_9	148 (1)	1·4490	0·9896		[64]
iso-C_5H_{11}—	—iso-C_4H_9	145 (2)	1·4458	0·9734		[64]
iso-C_5H_{11}—	—C_6H_{13}	171 (1)	1·4500	0·9618		[64]
C_6H_{13}—	—CH_3	125 (2)	1·4530	1·0489		[63]
C_6H_{13}—	—C_2H_5	136 (2)	1·4495	1·0110		[63]
C_6H_{13}—	—$C_2H_4OCH_3$	171 (2)	1·4560	1·0632		[63]
C_6H_{13}—	—$C_2H_4OC_2H_5$	188 (2)	1·4593	1·0348		[63]
C_6H_{13}—	—C_3H_7	138–139 (2)	1·4500	0·9891		[63]
C_6H_{13}—	—iso-C_3H_7	129 (2)	1·4402	0·9804		[63]
C_6H_{13}—	—C_4H_9	156 (1)	1·4496	0·9723		[63]
C_6H_{13}—	—iso-C_4H_9	151 (1)	1·4475	0·9660		[63]
C_6H_{13}—	—C_6H_{13}	190 (2)	1·4528	0·9515		[63]
C_6H_5—	—CH_3	128 (2)	1·5233	1·2871		[65]
C_6H_5—	—C_2H_5	140 (2)	1·5070	1·1367		[65]
C_6H_5—	—$C_2H_4OCH_3$	188 (2)	1·5070	1·1755		[65]
C_6H_5—	—$C_2H_4OC_2H_5$	198 (2)	1·5014	1·1386		[65]
C_6H_5—	—C_3H_7	147 (2)	1·4994	1·0934		[65]
C_6H_5—	—iso-C_3H_7	135 (2)	1·4970	1·0870		[65]
C_6H_5—	—C_4H_9	165 (2)	1·4971	1·0648		[65]
C_6H_5—	—iso-C_4H_9	157 (2)	1·4938	1·0596		[65]
C_6H_5—	—C_6H_{13}	204 (1)	1·4925	1·0237		[65]
$RSCH = CHPO(OR′)_2$						
R	R′					
C_2H_5—	—$C_2H_4OCH_3$	160–161 (1)	1·4925	1·1512		[42]
C_2H_5—	—$C_2H_4OC_2H_5$	168 (1)	1·4865	1·1056		[42]
C_2H_5—	—C_3H_7	147 (2)	1·4930	1·0807		[42]
C_2H_5—	—C_4H_9	168 (3)	1·4890	1·0317		[42]
C_2H_5—	—C_6H_{13}	165 (1)	1·4808	1·0059		[42]
C_4H_9—	—C_4H_9	153–154 (2)	1·4848	1·0235		[42]
C_4H_9—	—C_6H_{13}	201 (2)	1·4790	1·0009		[42]

TABLE 15. ESTERS OF THE TYPE $CH_2=CRPO(OR')_2$ WHERE
$R = CH_3$, CN, CO_2R, $C_2H_4CO_2C_2H_5$

Formula	b. p., °C (mm)	n_D^{20}	d_4^{20}	Yield (%)	Reference
$CH_2 = C(CH_3)PO(OCH_3)_2$	44–46 (1–2)	1·4340			[28, 53]
$CH_2 = C(CH_3)PO(OC_4H_9)_2$	86–87 (0·25)	1·4376			[28, 53]
$CH_2 = C(CH_3)PO(OC_6H_5)_2$	160–180 (0·4)				[28, 53]
$CH_2 = C(CN)PO(OCH_3)_2$ or $CN—CH = CHPO(OCH_3)_2$	95–96 (2)	1·4327	1·2458		[227]
$CH_2 = C(CN)PO(OC_2H_5)_2$ or $CN—CH = CH—PO(OC_2H_5)_2$	124–127 (1)	1·4350	1·1277*	26·4	[215]
$CH_2 = C(CN)PO(OC_4H_9)_2$	136–138 (15)	1·4208	1·0006	30·0	[82]
$CH_2 = C(COOCH_3)PO(OCH_3)_2$	106 (2)	1·4412	1·1268	76	[227]
$CH_2 = C(COOCH_3)PO(OC_2H_5)_2$	118–119 (3)	1·4348	1·1621	75	[227]
$CH_2 = C(COOCH_3)PO(OC_4H_9)_2$	125–126 (5)	1·4205	1·0143	20·7	[82]
$CH_2 = C(COOC_2H_5)PO(OC_2H_5)_2$	99–100 (17)	1·4114	1·0684	44·2	[82]
$CH_2 = C(C_2H_4COOC_2H_5)PO(OC_2H_5)_2$	145–165 (2)	1·4790			[233]

* d_{20}^{20}.

TABLE 16. ESTERS OF THE TYPE $RCH=CHPO(OR')_2$,
WHERE $R=CH_3$, ROOC, C_2H_5; $(CH_3)_2C=CHPO(OR)_2$;
$C_5H_{11}CCl=CHPO(OR)_2$; $ROOCCH=C(C_6H_5)P\langle\substack{C_2H_5 \\ \parallel \\ O}^{}\rangle OR$

Formula	b. p., °C (mm)	n_D^{20}	d_4^{20}	Yield (%)	Reference
$CH_3CH = CHPO(OC_2H_5)_2$	78–81 (2)	1·4320 (21)			[76]
$CH_3OOCCH = CHP\langle\substack{OCH_3 \\ \parallel \\ O}^{}\rangle OC_2H_5$	90–92 (1)				[100]
$CH_3OOCCH = CHPO(OC_2H_5)_2$	109–110 (1)	1·4483			[102]
$CH_3OOCCH = CHPO(OC_4H_9)_2$	130–133 (1)				[100]
$C_2H_5OOCCH = CHPO(OCH_3)_2$	80–81 (1)				[100]
$(CH_3)_2C = CHPO(OC_2H_5)_2$	107 (5)	1·441	1·038		[37]
$C_2H_5CH = CHPO(OC_2H_5)_2$	99–100 (1)	1·4376 (29·6°)	1·0112 (29·6°)	46·3	[78]
$C_5H_{11}CCl = CHPO(OC_2H_5)_2$	152 (17)				[14]
$C_2H_5OOCCH = C—POOC_2H_5$ (with C_2H_5 above and C_6H_5 below)	147–148 (0·5)	1·5082	1·1054	30	[74]

TABLE 17. ESTERS OF THE TYPE $C_6H_5CX=CHPO(OR)_2$,
WHERE $X=H$, Cl; $C_6H_5C(CH_3)=CHPO(OR_2)$;
$C_6H_8PO(OR_2)$, WHERE $C_9H_8 = $ INDENYL

Formula	b.p., °C (mm)	n_D^{20}	d_4^{20}	Yield (%)	Reference
$C_6H_5CH = CHPO(OR)_2$					
R					
—CH_3	m.p. 129 (2); 41–42°			57	[70]
—C_2H_5	138 (2)	1·5325	1·1082	67	[70]
—$C_2H_4OCH_3$	176 (2)	1·5246	1·1501		[70]
—$C_2H_4OC_2H_5$	187 (2)	1·5179	1·1114		[70]
—C_3H_7	158 (2)	1·5230	1·0700	75	[70]
—iso-C_3H_7	137 (1)	1·5164	1·0547	26	[70]
—C_4H_9	172–173 (2)	1·5153	1·0403	81	[70]
—iso-C_4H_9	159 (2)	1·5130	1·0342	67	[70]
—iso-C_5H_{11}	200–212 (4)				[234]
—C_6H_{13}	187·5 (2)	1·5500	1·0054		[70]
—C_7H_{15}	213 (2)	1·5020	0·9888	65	[70]
—C_8H_{17}	238–240 (3)		0·973		[37]
—C_6H_5	m.p. 109°			85	[37]
$C_6H_5CCl = CHPO(OR)_2$					
R					
—CH_3	148–149 (1)	1·5595	1·2812	48	[71]
—C_2H_5	159 (2)	1·5410	1·2070	65	[71]
—C_3H_7	166 (2)	1·5288	1·1584	66	[71]
—iso-C_3H_7	149 (1)	1·5220	1·1424		[71]
—C_4H_9	176 (1)	1·5212	1·1202	81	[71]
—iso-C_4H_9	165 (1)	1·5188	1·1168	60	[71]
$C_6H_5C(CH_3) = CHPO(OC_2H_5)_2$	149–150 (1·5)	1·5190	1·1009*	33·5	[215]
—PO(OR)$_2$					
R					
—CH_3	146 (2)	1·5603	1·2109	50·3	[72]
—C_2H_5	150 (1)	1·5398	1·1410	60	[72]
—C_3H_7	162 (1)	1·5298	1·1392	60	[72]
—C_6H_{13}	206 (2)	1·5100	1·0220	63	[72]

* d_{20}^{20}.

3*

TABLE 18. ESTERS OF THE TYPE

$$CX_2 = C\diagup^{A}_{\diagdown O-A} \; , \quad RCH = C\diagup^{A}_{\diagdown O-A} \; , \quad R_2C = C\diagup^{A}_{\diagdown O-A} \; ,$$

$$RC = CHA \atop | \atop O-A \quad , \quad R_2C = C\diagup^{A}_{\diagdown CHR-A} \; ,$$

where $A = PO(OR)_2$; $X = H, Cl$; $R = CH_3$

Formula	b.p., °C (mm)	n_D^{20}	d_4^{20}	Yield (%)	Reference
$CH_2 = CPO(OCH_3)_2$ | $OPO(OCH_3)_2$	141 (1)	1·4420	1·3214	84	[168]
$CH_2 = CPO(OC_2H_5)_2$ | $OPO(OC_2H_5)_2$	125–126 (0·5)	1·4396	1·1827	86·4	[168]
$CCl_2 = CPO(OCH_3)_2$ | $OPO(OCH_3)_2$	134–135 (0·75)	1·4770	1·4901	78·3	[168]
$CCl_2 = CPO(OC_2H_5)_2$ | $OPO(OC_2H_5)_2$	132–133 (0·5)	1·4660	1·3219		[168]
$CH_3CH = CPO(OC_2H_5)_2$ | $OPO(OC_2H_5)_2$	128–129 (1·5)	1·4450	1·1690	78·6	[168]
$CH_3C = CHPO(OC_2H_5)_2$ | $OPO(OC_2H_5)_2$	161–162 (1)	1·4478	1·1762	59	[167]
$(CH_3)_2C = CPO(OCH_3)_2$ | $OPO(OCH_3)_2$	131–132 (0·5)	1·4580	1·2756	92·3	[168]
$(CH_3)_2C = CPO(OC_2H_5)_2$ | $OPO(OC_2H_5)_2$	134–135 (1·5)	1·4503	1·1602	90·7	[168]
$(CH_3)_2C = CPO(OCH_3)_2$ | $CH(CH_3)PO(OCH_3)_2$	180–182 (6)	1·4782	1·2218		[103]
$(CH_3)_2C = CPO(OC_2H_5)_2$ | $CH(C_2H_5)PO(OC_2H_5)_2$	183–185 (6)	1·4598	1·1171		[103]
$(CH_3)_2C = CPO(OC_4H_9)_2$ | $CH(C_4H_9)PO(OC_4H_9)_2$	207–210 (3)	1·4612	1·0505		[103]

TABLE 19. ESTERS OF β,γ-UNSATURATED PHOSPHONIC ACIDS*

Formula		b.p., °C (mm)	n_D^{20}	d_4^{20}	Yield (%)	Reference
RPO(OR′)₂						
R	**R′**					
$CH_2 = CHCH_2-$	$-CH_3$	90–92 (13)	1·4320	1·1160⁺	76	[90]
$CH_2 = CHCH_2-$	$-CH_2\diagdown\diagup CH_2$ $-CH_2$	m.p. 78°			74·3	[91]
$CH_2 = CHCH_2-$	$-CH_3, -C_2H_5$	50–52 (1)				[235]
$CH_2 = CHCH_2-$	$-CH_2\diagdown CH_2\diagup$ $-CH$ CH_3	130–131 (3)	1·4680	1·1540⁺	74·4	[91]
$CH_2 = CHCH_2-$	$-C_2H_5$	90–91 (12) 100 (13)	1·4312	1·0380 1·0416*	17	[84] [89]
$CH_2 = CHCH_2-$	$-iso\text{-}C_3H_7$	96·5–97 (11)	1·4295 (17°)	1·0362 (17°)	70	[90]
		64–65 (35)	1·4277 (18°)	0·9828 (18°)	65	[90]
$CH_2 = CHCH_2-$	$-C_4H_9$	110 (0·4)	1·4336 (25°)	0·9548 (25°)		[92]
$CH_3OCH = CHCH_2-$	$-CH_3$	125–126 (8)	1·4432	1·1570	30·0	[236]
$CH_3OCH = CHCH_2-$	$-C_2H_5$	123–124 (3)	1·4435	1·0985	34·5	[236]
$C_2H_5OCH = CHCH_2-$	$-C_2H_5$	132–134 (3)	1·4442	1·0603	19·2	[236]
$C_3H_7OCH = CHCH_2-$	$-C_3H_7$	153–155 (5)	1·4426	1·0089	11·0	[236]
$C_4H_9OCH = CHCH_2-$	$-C_4H_9$	156–157 (3)	1·4460	0·9806	40·6	[236]
$iso\text{-}C_4H_9OCH = CHCH_2-$	$iso\text{-}C_4H_9$	150–151 (3)	1·4430	0·9750	17·4	[236]
$C_2H_5OCH = CHCH(CH_3)-$	$-C_2H_5$	136–138 (1)	1·4506	1·0436	17·1	[236]
$C_3H_7OCH = CHCH(CH_3)-$	$-C_3H_7$	152–154 (3)	1·4496	1·0046	12·9	[236]
$CH_2 = C(CH_3)CH_2-$	$-C_2H_5$	108–117 (17)	1·4710	0·9858	42	[235]
$CH_2 = C(CN)CH_2-$	$-CH_3$	137–140 (1)				[236]
$CH_2 = C(CN)CH_2-$	$-C_2H_5$	150–153 (2)				[236]
$CH_2 = C(CN)CH_2-$	$-C_3H_7$	174–176 (1–2)				[236]
$CH_2 = C(CN)CH_2-$	$-C_4H_9$	182–185 (2)				[236]
$CH_2 = C(COOCH_3)CH_2-$	$-C_2H_5$	172–174 (13)				[61]
$CH_3CH = CHCH_2-$	$-C_2H_5$	121·5–122 (19)	1·4380	1·0219	45	[94]

TABLE 19 — *(contd.)*

Formula	b. p., °C (mm)	n_D^{20}	d_4^{20}	Yield (%)	Reference
$[C_2H_5O)_2P(O)CH_2CH =]_2$	226 (15)	1·4547	1·1247	53	[95]
A compound with a similar structure, with the position of the double bond unknown	215–216 (10)	1·4559	1·1280		[237]

RPO(OR′)₂

R	R′					
$(CH_3)_2C = CHCH_2—$	$—C_2H_5$	117–118 (13)	1·4450	1·0080		[97]
$CH_3OC_2H_4CH = CHCH_2—$	$—CH_3$	144 (10)	1·4530	1·0950	37·6	[96]
$CH_3OC_2H_4CH = CHCH_2—$	$—C_2H_5$	146–147 (8)	1·4480	1·0380	63	[96]
$CH_3OC_2H_4CH = CHCH_2—$	$—iso\text{-}C_4H_9$	145–146 (3)	1·4455	0·9819	63	[96]
$C_4H_9OC_2H_4CH = CHCH_2—$	$—C_2H_5$	169–171 (9)	1·4462	0·9918	78·5	[98]
$C_4H_9OC_2H_4CH = CHCH_2—$	$—C_4H_9$	190–191 (7)	1·4478	0·9685	49	[98]
$C_2H_5OOCCH_2CH = CHCH_2—$	$—CH_3$	172–173 (11)	1·4552	1·1528		[237]
$C_2H_5OOCCH_2CH = CHCH_2—$	$—C_2H_5$	167–168 (10)	1·4489	1·0851		[237]
$CH_3OC_2H_4C(CH_3) = CHCH_2—$	$—C_2H_5$	140–142 (8)	1·4530	1·0131		[97]
$CH_3CH = CHCH—$ ꜜ $C_4H_9OOCCH_2$	$—C_4H_9$	200 (1·4)		0·997	18·3	[238]
$CH_2 = CHCH_2P(O)OCH_3$ ꜜ C_6H_5		107–111 (1–2)				[239]
$C_2H_5OCH = CHCH_2P(O)OC_2H_5$ ꜜ C_6H_5		150–152 (0·5)	1·5136	1·0389⁺	11·2	[240]
$CH_2 = CCH_2PO(OC_2H_5)_2$ ꜜ $OPO(OC_2H_5)_2$		193–195 (9)	1·4435	1·1623		[166]

* With the exception of esters of hydroxy- and keto-phosphonic acids which are listed in Table 20, amido-esters which are listed in Table 12, and esters of the type

$\diagdown C = CPO(OR)_2$ which are listed in Table 18.

CHP—PO (OR)₂

$+ d_{20}^{20}$

$* d_{20}^{17}$

TABLE 20. ESTERS OF β,γ-UNSATURATED HYDROXY- AND KETO-PHOSPHONIC ACIDS

Formula		b.p., °C (mm)	n_D^{20}	d_{20}^4	Yield (%)	Reference
RPO(OR')$_2$						
R	R'					
CH$_2$ = CHCHOH—	—CH$_3$	149–151 (13)	1·4575	1·2188	66·2	[108]
CH$_2$ = CHCHOH—	—C$_2$H$_5$	154–155 (13)	1·4506	1·1225	77·1	[108]
CH$_2$ = CHCHOH—	—iso-C$_3$H$_7$	140–141 (7)	1·4415	1·0465	69·8	[108]
CH$_2$ = CHCHOH—	—C$_4$H$_9$	169–172 (13)	1·4411	1·0130	15·0	[108]
CH$_2$ = CHCHOH—	—iso-C$_4$H$_9$	168–170 (13)	1·4348	0·9968	14·0	[108]
CH$_3$CH = CHCHOH—	—CH$_3$	150–152 (8)	1·4630	1·1690		[108]
CH$_3$CH = CHCHOH—	—C$_2$H$_5$	163–164 (9)	1·4555	1·1005		[108]
(CH$_3$)$_2$C = CHC(CH$_3$)OH—	—CH$_3$	136 (12)	1·4457	1·1163		[108]
(CH$_3$)$_2$C = CHC(CH$_3$)OH—	—C$_2$H$_5$	138 (11)	1·4400	1·0675		[108]
(CH$_3$)$_2$C = CHC(CH$_3$)OH—	—C$_4$H$_9$	171–172 (13)	1·4440	1·0084		[108]
(CH$_3$)$_2$C = CHC(CH$_3$)OH—	—iso-C$_4$H$_9$	162–163 (12)	1·4409	1·0029		[108]
⟨O⟩—CH = CH—CHOH—	—C$_2$H$_5$	106–107*			87·2	[108]
C$_6$H$_5$CH = CHCHOH—	—CH$_3$	101–102*			87·0	[108]
C$_6$H$_5$CH = CHCHOH—	—C$_2$H$_5$	104–105*			75·4	[108]
CH$_2$ = CHCOPO(OCH$_3$)$_2$+						[101]
CH$_2$ = CHCOPO(OC$_2$H$_5$)$_2$		200–207 (5–10)	1·4519 (25°)			[241]
CH$_2$ = C(CH$_3$)COPO(OC$_2$H$_5$)$_2$+						[99]
CH$_3$C = CHC(CH$_3$)$_2$P(O)OC$_4$H$_9$ with O bridge		82–100 (2×10^{-4})	1·4590	1·110	20	[31]
CH$_3$C = CHC(CH$_3$)$_2$P(O)OC$_{10}$H$_{21}$ with O bridge		104–145 (1×10^{-4})	1·4580	0·98	2	[31]

* Melting point.

+ Polymerizes on distillation *in vacuo*.

TABLE 21. ESTERS OF γ,δ-UNSATURATED ALKYL- AND CYCLOALKYL-PHOSPHONIC ACIDS

Formula	b.p., °C (mm)	n_D^{20}	d_4^{20}	Yield (%)	Reference
$CH_2 = CHCHClCH_2PO(OR)_2$					
R					
—CH_3	112–114 (2)	1·4770	1·2365	50	[43]
—C_2H_5	122·5–123·5 (3)	1·4672	1·1532	52	[43]
—$C_2H_4OCH_3$	157–160 (2)	1·4720	1·1844	50	[43]
—$C_2H_4OC_2H_5$	165–167 (2)	1·4700	1·1348	62	[43]
—C_3H_7	121–123 (1)	1·4650	1·1011	65	[43]
—iso-C_3H_7	113–116 (2)	1·4585	1·0845	44	[43]
—C_4H_9	147 (2)	1·4625	1·0634	62	[43]
—iso-C_4H_9	124–126 (2)	1·4608	1·0504	67	[43]
—C_6H_{13}	160–162 (1)	1·4628	1·0158	58	[43]
$CH_2 = CHCH(OC_2H_5)CH_2PO(OC_2H_5)_2$	119–120 (7)	1·4231	1·044	17	[242]
$CH_2 = C(CH_3)CHClCH_2PO(OR)_2$					
R					
—CH_3	119–121 (3)	1·4805	1·1971	50	[44]
—C_2H_5	134–135 (5)	1·4698	1·1237	84	[44]
—$C_2H_4OCH_3$	148–150 (2)	1·4738	1·1370	55	[44]
—$C_2H_4OC_2H_5$	155–157 (2)	1·4672	1·0981	50	[44]
—C_3H_7	136–137 (3)	1·4668	1·0828	73	[44]
—iso-C_3H_7	127–128 (2)	1·4618	1·0712	70	[44]
—C_4H_9	140–141 (1)	1·4665	1·0530	75	[44]
—iso-C_4H_9	141–142 (3)	1·4639	1·0456	83	[44]
—C_6H_{13}	160–162 (2)	1·4642	1·0043	61	[44]
$CH_3CH = CHCH_2CH(COOC_2H_5)$— —$PO(OC_2H_5)_2$	156–157 (10)	1·4458	1·0617		[243]
$C_2H_5OOCCH=CHCH_2CH(CH_3)$— —$PO(OCH_3)_2$	170–171 (20)	1·4585	1·1311		[237]
$C_2H_5OOCCH = CHCH_2CH(CH_3)$— —$PO(OC_2H_5)_2$	165–166 (10)	1·4500	1·0638		[237]
$CH_3COCH = CHCH_2CH(CH_3)$— —$PO(OCH_3)_2$	153–155 (11)	1·4635	1·1184		[237]
$CH_3COCH = CHCH_2CH(CH_3)$— —$PO(OC_2H_5)_2$	163–164 (14)	1·4549	1·0542		[237]

TABLE 21 — (contd.)

Formula	b.p., °C (mm)	n_D^{20}	d_4^{20}	Yield (%)	Reference
$CH_3OC_2H_4CH = CHCH_2CH-$ $-(COOC_2H_5)PO(OC_2H_5)$	167–169 (4)	1·4526	1·0718		[243]
	88–89 (0·2)	1·4726	1·0042	96·6	[225]
		1·519			[225]
	115–118 (1)				[226]
	118–119 (3)	1·4488	1·0166	63·5	[219]
	155–156 (3)	1·4801	1·0379	65·2	[219]
	125–127 (7)	1·4505	1·9992	44·0	[219]
	156–157 (2)	1·4710	1·0042	36·4	[219]

TABLE 22. ESTERS OF OTHER UNSATURATED PHOSPHONIC ACIDS WITH ONE DOUBLE BOND

Formula	b.p., °C (mm)	n_D^{20}	d_4^{20}	Yield (%)	Reference
(structure: chlorinated bicyclic with $CH_2PO(OC_2H_5)_2$, CCl_2, Cl substituents)		1·519			[225]
$(CH_3)_2C = C = CHPO(OC_2H_5)_2$ (dimer)	205–206 (5)	1·4795	1·0992		[103]
$CH_2 = C(CH_3)[CH_2]_3PO(OC_2H_5)_2$	124 (8·5)	1·4418		45	[244]
$CH_2 = C(CH_3)[CH_2]_2C(CH_3)PO(OCH_3)_2$	125 (12)	1·4492			[244]
$(CH_3)_2C = CHCOC_2H_4PO(OCH_3)_2$	169–171 (13)	1·4711	1·1130	59	[110]
$(CH_3)_2C = CHCOC_2H_4PO(OC_2H_5)_2$	149 (3)	1·4660	1·0658	52	[110]
$(CH_3)_2C = CHCOC_2H_4PO(OC_4H_9)_2$	198–100 (12)	1·4623	1·0111	57	[110]
$(CH_3)_2C = CHCOC_2H_4PO(OC_4H_9\text{-iso})_2$	188–190 (10)	1·4511	1·0013	48·5	[110]
$(CH_3)_3CCH_2C\begin{smallmatrix}CH_2\\C_2H_4\end{smallmatrix}CH(CH_3)PO(OCH_3)_2$	125–127 (3·5)	1·4530			[244]
$CH_2 = CHCH_2As(C_6H_5)PO(OC_2H_5)_2$	142–143 (1)		1·2568		[245]
$CH_2 = CHCH_2OC_2H_4PO(OC_4H_9)_2$	156 (molecular still)				[246]
$CH_2 = CHCH_2OC_3H_6PO(OC_4H_9)_2$	156 (5–10)				[247]
$C_{17}H_{33}COOC_2H_4PO(OC_2H_5)_2$	184 (0·1)	1·4532 (30°)	0·9680 (30°)	53	[248]

TABLE 23. ESTERS OF UNSATURATED PHOSPHONIC ACIDS WITH TWO DOUBLE BONDS OR ONE TRIPLE BOND

Formula	b.p., °C (mm)	n_D^{20}	d_4^{20}	Yield (%)	Reference
$CH_2 = C = CHPO(OC_2H_5)_2$	140 (10)			31	[83]
$(CH_3)_2C = C = CHPO(OCH_3)_2$	117 (10)	1·4682	1·0852		[236]
$(CH_3)_2C = C = CHPO(OC_2H_5)_2$	120–122 (10)	1·4555	1·0237		[236]
$(CH_3)_2C = C = CHPO(OC_4H_9)_2$	131–132 (4)	1·4310	0·9594		[236]
$CH_2 = CH—CH = CHPO(OR)_2$					
R					
—CH_3	77–78·5 (3)	1·4835	1·1021	60	[43]
—C_2H_5	84–87 (2)	1·4728	1·0465	75	[43]
—$C_2H_4OCH_3$	135–138 (2)	1·4775	1·1287	46	[43]
—$C_2H_4OC_2H_5$	145–147 (2)	1·4690	1·0954	43	[43]
—C_3H_7	103–104 (1)	1·4700	1·0163	90	[43]

TABLE 23 — (contd.)

Formula	b.p., °C(mm)	n_D^{20}	d_4^{20}	Yield (%)	Reference
—iso-C_3H_7	83–84·5 (2)	1·4632	1·0030	87	[43]
—C_4H_9	129 (2)	1·4680	0·9922	65	[43]
—iso-C_4H_9	111–113 (2)	1·4642	0·9819	86	[43]
—C_6H_{13}	150–153 (2)	1·4600	0·9839	48	[43]
$CH_2 = CClCCl = CHPO(OCH_3)_2$ and $CHCl = CHCCl = CHPO(OCH_3)_2$ (mixture)	122–123 (1)	1·4940	1·3470	56	[52]
$CH_2 = C(CH_3)CH = CHPO(OR)_2$ R					
—CH_3	95–96 (3)	1·4868	1·1015	74	[44]
—C_2H_5	93–95 (2)	1·4768	1·0415	85	[44]
—$C_2H_4OCH_3$	151–152 (3)	1·4798	1·0978	47	[44]
—$C_2H_4OC_2H_5$	154–155 (1)	1·4705	1·0670	49·5	[44]
—C_3H_6	127–128 (3)	1·4728	1·0108	81	[44]
—iso-C_3H_7	93–94 (2·5)	1·4660	0·9911	79	[44]
—C_4H_9	118–119 (1)	1·4711	0·9854	84	[44]
—iso-C_4H_9	138–139 (5)	1·4678	0·9781	78	[44]
—C_6H_{13}	137–138 (3)	1·4678	0·9588	60	[44]
$CH_3CH = CHCH = CHCHOH$——$PO(OCH_3)_2$	153–154 (13)	1·4866	1·1165	17·5	[108]
$CH_3CH = CHCH = CHCHOH$——$PO(OC_2H_5)_2$	167–168 (17)	1·4774	1·0717	10·9	[108]
$CH_3C \equiv CPO(OC_2H_5)_2$	108–110 (2·1)	1·4449		69	[249]
$C_6H_5C \equiv CPO(OC_2H_5)_2$	155 (1)	1·5312	1·1500		[71]
$C_6H_5C \equiv CPO(OC_4H_9$-iso$)_2$	159–161 (1)	1·5090	1·0423		[71]

TABLE 24. UNSATURATED ESTERS OF ALKOXYCARBONYLALKYL-PHOSPHONIC ACIDS OF THE TYPE RO_2C—R'—$PO(OR'')_2$, WHERE R = UNSATURATED RADICAL

Formula	b. p., °C (mm)	n_D^{20}	d_4^{20}	Yield (%)	Reference
$CH_2 = CHOOCCH_2PO(OC_2H_5)_2$	103–104 (2·5)	1·4340	1·1190		[250]
$CH_2 = CHCH_2OOCCH_2PO(OCH_3)_2$	114–114·5 (2)	1·4505	1·2064*		[105]
$CH_2 = CHCH_2OOCCH_2PO(OC_2H_5)_2$	157–158 (10)	1·4426	1·1203*	55	[105]
$CH_2 = CHCH_2OOCCH_2PO(OC_3H_7)_2$	146–147·5 (1)	1·4470	1·0492		[105]
$CH_2 = CHCH_2OOCCH_2PO(OC_3H_7$-iso$)_2$	152–153 (6)	1·4357	1·0520		[105]
$CH_2 = CHCH_2OOCCH_2PO(OC_4H_9)_2$	146–147·5 (1)	1·4470	1·0492		[250]
$CH_2 = CHCH_2OOCCH_2PO(OC_4H_9$-iso$)_2$	154–156 (2)	1·4438	1·0356		[105]
$CH_2 = CHCH_2OOCCH(CH_3)CH_2PO(OC_2H_5)_2$	117–119 (2·5)	1·4396	1·0799	41	[107]
$CH_2 = CHCH_2OOCCH$—$PO(OC_4H_9)_2$ $CH_2 = CHCH_2OOCCH_2$	122 (0·35)	1·4568	1·0755		[251]

* d_D^{20}

+ At 15°.

TABLE 25. ESTERS OF α,β-UNSATURATED PHOSPHONODITHIOLIC ACIDS OF THE TYPE RPO(SR')$_2$

Formula		b. p., °C (mm)	n_D^{20}	d_4^{20}	Yield (%)	Reference
RCH = CHPO(SR')$_2$						
R	R'					
C$_2$H$_5$O—	—C$_2$H$_5$	135 (2)	1·5475	1·1366	55·8	[67]
CH$_3$OC$_2$H$_4$O—	—C$_2$H$_5$	150 (1)	1·5511	1·1435	80	[69]
C$_4$H$_9$OC$_2$H$_4$O—	—C$_2$H$_5$	186 (2)	1·5365	1·1180	87	[69]
C$_4$H$_9$O—	—C$_2$H$_5$	154 (2)	1·5544	1·1410	52	[67]
iso-C$_4$H$_9$O—	—C$_2$H$_5$	145 (2)	1·5370	1·0961	63	[67]
iso-C$_4$H$_9$O—	—C$_6$H$_5$	72–73*			60	[67]
C$_6$H$_5$O—	—C$_2$H$_5$	162 (1)	1·5860	1·1535		[67]
C$_6$H$_5$—	—C$_2$H$_5$	168 (1)	1·6248	1·1469	58·8	[58]
C$_6$H$_5$—	—C$_6$H$_5$	117*				[58]

* Melting point.

TABLE 26. ESTERS OF α,β AND β,γ-UNSATURATED PHOSPHONOTHIONIC ACIDS OF THE TYPE RPS(OR')$_2$

Formula		b. p., °C (mm)	n_D^{20}	d_4^{20}	Yield (%)	Reference
ROCH = CHPS(OR')$_2$						
R	R'					
C$_2$H$_5$—	—CH$_3$	86 (1)	1·4852	1·1373	60	[66]
C$_2$H$_5$—	—C$_2$H$_4$	107 (3)	1·4879	1·0970	50	[66]
CH$_3$OC$_2$H$_4$—	—CH$_3$	119 (6)	1·4775	1·1624	58	[69]
CH$_3$OC$_2$H$_4$—	—C$_2$H$_5$	120 (1)	1·4760	1·0904	73	[69]
C$_2$H$_5$OC$_2$H$_4$—	—CH$_3$	127 (2)	1·4712	1·1321	78	[69]
C$_2$H$_5$OC$_2$H$_4$—	—C$_2$H$_5$	133 (2)	1·4695	1·0081	82	[69]
iso-C$_4$H$_9$OC$_2$H$_4$—	—CH$_3$	141 (1)	1·4690	1·0922	83	[69]
iso-C$_4$H$_9$OC$_2$H$_4$—	—C$_2$H$_5$	145 (1)	1·4680	1·0296	80	[69]
iso-C$_3$H$_7$—	—CH$_3$	95 (1)	1·4780	1·1035		[66]
iso-C$_3$H$_7$—	—C$_2$H$_5$	105 (1)	1·4741	1·0510	63	[66]
C$_4$H$_9$—	—CH$_3$	107 (1)	1·4790	1·1018	70	[66]
C$_4$H$_9$—	—C$_2$H$_5$	117 (1)	1·4705	1·0687	60	[66]
C$_6$H$_5$—	—CH$_3$	151 (2)	1·5331	1·1945	50	[66]

TABLE 26 — *(contd.)*

Formula		b.p., °C(mm)	n_D^{20}	d_4^{20}	Yield (%)	Reference
C_6H_5—	—C_2H_5	159 (2)	1·5375	1·1263	75	[66]
RPS(OR′)$_2$						
R	**R′**					
$CH_3C(CH_3) = CH$—	—$C_6H_4NO_2$	103–105*				[5]
C_8H_{15}—	—$C_6H_4NO_2$	81–82*				[5]
$C_6H_5CH = CH$—	—CH_3	124 (1)	1·5890	1·1704	65·3	[58]
$C_6H_5CH = CH$—	—C_2H_5	130 (1)	1·5658	1·1067	55·4	[58]
$C_6H_5CH = CH$—	—C_6H_5	83*	1·5369			[37]
$C_2H_5OOCCH = C(C_6H_5)PS(OC_2H_5)_2$		168–169 (1)	1·4710	1·1534	32	[79]
$CH_2 = CHCH_2PS(OC_4H_9)_2$		120 (3)	1·4828	0·9858	42	[93]
$CH_2 = CHCHOHPS(OC_2H_5)_2$		120–122 (10)	1·4846	1·1158	46·2	[109]
$CH_3CH = CHCHOHPS(OC_2H_5)_2$		130–132 (8)	1·5280	1·1019	43·7	[109]
$\underset{O}{\square}$—CH=CHCHOHPS(OC_2H_5)_2		101–102 (10)		1·0785	46·1	[109]

* Melting point.

TABLE 27. ESTERS OF α,β-UNSATURATED PHOSPHONOTRITHIONIC ACIDS OF THE TYPE $ROCH=CHPS(SC_2H_5)_2$

Formula	b.p., °C (mm)	n_D^{20}	n_4^{20}	Yield (%)	Reference
C_2H_5—	134 (1)	1·5858	1·1734	65·9	[67]
$CH_3OC_2H_4$—	157 (2)	1·5890	1·1579	75	[69]
$C_2H_5OC_2H_4$—	176 (2)	1·5745	1·1417	83	[69]
iso-C_3H_7—	136 (2)	1·5672	1·1198	59·2	[67]
iso-C_4H_9—	145 (1)	1·5662	1·1060	60	[67]
C_6H_5—	155 (1)	1·6336	1·3142	47	[67]

ESTERS OF ACIDS OF PHOSPHORUS AND UNSATURATED ALCOHOLS

Esters of inorganic acids of phosphorus
(phosphorous, phosphoric, phosphorothionic, phosphoramidic)

The starting materials for these compounds are usually phosphorus trichloride, phosphoryl chloride and thiophosphoryl chloride.

The first completely unsaturated ester of phosphorous acid was triallyl phosphite, which was prepared by Zoroastrova [111] in two ways: by the reaction of allyl phosphorodichloridite [112] with sodium alloxide:

$$CH_2 = CHCH_2OPCl_2 + 2NaOCH_2CH = CH_2 \longrightarrow P(OCH_2CH = CH_2)_3 + NaCl$$

and by the reaction of phosphorus trichloride with allyl alcohol and pyridine [113]

$$PCl_3 + 3CH_2 = CH \cdot CH_2OH + 3C_5H_5N \longrightarrow P(OCH_2CH = CH_2)_3 + 3C_5H_5N \cdot HCl$$

The preparation of unsaturated esters of phosphorous acid by the treatment of phosphorus trichloride with unsaturated alcohols in the presence of an organic base has been frequently utilized. In this way, for example, Kama and Chadayeva [114, 115] synthesized a range of a-substituted allyl esters of phosphorous acid using dimethylaniline as organic base [116], and Kuznetzov and Baletdinov [117] a range of allyl cyanoalkyl phosphites.

Recently, the allyl and methallyl esters of phosphorous acid have been obtained by the transesterification of triaryl phosphites with the corresponding unsaturated alcohols [118]. There is great interest in the mixed esters of phosphorous acid, containing rings. Such compounds have been studied in detail by Arbusov and Zoroastrova [91], who made then by the reaction of allyl alcohol with the acid chlorides of the esters of ethylene, trimethylene and 1-methyltrimethylene glycols with phosphorous acid, in the presence of pyridine:

$$\begin{array}{c} CH_2O \\ | \quad\quad PCl + CH_2 = CH \cdot CH_2OH + C_5H_5N \longrightarrow \\ CH_2O \end{array}$$

$$\longrightarrow \begin{array}{c} CH_2O \\ | \quad\quad P{-}OCH_2CH = CH_2 + C_5H_5N \cdot HCl \\ CH_2O \end{array}$$

Morris and Winkle have obtained esters of phosphorous acid with a triple bond in the molecule in an analogous way [119].

Vinyl esters of phosphorous acid and substituted phosphorous acids have been synthesized by the reaction of the acid chlorides of these acids with triethylamine and acetaldehyde [120] or mercury bis(acetaldehyde) [121]; the first of these reactions is described in detail on p. 81.

Allyl phosphorodichloridite $CH_2 = CHCH_2OPCl_2$ [112]

$$CH_2 = CHCH_2OH + PCl_3 \longrightarrow CH_2 = CHCH_2OPCl_2 + HCl$$

A round-bottomed flask, provided with a stirrer, was charged with freshly distilled phosphorus trichloride (135 g), and then, with stirring and cooling, allyl alcohol (60 g) was carefully added dropwise. The reaction was accompanied by a vigorous evolution of hydrogen chloride. After the addition the flask was heated on a water bath for 6 hr while carbon dioxide gas was passed through it. On the following day the liquid was poured off from the residue of yellow phosphorus and polyphosphines and distilled at atmospheric pressure to give a colourless, refracting liquid, b. p. $137°/756$ mm, d^{18} $1 \cdot 2772$, which fumed in air and had a sharp penetrating smell. By the action of water this liquid decomposed into allyl alcohol and phosphorous acid.

Triallyl phosphite $P(OCH_2CH = CH_2)_3$ [111]

$$PCl_3 + 3CH_2 = CHCH_2OH + 3C_5H_5N \longrightarrow P(OCH_2CH = CH_2)_3 + 3C_5H_5N \cdot HCl$$

A flask, fitted with a condenser and dropping funnel, was charged with a mixture of absolute allyl alcohol (87 g), pyridine (113·5 g) and absolute ether (200 ml). Freshly distilled phosphorus trichloride ($68 \cdot 7$ g) was added dropwise, with stirring and exterior cooling to $0°$ in ice. When all the phosphorus trichloride had apparently reacted, the mixture was stirred at $0°$ for 20–25 min. The pyridine hydrochloride was then filtered off and washed several times with dry ether. Evaporation of the ether solution and distillation of the residue *in vacuo* yielded the ester ($71 \cdot 77$ g, $71 \cdot 6\%$), b.p. $89°/10.5$ mm, n_D^{16} $1 \cdot 4600$, d_0^{20} $0 \cdot 9967$.

A few acidic unsaturated esters of phosphorous acid, with general formula $HPO(OR)_2$, where R = unsaturated radical, have been synthesized, usually by the following reaction [122–126]:

$$PCl_3 + 3ROH \longrightarrow P(OR)_3 + 3HCl \longrightarrow \left[\begin{array}{c} H \diagdown \quad \diagup (OR)_2 \\ P \\ Cl \diagup \quad \diagdown OH \end{array} \right] + 2HCl \longrightarrow$$

$$\longrightarrow HPO(OR)_2 + 2HCl + RCl$$

Henry [125] has prepared bis-(2,3-di-iodo-allyl) hydrogen phosphite by the reaction of propargyl alcohol, iodine and red phosphorus; and Kennedy [127], diallyl hydrogen phosphite by treating triallyl phosphite with allyl alcohol.

Diallyl hydrogen phosphite $HPO(OCH_2CH = CH_2)_2$ [123]

$$PCl_3 + 3CH_2 = CHCH_2OH \longrightarrow HPO(OCH_2CH = CH_2)_2 + CH_2 = CHCH_2Cl + 2HCl$$

To cooled allyl alcohol (117 g) in a 250 ml flask was added dropwise, with stirring, freshly distilled phosphorus trichloride ($91 \cdot 9$ g) (i. e. 1 mole of phosphorus trichloride to 3 moles of allyl alcohol). The addition of each portion of phosphorus trichloride was accompanied by a strong crackling noise and the evolution of hydrogen chloride. The addition was carried out over 2 hr and carbon dioxide gas was passed through the apparatus throughout. When all the phosphorous trichloride had been added, the cooling bath was removed and replaced by a water bath; the flask was fitted with a reflux condenser connected via a cooled receiver to a vacuum pump. The water bath was carefully heated and the allyl chloride distilled and the hydrogen chloride volatilized. After 3–5 hr the residue was distilled in a carbon dioxide stream under reduced pressure (Care! Not more than two-thirds of the material should be distilled: otherwise a powerful explosion may result). Distillation at 8 mm afforded the following fractions: (i) up to 95° (8 g), (ii) 98° (52 g), (iii) 98–102° [43]. The second and third fractions were redistilled, when diallyl hydrogen phosphite came over easily, without decomposition, as a clear liquid. The pure product (71 g, 65·7%) boiled at 97·5–98·5°/8 mm.

Diallyl hydrogen phosphite is a colourless, mobile liquid with a characteristic smell, easily soluble in water and organic solvents: d_0^0 1·1001, d_0^{20} 1·079, n_D^{20} 1·4430.

However, attempts to obtain dipropenyl and di-isobutenyl hydrogen phosphites by this method failed, even though diallyl hydrogen phosphite can be obtained without difficulty.

Unsaturated esters of phosphoric and phosphoramidic acid are synthesized by the reaction of phosphoryl chloride, various phosphorochloridates and phosphoramidochloridates with alkoxides of unsaturated alcohols or with most alcohols in the presence of organic bases [129–138]; for example:

$$POCl_3 + 3CH_2 = CHCH_2OH + 3C_5H_5N \longrightarrow PO(OCH_2CH = CH_2)_3 + 3C_5H_5N \cdot HCl$$

or by the reaction of diallyl hydrogen phosphite with carbon tetrachloride and ammonia (135). Kuznetsov and Baletdinov have discovered a new method for preparing triallyl phosphate; the oxidation of triallyl phosphite [139]. (A similar method for saturated phosphates was described earlier [140–144].) It is interesting to note that the ester prepared by these authors was purified by distillation in vacuo without any complications, whereas the triallyl phosphate prepared by the old method exploded with great force on distillation [145].

Tri(2-chloroallyl) phosphate PO(OCH₂CCl = CH₂)₃ [130]

$$POCl_3 + 3CH_2 = CClCH_2OH + 3C_5H_5N \longrightarrow PO(OCH_2CCl = CH_2)_3 + 3C_5H_5N \cdot HCl$$

To a mixture of 2-chloroallyl alcohol (240 g, 2·59 mole), toluene (240 g) and dry pyridine (400 g) in a 2-l. three-necked flask fitted with a thermometer, mechanical stirrer and dropping funnel, was added over 1 hr a mixture of phosphoryl chloride (111 g, 0·72 mole) and toluene (111 g). The temperature of the reaction was maintained between −30° and −40°. After the addition, the mixture was allowed to warm up to room temperature, and then washed with water to remove the pyridine hydrochloride. The toluene layer was separated, washed with water, dried (NaOH) and the toluene distilled to leave crude tri(2-chloroallyl) phosphate (167 g, 71·8%).

The crude product (21·4 g) was distilled in vacuo in the presence of hydroquinone (0·3 g) and soda (3 g) (for the prevention of explosions) to give the pure material (14·6 g), b. p. 131–133°/1 mm, n_D^{20} 1·4866.

Triallyl phosphate PO(OCH₂CH = CH₂)₃ [139]

$$P(OCH_2CH = CH_2)_3 + \frac{1}{2}O_2 \longrightarrow PO(OCH_2CH = CH_2)_3$$

Triallyl phosphite (150 g) was placed in a long glass cylinder fitted with a stirrer. The apparatus was heated in a thermostat with carbon tetrachloride vapour. Oxygen from a cylinder, dried with concentrated sulphuric acid and calcium chloride, was passed through the phosphite for 6 hr. During this time the refractive index of the reaction mass changed from $1\cdot4560$ to $1\cdot4500$. Two distillations at 1 mm gave triallyl phosphate (125 g, 83%), b. p. 93–95°/1 mm. The compound was distilled once more and the constants determined. Pure triallyl phosphate has the following constants: b. p. 93–94°/1 mm, n_D^{20} $1\cdot4500$, d_4^{20} $1\cdot0815$.

Allyl phosphorodichloridothionate, which is the starting material for esters of this acid, was obtained by Pletz [146] by the addition of sulphur to allyl phosphorodichloridite, and by the treatment of thiophosphoryl chloride with allyl alcohol:

$$CH_2 = CHCH_2OPCl_2 + S$$
$$CH_2 = CHCH_2OH + PSCl_3 \longrightarrow CH_2 = CHCH_2OPSCl_2$$

However, unsaturated esters of phosphorothionic acid are, as a rule, synthesized by the addition of sulphur to the corresponding trialkenyl phosphite [91, 111, 121].

Triallyl phosphorothionate $PS(OCH_2CH = CH_2)_3$ [111]

$$P(OCH_2CH = CH_2)_3 + S \longrightarrow PS(OCH_2CH = CH_2)_3$$

Finely ground crystalline sulphur ($3\cdot2$ g) was added to triallyl phosphite ($20\cdot2$ g): an exothermic reaction proceeded on mixing, and all the sulphur dissolved. Distillation afforded triallyl phosphorothionate ($18\cdot87$ g, $80\cdot6$%), b. p. 125–127°/9 mm, n_D^{18} 1.4832, d_0^{18} $1\cdot0827$.

The 3-chloropropenyl esters of dialkyl hydrogen phosphorothiolothionates were obtained by Tichy [147] by the reaction of salts of these acids with 1,3-dichlorobut-2-ene and soda.

Unsaturated acid esters of phosphoric acid of the type:

$$\begin{array}{c} RO \\ \diagdown \\ R'O \diagup \end{array} P(O)OH \text{ or } RO—PO(OH)_2$$

where R is an unsaturated radical, are crystalline substances or undistillable syrups (in distinction from the full esters, which are rather mobile liquids). They are obtained by the reaction of allyl alcohol with phosphorus pentoxide [148–150]:

$$3CH_2 = CHCH_2OH + P_2O_5 \longrightarrow CH_2 = CHCH_2OPO(OH)_2 + (CH_2 = CHCH_2O)_2PO(OH)$$

by the hydrolysis of unsaturated trialkyl phosphates or phosphorochloridates [151–153]; by the reaction of alkyl halides with trisodium phosphate [154];

and also by the reaction of phosphoryl chloride with sodium acetoacetate followed by hydrolysis of the phosphorodichloridate which forms: [155]

$$CH_3C\underset{CHCOOC_2H_5}{\overset{ONa}{\big<}} + POCl_3 \longrightarrow CH_3C\underset{CHCOOC_2H_5}{\overset{OPOCl_2}{\big<}} \xrightarrow{2H_2O}$$

$$\longrightarrow CH_3C\underset{CHCOOC_2H_5}{\overset{OPO(OH)_2}{\big<}}$$

Unsaturated esters of phosphoric acid containing vinyl and substituted vinyl groups were not known in the past. However, a range of methods for obtaining these compounds have been developed recently.

Thus, Upson [156] has published a method for obtaining diethyl vinyl phosphate by removing the elements of hydrogen chloride from diethyl 2-chloroethyl phosphate with alkali.*

$$ClCH_2CH_2OPO(OC_2H_5)_2 \xrightarrow{-HCl} CH_2 = CH-OPO(OC_2H_5)_2$$

Some very interesting results were obtained by a detailed study of the reaction of a-halogenocarbonyl-compounds with esters of acids of trivalent phosphorus. This is considered in detail later (cf. pp. 75–79); it suffices to say here that Perkow and his co-workers [158–160) and then also a number of other workers [161–173], first showed, that reaction between a-halogeno-carbonyl-compounds and trialkyl phosphites can occur not only via the classical Arbusov rearrangement, but also in another way to produce vinyl and substituted vinyl esters of dialkyl phosphoric acids:

$$P(OR)_3 + R'R''CX-CO-R''' \longrightarrow (RO)_2P(O)OCR''' = CR'C'' + RX$$

where X = halogen.

Diethyl vinyl phosphate $CH_2 = CHOPO(OC_2H_5)_2$ [169]

$$ClCH_2CHO + P(OC_2H_5)_3 \longrightarrow CH_2 = CHOPO(OC_2H_5)_2 + C_2H_5Cl$$

Triethyl phosphite (665 g, 4 mole) was added over 40 min to chloroacetal-dehyde (314 g, 4 mole). Exterior cooling kept the temperature in the range 50–60°. The mixture was then heated to 110° and ethyl chloride (178 g, 70%) was distilled out; the residue was fractionally distilled through a 60 cm column packed with glass rings to give diethyl vinyl phosphate (482 g, 67%), b. p. 79°/6 mm, n_D^{35} 1·4100, d_4^{35} 1·0724.

2-Acetyl-1-methylvinyl diethyl phosphate $CH_3COCH = C(CH_3)OPO(OC_2H_5)_2$ [167]

$$CH_3COCHClCOCH_3 + P(OC_2H_5)_3 \longrightarrow CH_3COCH = C(CH_3)OPO(OC_2H_5)_2$$

Triethyl phosphite (37 g) was slowly added, dropwise, to 3-chloroacetyl-acetone (30 g) in a round-bottomed flask fitted with a reflux condenser, drop,

* Allen and his co-workers [157] have made several unsuccessful attempts to repeat Upson's results.

ping funnel and a thermometer immersed in the liquid. After about one-third of the triethyl phosphite had been added the reaction mixture began to warm up and ethyl chloride was evolved. The further addition of triethyl phosphite was carried out at a rate such that the temperature did not exceed 100–110° and at the very end of the reaction, not above 140°. After heating for 30 min on an oil-bath at 130–140° the reaction mixture was distilled *in vacuo*. The main bulk of the product distilled at 117–120°/2 mm; redistillation of this gave 2-acetyl-1-methylvinyl diethyl phosphate (34·5 g), b.p. 119–120°/2 mm, n_D^{20} 1·4489, d_4^{20} 1·1237.

An interesting rearrangement has been discovered by American and German investigators: they have found that the action of aqueous or alcoholic alkali on esters of β,β-dichloro- or β,β,β-trichloro-α-hydroxyethylphosphonic acid results not only in the removal of hydrogen chloride, but also in a change in the skeleton of the molecule: the esters of the phosphonic acid are rearranged into halogeno-vinyl esters of phosphoric acid [174—176]:

$$CCl_3\text{—}CHOHPO(OR)_2 \xrightarrow{\ulcorner-HCl} CCl_2 = CHOPO(OR)_2$$

[Details of this reaction will be described later (see pp. 79–80).]

Gefter and Kabachnik [120] have synthesized trivinyl phosphate by the reaction of phosphoryl chloride with acetaldehyde and triethylamine (see also p. 81):

$$POCl_3 + 3CH_3CHO + 3N(C_2H_5)_3 \longrightarrow PO(OCH = CH_2)_3 + 3N(C_2H_5)_3 \cdot HCl$$

A recent American patent (with experimental details) has described how vinyl and substituted vinyl esters of phosphoric acids can be obtained by the treatment of the acids with acetylene or its derivatives in the presence of mercury salts. [177]

The properties of the acid chlorides and esters of the inorganic acids of phosphorus are shown in Tables 28–39 (see pp. 51–65).

TABLE 28. UNSATURATED ACID CHLORIDES OF O- AND N-ALLYL
PHOSPHOROUS, PHOSPHORIC, PHOSPHOROTHIONIC
AND PHOSPHORAMIDIC ACIDS

Formula	b.p., °C (mm)	d_D^{20}	n_4^{20}	Yield (%)	Reference
$CH_2 = CHCH_2OPCl_2$	137		1·2792 (18°)	50	[146]
$(CH_2 = CHCH_2O)_2PCl$ $\overset{\|}{O}$	65–85 (3–4)	1·4504		22	[138]
$CH_2 = CHCH_2OPSCl_2$	74 (25)				[146]
$CH_2 = CHCH_2NHPOCl_2$	125–126 (8)				[134]
$(CH_2 = CHCH_2)_2NPOCl_2$	122–123 (19)		1·2317 (15°)		[134]

TABLE 29. UNSATURATED ESTERS OF PHOSPHOROUS ACID*

Formula	b. p., °C (mm)	n_D^{20}	d_4^{20}	Yield (%)	Reference
$CH_2 = CHOP \Big\langle \begin{matrix} O-CH_2 \\ \mid \\ O-CH_2 \end{matrix}$	58–59 (15)	1·4577	1·1672	24	[120]
$CH_2 = CHOP(OCH_3)_2$	55–56 (80)	1·4255	1·0406	46	[121]
$CH_2 = CHOP(OC_2H_5)_2$	58–59 (28)	1·4258	0·9787	67	[121]
$CH_2 = CHOP(OC_3H_7)_2$	53–54 (3)	1·4322	0·9518	62	[121]
$CH_2 = CHOP(OC_4H_9)_2$	85–86 (4)	1·4360	0·9381	70	[121]
$CH_2 = CHOP \Big\langle \begin{matrix} O \\ O \end{matrix}$ (benzodioxaphosphole)	71 (2–2·5)	1·5357	1·2306	30	[120]
$CH_2 = CHOP(OC_6H_5)_2$	143–144 (3)	1·5575	1·1567	80	[121]
$(CH_2 = CHO)_2POCH_3$	60–61 (60)	1·4390	1·0368	56	[121]
$(CH_2 = CHO)_2POC_2H_5$	57–58 (30)	1·4380	1·0015	60	[121]
$(CH_2 = CHO)_2POC_3H_7$	56–57 (11)	1·4392	0·9908	62	[121]
$(CH_2 = CHO)_2POC_4H_9$	63 (7)	1·4412	0·9873	60	[121]
$(CH_2 = CHO)_2POC_6H_5$	108–109 (10)	1·5151	1·1037	55	[121]
$(CH_2 = CHO)_3P$	51–52 (30)	1·4485	1·0262	46	[121]
$CH_2 = CHCH_2OP \Big\langle \begin{matrix} O-CH_2 \\ \mid \\ O-CH_2 \end{matrix}$	69–70 (11)	1·4635	1·1553	58·6	[91]
$CH_2 = CHCH_2OP \Big\langle \begin{matrix} O-CH_2 \\ O-CH_2 \end{matrix} \Big\rangle CH_2$	82–82·5 (12)	1·4625	1·1214	52·7	[91]
$CH_2 = CHCH_2OP \Big\langle \begin{matrix} O-CH_2 \\ O-CH \end{matrix} \Big\rangle CH_2$ $\qquad\qquad\mid$ $\qquad\qquad CH_3$	82–83 (10)	1·4580	1·0777	62·5	[91]
$CH_2 = CHCH_2OP \Big\langle \begin{matrix} O \\ O \end{matrix} (CH_2)_4$	Explodes on distillation (even at 1 mm)				[91]
$CH_2 = CHCH_2OP(OCH_2CH_2CN)_2$	165–170 (8·5)	1·4580	1·0989		[117]
$CH_2 = CHCH_2OP[OC(CH_3)_2CN]_2$	153–156 (10)	1·4450	1·0546	36	[117]

* A number of mixed and acid esters are included.

TABLE 29 — *(contd.)*

Formula	b. p., °C (mm)	n_D^{20}	d_4^{20}	Yield (%)	Refer-ence
$CH_2 = CHCH_2OCH_2-CHO \underset{CH_2O}{\overset{CH_2O}{\diagup}} POCH_3$	74–76 (1)	1·4580 (35)		89	[169]
$(CH_2 = CHCH_2O)_2PHO$	97·5–98·5 (8)	1·4430	1·0793	65·7	[122]
$(CH_2 = CHCH_2O)_2POCH_2CH_2CN$	140–145 (8·5)	1·4636	1·0691		[117]
$(CH_2 = CHCH_2O)_2POC(CH_3)_2CN$	111–116 (9)	1·4425	1·0230	72	[117]
$(CHI = CICH_2O)_2PHO$	m. p. 48–49°				[125]
$(CH_2 = CHCH_2O)_3P$	85·5–86·5 (9)	1·4595	0·9974	71·6	[111]
$[CH_2 = CHCH(CH_3)O]_3P$	91–93 (9)	1·4531	0·9557	49	[114]
$[CH_2 = CHCH(C_2H_5)O]_3P$	102–103 (3); 123–124 (10)	1·4521	0·9467	84	[114]
$[CH_2 = CHCH(C_3H_7)O]_3P$	137–139 (13)	1·4519	0·9365		[114]
$[CH_2 = CHCH(C_4H_9)O]_3P$	155–157 (15)	1·4521	0·9230	63	[114]
$[CH_2 = CHCH(C_6H_5)O]_3P$	Decomposes and polymerizes on distillation *in vacuo*				[114]
$(CH_3CH = CHCH_2O)_3P$	98–99 (1)	1·4680	0·9757		[252]
$[CH_2 = CHCH_2CH(CH_3)O]_3P$	132–133 (12)	1·4538	0·9323		[115]
$[CH_2 = CHCH_2CH(C_6H_5)O]_3P$	Decomposes and polymerizes on distillation *in vacuo*				[115]
$CH \equiv CCH_2OP \underset{O-CH_2}{\overset{O-CHCH_3}{\diagup}}$	22 (55)	1·4962	1·2498		[119]
$\left[\equiv CCH_2OP \underset{O-CH_2}{\overset{O-CHCH_3}{\diagup}} \right]_2$	25 (12)	1·4957	1·2675		[119]
$(CH \equiv CCH_2O)_2PHO$ (presumed structure)	105 (5)				[126]
$(CH \equiv CCH_2O)_3P$	25 (23)	1·4935	1·1445		[119]
$[CH \equiv CC(CH_3)_2O]_3P$	Oil			52	[253]

Table 30. Esters of the type

$XCH=CHOPO(OR)_2$, where $X=H$, Cl; $CX_2=CHOPO(OR)_2$, where $X=Cl$, Br; $CCl_2=$

$$=CXOPY_2,$$ where $X=H$, RO, $Y=RO$, $N(R)_2$ or RO and $N(R)_2$; $CCl_2=CHOP(O)N$—X R'

—$PO(OR)_2$, where $X=H$, $N(R)_2$; $CCl_2=CHOPO(OCH_2CH=CH_2)_2$

Formula	b. p., °C (mm)	n_D^{20}	d_4^{20}	Yield (%)	Reference
$CH_2 = CHOPO(OC_2H_5)_2$	79 (6)	1·4100 (35°)	1·0724 (35°)	67	[169]
$ClCH = CHOPO(OC_2H_5)_2$	121–122 (13)	1·4345 (25°)	1·204 (25°)+	13	[174]
	80 (0·2)		1·159	60	[160]
$ClCH = CHOPO(OCH_2CH_2Cl)_2$	152–157 (1)			70	[169]
$ClCH = CHOPO(OC_3H_7)_2$	94–100 (0·1)	1·4364 (25°)		56	[169]
$ClCH = CHOPO(OC_3H_6\text{-iso})_2$	89–91 (0·3)	1·4307	1·111	45	[160]
	74–87 (0·1)			37	[169]
$ClCH = CHOPO[OCH_2CH(C_2H_5)C_4H_9]_2$	156–173 (0·1)	1·4492 (25°)		82	[169]
$CCl_2 = CHOP\langle\begin{smallmatrix}O—CH_2\\ \|\\ O—CH_2\end{smallmatrix}$ (‖O)	110–117 (0·5)			24	[169]
$CCl_2 = CHOPO(OCH_3)_2$	100–104 (25)		1·4243	60	[159]
	74–87 (2)			53	[169]
	120 (14)	1·4524	1·413	57	[174]
$CCl_2 = CHOP\langle\begin{smallmatrix}O—CHCH_3\\ \|\\ O—CH_2\end{smallmatrix}$ (‖O)	118–123 (2)			54	[169]
$CCl_2 = CHOP\langle\begin{smallmatrix}O—CHCH_2OC_2H_5\\ \|\\ O—CH_2\end{smallmatrix}$ (‖O)				99	[169]
$CCl_2 = CHOP\langle\begin{smallmatrix}OCH_3\\ OC_2H_5\end{smallmatrix}$ (‖O)	80–96 (1)			67	[169]
$CCl_2 = CHOP\langle\begin{smallmatrix}OCH—CH_3\\ OCH_2\end{smallmatrix}CH_2$ (‖O)	132–140 (1)			97	[169]
$CCl_2 = CHOPO(OC_2H_5)_2$	113–115 (2)		1·299	85–90	[159]
	69–71 (0·5)	1·4498		98	[171]
	131–132 (14)	1·4479	1·295	51	[174]
$CCl_2 = CHOPO(OCH_2CH_2Cl)_2$	93–112 (0·1)	1·4820 (35°)		68	[169]

TABLE 30 — *(contd.)*

Formula	b. p., °C (mm)	n_D^{20}	d_4^{20}	Yield (%)	Reference
$CCl_2 = CHOPO[OC_2H_4)_2OCH_3]_2$				75	[169]
$CCl_2 = CHOP\begin{subarray}{l} OC_2H_5 \\ \| \quad OCH(CH_3)_2 \\ O \end{subarray}$	162–164 (1)	1·4580	1·2716	51·7	[254]
$CCl_2 = CHOP\begin{subarray}{l} OCH{-}C_2H_5 \\ \| \quad CH_3 \\ OCH \\ O \quad \| \\ \quad CH_3 \end{subarray}$				81	[169]
$CCl_2 = CHOPO(OC_3H_7)_2$	107 (0·3) / 118–120 (0·7)	1·4450	1·215+ / 1·216	36 / 70	[174] / [159]
$CCl_2 = CHOPO(OC_3H_7\text{-iso})_2$	96·5 (2) / 99–105 (0·7) / 106–108 (0·8)	1·4372 (35°) / 1·4423	1·1924 (35°) / 1·201+ / 1·210	62 / 26 / 72	[169] / [174] / [159]
$CCl_2 = CHOPO(OC_4H_9)_2$	107–121 (0·5) / 125–128 (0·35)	1·4487	1·166+	80 / 53	[169] / [174]
$CCl_2 = CHOPO[OCH_2CH(C_2H_5)C_4H_9]_2$				100	[169]
$CCl_2 = CHOP\begin{subarray}{l} OC_2H_5 \\ \| \quad OC_6H_5 \\ O \end{subarray}$	116–130 (0·5)			84	[169]
$CCl_2 = CHOPO[OC_6H_4C(CH_3)_3\text{-}4]_2$				89	[169]
$CCl_2 = CHOP\begin{subarray}{l} OC_2H_5 \\ \| \quad N(CH_3)_2 \\ O \end{subarray}$	90–91·5 (3)	1·4580	1·2801	42·7	[254]
$CCl_2 = CHOP\begin{subarray}{l} OC_3H_7 \\ \| \quad N(CH_3)_2 \\ O \end{subarray}$	103–104 (2)	1·4580	1·2333	56·3	[254]
$CCl_2 = CHOP\begin{subarray}{l} OCH_2CH_2Cl \\ \| \quad N(C_2H_5)_2 \\ O \end{subarray}$	113–123 (0·2)			73	[169]
$CCl_2 = CHOPO[N(CH_3)_2]_2$	89·5–90 (1)	1·4785	1·2607	60·7	[254]
$CCl_2 = CHOPO[N(C_2H_5)_2]_2$	115–125 (1)			74	[169]
$CCl_2 = C(OC_2H_5)OPO(OC_2H_5)_2$	103 (0·5)	1·4284		40	[171]
$CBr_2 = CHOPO(OC_2H_5)_2$	139–140 (1·5)		1·661	70	[159]
$CBr_2 = CHOPO(OC_3H_7\text{-iso})_2$	139–142 (2)		1·482	45	[159]
$CBr_2 = CHOPO(OC_4H_9\text{-iso})_2$	159–160 (1·5)		1·465	30	[159]

TABLE 30 — *(contd.)*

Formula	b. p., °C (mm)	n_D^{20}	d_4^{20}	Yield (%)	Reference
$CCl_2 = CHO$ $\overset{C_2H_5}{P(O)N}$ C_2H_5O —$PO(OC_2H_5)_2$	164–165 (1)	1·4610	1·2792	70·4	[254]
$CCl_2 = CHO$ $\overset{C_2H_5}{P(O)N}$ C_3H_7O —$PO(OC_3H_7)_2$	160–162·5 (1)	1·4580	1·1951	36·4	[254]
$CCl_2 = CHO$ $\overset{CH_3}{P(O)N}$ $(CH_3)_2N$ —$PO(OC_2H_5)_2$	148–149 (1)	1·4700	1·2947	40	[254]
$CCl_2 = CHO$ $\overset{C_2H_5}{P(O)N}$ $(CH_3)_2N$ —$PO(OC_2H_5)_2$	145–145·5 (1)	1·4715	1·2711	51·2	[254]
$CCl_2 = CHO$ $\overset{C_2H_5}{P(O)N}$ $(C_2H_5)_2N$ —$PO(OC_2H_5)_2$	154–155 (1·5)	1·469	1·2263	25	[254]
$\left[CCl_2 = CHOP \underset{\overset{\parallel}{O}}{\overset{OCH_2-}{<_{OCH_2-}}} \right]_2$	130- 132‡			68	[169]
$CCl_2 = CHOPO(OCH_2CH = CH_2)_2$	105 (0·5)	1·460		72	[173]

* Esters which have the skeletons $\underset{OPO(OR)_2}{>C=CPO(OR)_2}$ and $\underset{OPO(OR)_2}{-C=CHPO(OR)_2}$ are listed

in Table 18, and esters with the skeleton $>C=C<_{OPO(OR)_2}^{CH_2PO(OR)_2}$ in Table 19.

+ This substance was obtained by Perkow.

‡ Melting point.

TABLE 31. ESTERS OF THE TYPE $CH_2=C(R)OPO(OR')_2$,
WHERE $R=CH_3$, CH_2Cl, CH_2Br, C_6H_5;
$CHX=C(CH_3)OPO(OR)_2$ AND $CH_2XCH=CHOPO(OR)_2$,
WHERE $X=Cl$, Br; $CH_3CX=C(CH_3)OPO(OR)_2$, WHERE

$$X=H,\ Br,\ RO;\ \begin{matrix} C(CH_3)-O \\ \| \\ C(CH_3)-O \end{matrix}\Big\rangle P(OR)_3$$

Formula	b. p., °C (mm)	n_D^{20}	d_4^{20}	Yield (%)	Reference
$CH_2 = C(CH_3)OPO(OCH_3)_2$	84–85 (9)	1·4175	1·1449		[163]
$CH_2 = C(CH_3)OPO(OC_2H_5)_2$	96 (12)	1·4190	1·0708	94	[164]
$CH_2 = C(CH_3)OPO(OC_4H_9)_2$	125–126 (5)	1·4268	1·0049		[163]
$CH_2 = C(CH_3)OPO(OC_4H_9\text{-iso})_2$	122–123 (9)	1·4245	0·9955		[163]
$CH_2 = C(CH_2Cl)OPO(OC_2H_5)_2$	135·5–134·5(11) 76–89 (1)	1·4435	1·1934	44·8 82	[166] [169]
$ClCH = C(CH_3)OPO(OC_2H_5)_2$	116·5–117 (10)	1·4370	1·1833	82	[166]
$ClCH = C(CH_3)OPO(OC_4H_9)_2$	154–155 (11)	1·4400	1·0892	76	[166]
$ClCH_2CH = CHOPO(OC_2H_5)_2$	115–118 (0·8)			41	[160]
$ClCH_2CH = CHOPO(OC_3H_7\text{-iso})_2$	124 (0·4)			39	[160]
$ClCH_2CH = CHOPO(OC_4H_9\text{-iso})_2$	136–137 (0·4)			52	[160]
$CH_2 = C(CH_2Br)OPO(OC_2H_5)_2$	142·5–143 (11)	1·4622	1·3928	40·2	[166]
$BrCH = C(CH_3)OPO(OC_2H_5)_2$	126–127 (10)	1·4540	1·3643	36·7	[166]
$CH_3CH = C(CH_3)OPO(OC_2H_5)_2$	110–111·5 (10)	1.4272	1·0578	70	[255]
$CH_3CBr = C(CH_3)OPO(OC_2H_5)_2$	147–148 (10)	1·4655	1·3481	38	[255]
$C_2H_5OC(CH_3) = C(CH_3)OPO(OC_2H_5)_2$	127–130 (10)	1·4250	1·1061	23·3	[256]
$C_3H_7OC(CH_3) = C(CH_3)OPO(OC_3H_7)_2$	140–142 (10)	1·4230	1·0752	46·7	[256]
$C_4H_9OC(CH_3) = C(CH_3)OPO(OC_4H_9)_2$	148–150 (10)	1·4240	1·0192	42·6	[256]
$CH_2 = C(C_6H_5)OPO(OC_2H_5)_2$	171 (11)	1·5009	1·1422		[164]
$CHCl = C(C_6H_5)OPO(OC_2H_5)_2$	139–140 (0·5)	1·5170	1·2353	92·4	[255]
$CCl_2 = C(C_6H_5)OPO(OC_2H_5)_2$	105–110 (10⁻³)	1·5195		91	[171]
$\begin{matrix} CH_3-C-O \\ \| \\ CH_3-C-O \end{matrix}\Big\rangle P(OC_2H_5)_3$	104–105 (10)	1·4290	1·0825	47·2	[256]
$\begin{matrix} CH_3-C-O \\ \| \\ CH_3-C-O \end{matrix}\Big\rangle P(OC_3H_7)_3$	127–130 (10)	1·4305	1·0256	37·1	[256]

TABLE 32. ESTERS OF THE TYPE $RO_2CCX=C(CH_3)OPO(OR')_2$, $CH_3COCX=C(CH_3)OPO(OR)_2$ WHERE $X=H$, Cl AND OTHERS; $CCl_2=CHCH=CHOPO(OC_2H_5)_2$; $(CH_2=CHO)_3PO$

Formula	b. p., °C (mm)	n_D^{20}	d_4^{20}	Yield (%)	Reference
$CH_3OOCH = C(CH_3)OPO(OCH_3)_2$	106–107·5 (1)	1·4494	1·25		[160]
$C_2H_5OOCCH = C(CH_3)OPO(OC_2H_5)_2$	155–156 (10)	1·4451	1·1349	91	[167]
$C_2H_5OOCCH = C(CH_3)OPO(OC_4H_9\text{-iso})_2$	175 (10)	1·4445	1·0569	71	[167]
$C_2H_5OOCCCl = C(CH_3)OPO(OC_2H_5)_2$	136 (1)	1·4572	1·1203	97	[167]
$C_2H_5OOC\overset{CCl}{\diagup}C(CH_3)OPO(OC_4H_9\text{-iso})_2$	154 (1)	1·4547	1·1289	90	[167]
$C_2H_5OOCC(C_2H_5) = C(CH_3)OPO(OC_2H_5)_2$	133–134 (1·4)	1·4470	1·1217	75	[257]
$CH_3CHCl—CCl = CHOPO(OC_2H_5)_2$	140–142 (2)	1·219		45	[160]
$CH_3COCH = C(CH_3)OPO(OCH_3)_2$	103–104 (2)	1·4572	1·2040		[258]
$CH_3COCH = C(CH_3)OPO(OC_2H_5)_2$	119–120 (2)	1·4489	1·1237	66	[167]
$CH_3COCH = C(CH_3)OPO(OC_4H_9)_2$	125–127 (1)	1·4510	1·0503		[258]
$CH_3COCH = C(CH_3)OPO(OC_4H_9\text{-iso})_2$	137–138 (2·5)	1·4468	1·0425	80	[167]
$CH_3COCCl = C(CH_3)OPO(OCH_3)_2$	115 (2)	1·4710	1·3085		[258]
$CH_3COCCl = C(CH_3)OPO(OC_2H_5)_2$	135 (3)	1·4626	1·2292	63	[167]
$CH_3COCCl = C(CH_3)OPO(OC_4H_9)_2$	138–139 (2)	1·4615	2·1202*		[258]
$CH_3COCCl = C(CH_3)OPO(OC_4H_9\text{-iso})_2$	150–151 (4)	1·4575	1·1240	80	[167]
$CH_3COCH = C(C_6H_5)OPO(OCH_3)_2$	138–139 (1)	1·5262	1·2278		[258]
$CH_3COCH = C(C_6H_5)OPO(OC_2H_5)_2$	170–172 (2)	1·5135	1·1611		[258]
$CH_3COCCl = C(C_6H_5)OPO(OCH_3)_2$	156–157 (2·5)	1·5223	1·2969		[258]
⬡—$OPO(OC_2H_5)_2$	143 (11)	1·4523	1·1032	88	[164]
(cyclohexenone)—$OPO(OC_2H_5)_2$	126 (3)	1·4576	1·1252	88·4	[255]
$(CH_3)_2C$—(ring)—$OPO(OC_2H_5)_2$	166–168 (10)	1·4781			[258]
(not a completely pure substance)					
$(CH_3)_2C$—(ring)—$OPO(OC_2H_5)_2$, —Cl	160–161 (2·5)	1·4818			[258]

TABLE 32 — *(contd.)*

Formula	b. p., °C(mm)	n_D^{20}	d_4^{20}	Yield (%)	Reference
[structure] —Br / —OPO(OC₂H₅)₂ ;$C_{14}H_{24}O_4BrP$				81	[169]
$C_6H_5CHClCH = CHPO(OC_2H_5)_2$				100	[169]
$C_6H_5COCH = C(C_6H_5)OPO(OC_2H_5)_2$	208 (3)	1·5490			[258]
$CCl_2 = CHCH = C(C_6H_5)OPO(OC_2H_5)_2$				100	[169]
$(CH_2 = CHO)_3PO$	84–85 (10)	1·4314	1·1240	10	[120]

* This is obviously a misprint in the original paper [258]. The correct figure is most probably 1·1202.

TABLE 33. β,γ-UNSATURATED ESTERS OF PHOSPHORIC ACIDS*

Formula	b. p., °C (mm)	n_D^{20}	d_{25}^{25}	Yield (%)	Reference
$CH_2 = CHCH_2OPO(OC_2H_5)_2$	63 (0·5)	1·4216	1·073	72·5	[186]
$CH_2 = C(CH_3)CH_2OPO(OC_6H_5)_2$		1·5242 (Undistilled)	1·162		[132]
$(CH_2 = CHCH_2O)_2P(O)OCH_3$	60 (0·5)			30	[173]
$(CH_2 = CHCH_2O)_2P(O)OC_2H_5$	{ 72 (1–2) / 66 (0·5)	1·4350		34 / 62	[138] / [173]
$(CH_2 = CHCH_2O)_2P(O)OC_6H_5$	102 (0·5)	1·4957	1·142	64	[186]
$(CH_2 = CHCH_2O)_2P(O)OC_6H_3Cl_2\text{-}2,5$	154 (2·8)	1·4805 (11°)		52	[259]
$[CH_2 = C(CH_3)CH_2O]_2P(O)OC_2H_5$	120–135 (6)	1·4390	1·040	45	[132]
$[CH_2 = C(CH_3)CH_2O]_2P(O)O$—⟨benzene⟩ C_6H_5		1·5331 (Undistilled)	1·1149		[132]
$(CH_2 = CHCH_2O)_3PO$	{ 80 (0·5) / 93–94 (1)	1·4500	1·0815	83	[129] / [139]
$(CH_2 = CClCH_2O)_3PO$	131–133 (1)	1·4866 (20°)		71·8 (Undistilled)	[130]
$(CHCl = CHCH_2O)_3PO$	160–170⁺		1·350 (23°)		[260]
$[CH_2 = C(CH_3)CH_2O]_3PO$	135·5–140 (5)	1·4470 (26°)	0·988 (26°)	51·5	[132]
$(CH_3CCl = CHCH_2O)_3PO$	Decomposes		1·20 (20°)		[260]
$(CH \equiv CCH_2O)_2P(O)OC_6H_2Cl_3\text{-}2,4,5$		1·5370	1·4058		[261]
$(CH \equiv CCH_2O)_2P(O)OCH_2CH_2O$——$C_6H_2Cl_3\text{-}2,4,5$		1·5145	1·4144		[261]

* The compound $CCl_2=CHOPO(OCH_2CH=CH_2)_2$ is listed in Table 30.

⁺ Pressure not known.

TABLE 34. ESTERS OF THE TYPE

$$R-ArOPO(OAr')_2, \quad \underset{R'}{\overset{R}{\diagdown}} ArOPO(OAr')_2, (R-ArO)_2P(O)OAr', (R-ArO)_3PO,$$

$$(ROOC-ArO)_3PO, \text{ WHERE } R=CH_2=CHCH_2, CH_2=CClCH_2, CH_2=C(CH_3)CH_2$$

Formula	b. p., °C (mm)	n_D^{29}	d_4^{20}	Reference
—CH₂CH=CH₂ / —OPO(OC₆H₅)₂	250–260 (6·5)	1·5640		[132]
—CH₂CH=CH₂ / —OPO[OC₆H₄(CH₃)-4]₂	291–297 (8)	1·5421	1·100	[132]
—CH₂CCl=CH₂ / —OPO(OC₆H₄CH₃-2)₂	258–267 (7)	1·5720	1·226	[132]
CH₂CH=CH₂ / —OPO(OC₆H₅)₂ / CH₂CH=CH₂	254–258 (5)	1·5637	1·190	[132]
$C_6H_5OPO\left(O-\underset{CH_2CH=CH_2}{\bigcirc}\right)_2$	254–262 (6)	1·5669	1·177	[132]
$2\text{-}C_6H_5C_6H_4OPO\left(O-\underset{CH_2CH=CH_2}{\bigcirc}\right)_2$	293–296 (6)	1·5872	1·188	[132]
$C_6H_5OPO\left(O-\underset{CH_2C(CH_3)=CH_2}{\bigcirc}\right)_2$	267–269 (7·5)	1·5647	1·152	[132]
$\left(CH_2=CHCH_2-\underset{CH_3}{\bigcirc}-O-\right)_3 PO$	Undistillable oil			[262]
$\left(CH_2=CHCH_2OOC-\underset{CH_3O}{\bigcirc}-O-\right)_3 PO$	m. p. 63–63·7°			[259]

TABLE 35. UNSATURATED ACID ESTERS OF PHOSPHORIC ACID

Formula	m. p., (°C)	Reference
$C_2H_5OOCCH = C(CH_3)OPO(OH)_2$		[155]
$CH_2 = CHCH_2OPO(OH)_2$		[149]
$CH_2 = CHCH_2O$ $>P(O)OH$ $ClCH_2CH_2O$	Undistillable syrups	[154]
$(CH_2 = CHCH_2O)_2P(O)OH$		[150]
$CH_3CH = CH-\!\!\!\!\diagup\!\!\diagdown\!\!-OPO(OH)_2$ with OCH_3	133	[153]
$CH_2 = CHCH_2-\!\!\!\!\diagup\!\!\diagdown\!\!-OPO(OH)_2$ with OCH_3	105	[153]

TABLE 36. β,γ-UNSATURATED ESTERS OF N-SUBSTITUTED
PHOSPHORAMIDIC ACIDS

Formula	b. p., °C (mm)	n_D^{20}	d_4^{20}	Yield (%)	Reference
$CH_2 = CHCH_2NHPO(OC_2H_5)_2$	118–120 (3·5)				[134]
$CH_2 = C(CH_3)CH_2NHPO(OC_2H_5)_2$	96 (0·5)	1·4412	1·124	81·3	[186]
$(CH_2 = CHCH_2)_2NPO(OC_2H_5)_2$	77–81 (1)	1·4430	1·013	72·0	[186]
$(CH_2 = CHCH_2O)_2PNH_2$ $\overset{\|}{O}$	130 (2) 12—14*				[135]
$(CH_2 = CHCH_2O)_2PNHCH_2OH$ $\overset{\|}{O}$	Oil				[135]
$(CH_2 = CHCH_2O)_2PN(CH_3)_2$ $\overset{\|}{O}$	75 (0·5) 113–114 (11)	1·4465 (25°)	1·0561 (25°) 1·0570 (19·5°)	71·4	[186] [134]
$(CH_2 = CHCH_2O)_2PN(C_2H_5)_2$ $\overset{\|}{O}$	129–130 (13) 105–110 (2)		1·0225 (22°)		[134] [135]
$(CH_2 = CHCH_2O)_2PNHCH_2CH = CH_2$ $\overset{\|}{O}$	115–120 (2); 35–36*				[135]
$(CH_2 = CHCH_2O)_2PN(CH_2CH = CH_2)_2$ $\overset{\|}{O}$	104·5–106·5 (2)				[134]
$(CH \equiv CCH_2O)_2PNH_2$ $\overset{\|}{O}$	155–160 (2); 35*				[135]

* Melting point.

TABLE 37. α,β-AND β-γ-UNSATURATED ESTERS OF PHOSPHOROTHIONIC PHOSPHOROTHIOLOTHIONIC AND N-SUBSTITUTED PHOSPHORAMIDOTHIONIC ACIDS

Formula	b. p., °C (mm)	n_D^{20}	d_4^{20}	Yield (%)	Reference
$CH_2 = CHOPS(OC_2H_5)_2$	82 (7·5)	1·4562	1·0904	79	[121]
$CH_2 = CHOPS(OC_3H_7)_2$	97 (6)	1·4581	1·0505	64	[121]
$CH_2 = CHOPS(OC_4H_9)_2$	126–127 (8)	1·4575	1·0195	67	[121]
$CH_2 = CHOPS(OC_6H_5)_2$	163–164 (2)	1·5655	1·2164	50	[121]
$C_2H_5OOC—CH = C(CH_3)OPS(OC_2H_5)_2$	154 (5)				[263]
$(CH_2 = CHO)_2P(S)OC_2H_5$	72–73 (7)	1·4634	1·1017	62	[121]
$(CH_2 = CHO)_2P(S)OC_4H_9$	96 (6)	1·4654	1·0617	65	[121]
$(CH_2 = CHO)_2P(S)OC_6H_5$	134–135 (10)	1·5268	1·1719	74	[121]
$CH_2 = CHCH_2OP{\overset{\displaystyle O—CH_2}{\underset{\displaystyle O—CH_2}{}}}$, $\Vert S$	130–132 (4)	1·5025	1·2619	40	[91]
$CH_2 = CHCH_2OP{\overset{\displaystyle O—CH—CH_3}{\underset{\displaystyle O—CH_2}{}CH_2}}$, $\Vert S$	158–160 (5)	1·5025	1·2111	43	[91]
$CH_2 = CHCH_2OP{\overset{\displaystyle N(CH_3)_2}{\underset{\displaystyle OC_6H_4NO_2\text{-}4}{}}}$, $\Vert S$		1·5388 (35°)	1·16 (31°)		[264]
$CH_3CCl = CHCH_2SPS(OCH_3)_2$	118–121 (2·5)	1·5437	1·2605		[147]
$CH_3CCl = CHCH_2SPS(OC_2H_5)_2$	117–120 (1—1·2)	1·5284	1·1898	78·4*	[147]
$CH_3CCl = CHCH_2SPS(OC_3H_7)_2$	138–141 (1·5)	1·5184	1·1417	91·1*	[147]
$CH_3CCl = CHCH_2SPS(OC_3H_7\text{-iso})_2$	141–142 (2)	1·5132	1·1308	95·1*	[147]
$CH_3CCl = CHCH_2SPS(OC_4H_9)_2$	Undistillable oil	1·5129	1·1068	83·2*	[147]
$(CH_2 = CHCH_2O)_3PS$	125–127 (11)	1·4815	1·0827	80·6	[111]
$CH \equiv CCH_2OP{\overset{\displaystyle OC_2H_5}{\underset{\displaystyle OC_6H_2Cl_3\text{-}2,4,5}{}}}$, $\Vert S$		1·5585	1·3754		[261]

* The yields refer to undistilled materials.

TABLE 38. COMPLEX (CONTAINING RINGS) UNSATURATED ESTERS
OF PHOSPHOROTHIONIC AND PHOSPHOROTHIOLOTHIONIC ACIDS

Formula	b. p., °C(mm)	n_D^{20}	d_4^{20}	Yield (%)	Reference
$(C_2H_5O)_2P(S)O-$ [ring structure with O, CO]	170 (8); 46*				[265]
$(CH_3O)_2P(S)O-$ [ring structure with O, CO, CH_3]	42*				[265]
$(C_3H_5O)_2P(S)O-$ [ring structure with O, CO, CH_3]	Liquid				[265]
$(CH_3O)_2P(S)O-$ [ring structure with O, CO, CH_3]	77*		1·31		[265]
$CH_3O{,}\ C_2H_5O{>}P(S)O-$ [ring structure with O, CO, CH_3]	Liquid				[265]
$(C_2H_5O)_2P(S)O-$ [ring structure with O, CO, CH_3]	210 (1); 38*	1·5685 (37°)	1·260 (38°)		[265]
[CCl ring structure] $-CH_2SPS(OC_2H_5)_2$		1·5660	1·4859	56	[266]
[CCl ring structure with CHO—] PSSH, bracketed ×2		1·6965		96	[267]

TABLE 38 — (contd.)

Formula	b. p., °C (mm)	n_D^{20}	d_4^{20}	Yield (%)	Reference
$\left[\text{Cl–C} \overset{\text{CCl}}{\underset{\text{CCl}}{\diamondsuit}} \underset{\text{CH}_2}{\overset{\text{CCl}_2}{}} \text{CHCH}_2\text{O–} \right]_2 \text{PSSH}$		1·5965		98	[267]
$\left[\text{Cl–C} \overset{\text{CCl}}{\underset{\text{CCl}}{\diamondsuit}} \underset{\text{CH}_2}{\overset{\text{CCl}_2}{}} \text{CHO–} \right]_2 \text{PSS–CHCOOH} \quad \text{CH}_2\text{–COOH}$	143*			93	[267]
$\left[\text{Cl–C} \overset{\text{CCl}}{\underset{\text{CCl}}{\diamondsuit}} \underset{\text{CH}_2}{\overset{\text{CCl}_2}{}} \text{CHCH}_2\text{O–} \right]_2 \text{PSSCH–COOH} \quad \text{CH}_2\text{–COOH}$		1·5539		78	[267]
$\left[\text{Cl–C} \overset{\text{CCl}}{\underset{\text{CCl}}{\diamondsuit}} \underset{\text{CH}_2}{\overset{\text{CCl}_2}{}} \text{CHO–} \right]_3 \text{PS}$		1·5378		84	[267]
$\left[\text{Cl–C} \overset{\text{CCl}}{\underset{\text{CCl}}{\diamondsuit}} \underset{\text{CH}_2}{\overset{\text{CCl}_2}{}} \text{CHCH}_2\text{O–} \right]_3 \text{PS}$		1·5240		97	[267]
$\left[\text{Cl–C} \ldots \text{CHOCH}_2\text{O–} \right]_2 \text{PSSH}$		1·5761		96	[267]
$\text{Cl–C} \ldots \text{C} \overset{\text{CH}_2\text{O}}{\underset{\text{CH}_2\text{O}}{}} \text{PSSH}$	206–207*			84	[267]

* Melting point

TABLE 39. UNSATURATED ESTERS OF PHOSPHORAMIDOTHIONIC

ACIDS OF THE TYPE $\begin{array}{c}R \\ R'\end{array}\Big\rangle NPS(OC_6H_4CH_2CH{=}CH_2\text{-}2)$ [268]

$RPS\left(O-\overset{CH_2-CH=CH_2}{\underset{}{\bigcirc}}\right)_2$	n_D^{35}	d
R		
CH_3NH-	1·5302	1·09 (26°)
iso-C_3H_7NH-	1·5170	0·97 (19°)
$(CH_3)_2N-$	1·5428	1·06 (25°)
$(C_2H_5)_2N-$	1·5233	1·04 (25°)

Esters of saturated and aromatic phosphonous, phosphinous, phosphonic, phosphinic and phosphonothionic acids

Esters of alkoxycarbonylalkylphosphonic acids of the type $ROOC-R'-PO(OR'')_2$, *where R and R' are saturated and R'' is an unsaturated radical*

Of the unsaturated esters of the phosphinous and phosphonous acids, the allyl and thioallyl esters with the general formulae $RP(XR')_2$ and $(C_6H_5)_2P-X-R'$ (X = oxygen or sulphur; R' = allyl or its derivatives) are known, and they are prepared by the reaction of the corresponding acid chlorides and alcohols in the presence of an organic base [101, 178, 179].

For the synthesis of esters of phosphonic and alkoxycarbonylalkylphosphonic acids, the Arbusov rearrangement is often used [101, 105, 180–183], or the reaction between the corresponding acid chlorides and unsaturated alcohols in the presence of organic bases [184–189]. Abramov and his co-workers [190, 191] have described a method of obtaining unsaturated (allylic) esters of *a*-hydroxyalkylphosphonic acids by the addition of diallyl hydrogen phosphite to aldehydes in the presence of a metallic sodium catalyst:

$$RCHO + HPO(OCH_2CH = CH_2)_2 \longrightarrow RCHOHPO(OCH_2CH = CH_2)_2$$

By means of the catalysed addition of diallyl hydrogen phosphite to various unsaturated compounds, Pudovik and Khlyupina [128] obtained a range of diallyl alkoxycarbonylalkylphosphonates with the general formula $ROOC-R'-PO(OCH_2CH = CH_2)_2$.

It is obvious that of the unsaturated esters of the various phosphorus acids, the allyl compounds have received most study: this reflects the greater availability of allyl alcohol as compared with other unsaturated alcohols.

Diallyl phenylphosphonate $C_6H_5PO(OCH_2CH = CH_2)_2$ [184]

$$C_6H_5POCl_2 + 2CH_2 = CHCH_2OH + 2C_5H_5N \longrightarrow C_6H_5PO(OCH_2CH = CH_2)_2 +$$
$$+ 2C_5H_5N \cdot HCl$$

A 3-l. three-necked flask, fitted with a stirrer, thermometer, dropping funnel and reflux condenser was charged with allyl alcohol (464 g, 8 moles) and pyridine (632 g, 8 moles). Phenylphosphonic dichloride (780 g, 4 moles) was added to this mixture over a period of 6 hr. The temperature of the reaction was kept at 2–5° by exterior cooling with an ice-salt bath. At the end of the addition the mixture was allowed to warm up to room temperature. Water (400 ml) was then added, the oily layer was separated and promptly distilled *in vacuo*: long standing of the crude wet ester caused hydrolysis. In effecting the distillation it was necessary to raise the temperature slowly and to maintain the pressure at about 20 mm up to 50°, at less than 10 mm from 50° to 100°, and at less than 5 mm up to 120°.

In heating the crude ester to the temperature of distillation, gaseous products were formed which made it difficult to maintain the necessary low pressure. Heating the substance too rapidly at too high a pressure caused some decomposition and resulted in low yields of the product. In any event it was essential to avoid heating the residue to a temperature much above 170° to prevent rapid decomposition.

The distillation of the product is best done at 1–2 mm in the presence of a small quantity of an inhibitor — copper resinate. The yield of distilled product was 777 g (81·6%), b. p. 128°/1 mm, n_D^{25} 1·5128, d_4^{25} 1·1097.

Vinyl esters of alkyl- and aryl-phosphonic acids have been synthesized by other methods, namely by the removal of hydrogen chloride from the corresponding 2-chloroethyl ester [156],* and by the reaction of α-halogeno-carbonyl compounds with esters of phenylphosphonic acid [169] (see pp. 75–79):)

$$C_6H_5P(OR)_2 + R'—CO—CR''R'''X \to C_6H_5P\!\!\begin{array}{c} \diagup OR \\ \Vert \quad \diagdown OCR' = CR''R''' \\ O \end{array} + RX$$

where X = halogen. Vinyl esters of phosphinic acids have been synthesized by the reaction of phosphinic chlorides with acetaldehyde and triethylamine [120, 192] (cf. p. 81) as follows:

$$\begin{array}{c} R \diagdown \\ \qquad P—Cl + CH_3CHO + N(C_2H_5)_3 \longrightarrow \\ R \diagup \Vert \\ O \end{array} \begin{array}{c} R \diagdown \\ \qquad POCH = CH_2 + N(C_2H_5)_3 \cdot HCl \\ R \diagup \Vert \\ O \end{array}$$

Divinyl methylphosphonate $CH_3PO(OCH = CH_2)_2$ [120]

$$CH_3POCl_2 + 2CH_3CHO + 2N(C_2H_5)_3 \longrightarrow CH_3PO(OCH = CH_2)_2 + 2N(C_2H_5)_3 \cdot HCl$$

A solution of methylphosphonic dichloride (20 g) in benzene (20 ml) was added dropwise over a period of 2 hr to a mixture of acetaldehyde (40 g),

* See footnote, p. 50

triethylamine (62 g) and phenyl-β-naphthylamine (0·5 g). During the addition the temperature was kept between $-8°$ and $-10°$, and then the reaction mixture was allowed to stand for 1 hr at room temperature. On the following day it was distilled without previously removing the triethylamine salt. Redistillation of the distillate from orthophosphoric acid at 8 mm pressure gave pure divinyl methylphosphonate (5 g, 23%) as a colourless, transparent liquid, which turned a pale yellow after being kept for 1–2 days in the light or for 1–2 weeks in the dark. It has b. p. 64–65°/8 mm, n_D^{20} 1·4394, d_4^{20} 1·1097.

The properties of esters of saturated organophosphorus acids and unsaturated alcohols are recorded in Tables 40–45 (see pp. 67–72).

TABLE 40. ESTERS OF PHOSPHONOUS ACIDS WITH
β,γ-UNSATURATED ALCOHOLS

Formula	b.p., °C (mm)	n_D^{12}	d^{12}	Yield (%)	Reference
H │ $C_8H_{17}POCH_2CH = CH_2$ ‖ O	134 (1)	1·4536 (20°)			[183]
H │ $C_6H_5POCH_2CH = CH_2$ ‖ O	121–123 (1·5)				[183]
$(C_6H_5)_2POCH_2CH = CH_2$	isomerizes into $(C_6H_5)_2P(O)CH_2CH= = CH_2$				[178]
$(C_6H_5)_2PSCH_2CH = CH_2$	isomerizes into $(C_6H_5)_2P(S)CH_2CH= = CH_2$				[178]
$C_2H_5P(OCH_2CH = CH_2)_2$	65–67 (11)	1·4553	0·9396		[269]
$C_4H_9P(OCH_2CH = CH_2)_2$	99–100 (11)	1·4550	0·9340	64	[270]
$C_6H_5P(OCH_2CH = CH_2)_2$	116–117 (3)	1·5240 (20°)	1·0443 (20°)		[105]
$4\text{-}ClC_6H_4P(OCH_2CH = CH_2)_2$	126–127 (3)	1·5376 (20°)	1·1490 (20°)		[105]
$C_2H_5P(OCH_2C \equiv CH)_2$	126–127 (6)	1·5015	1·0801		[270]
$C_3H_7P(OCH_2C \equiv CH)_2$	136–136·5 (6)	1·5001	1·0598		[270]
$C_4H_9P(OCH_2C \equiv CH)_2$	146–147 (6)	1·4949	1·0406		[270]

TABLE 41. ESTERS AND ESTER-AMIDES OF ALKYL- AND ARYL-PHOSPHONIC ACIDS WITH α,β-UNSATURATED ALCOHOLS

Formula	b.p., °C (mm)	n_D^{20}	d_4^{20}	Yield (%)	Reference
$CH_3P\begin{cases}OCH=CH_2\\OCH_2CH_2Cl\end{cases}$, $\Vert$ O	96–98 (3·5–4)	1·4540	1·2351	34	[120]
$CH_3P\begin{cases}OCH=CH_2\\OC_4H_9\end{cases}$, $\Vert$ O	63–65 (2·5–3)	1·4278	1·0208	23	[120]
$C_6H_5P\begin{cases}OCH=CH_2\\(OC_2H_4)_2OCH_3\end{cases}$, $\Vert$ O				100	[169]
$CCl_3P\begin{cases}OCH=CH_2\\N(CH_3)_2\end{cases}$, $\Vert$ O	100–105 (0·5)				[271]
$\begin{array}{c}CH_3\\C_6H_5\end{array}\!\!>\!P(O)OCH=CH_2$	102–104 (2)	1·5224	1·1166	24	[120]
$(C_4H_9)_2P(O)OCH=CHCl$	96 (0·5)	1·4392 (25°)		85	[172]
$C_6H_5P\begin{cases}OCH=CHCl\\OC_2H_5\end{cases}$, $\Vert$ O	118–134 (0·1–0·4)	1·5174 (25°)		79	[169]
$(C_6H_5)_2P(O)OCH=CHCl$				100	[169]
$C_2H_5P\begin{cases}OCH_3\\OCH=CCl_2\end{cases}$, $\Vert$ O	65–66 (0·5)	1·4680	1·3333		[269]
$C_2H_5P\begin{cases}OC_2H_5\\OCH=CCl_2\end{cases}$, $\Vert$ O	71–72 (1)	1·4637	1·2734		[269]
$C_2H_5P\begin{cases}OC_3H_7\\OCH=CCl_2\end{cases}$, $\Vert$ O	83–86 (0·5)	1·4620	1·2314		[269]
$C_2H_5P\begin{cases}OC_3H_7\text{-iso}\\OCH=CCl_2\end{cases}$, $\Vert$ O	73–74 (0·5)	1·4575	1·2260		[269]
$C_2H_5P\begin{cases}OC_4H_9\\OCH=CCl_2\end{cases}$, $\Vert$ O	92–93 (0·5)	1·4624	1·2002		[269]

TABLE 41 — *(contd.)*

Formula	b. p., °C (mm)	n_D^{20}	d_4^{20}	Yield (%)	Reference
$C_2H_5P \begin{smallmatrix} OC_4H_9\text{-iso} \\ OCH = CCl_2 \end{smallmatrix}$ \; $\parallel O$	89–90 (0·5)	1·4570	1·1899		[269]
$C_2H_5P \begin{smallmatrix} OC_5H_{11} \\ OCH = CCl_2 \end{smallmatrix}$ \; $\parallel O$	100–101 (0·5)	1·4591	1·1672		[269]
$C_2H_5P \begin{smallmatrix} OCH_2C_6H_5 \\ OCH = CCl_2 \end{smallmatrix}$ \; $\parallel O$	132–133 (0·5)	1·5220	1·2805		[269]
$C_2H_5P \begin{smallmatrix} N(CH_3)_2 \\ OCH = CCl_2 \end{smallmatrix}$ \; $\parallel O$	80–82 (2)	1·4714	1·2482		[269]
$C_2H_5P \begin{smallmatrix} N(C_2H_5)_2 \\ OCH = CCl_2 \end{smallmatrix}$ \; $\parallel O$	92–93 (1)	1·4758	1·1974		[269]
$(C_2H_5)_2POCH = CCl_2$	81–83 (0·5)	1·4810	1·2465		[269]
$C_6H_5P \begin{smallmatrix} OCH = CCl_2 \\ OCH_3 \end{smallmatrix}$ \; $\parallel O$	125–137 (1)			73	[169]
$C_6H_5P \begin{smallmatrix} OCH = CCl_2 \\ OC_2H_5 \end{smallmatrix}$ \; $\parallel O$	131–144 (2–3)			68	[169]
$C_6H_5P \begin{smallmatrix} OC(CH_3) = CH_2 \\ OCH_3 \end{smallmatrix}$ \; $\parallel O$	137–138 (8)	1·5120	1·1421		[165]
$CH_3P \begin{smallmatrix} OC(CH_3) = CHCH_3 \\ OCH(CH_3)CHOHCH_3 \end{smallmatrix}$ \; $\parallel O$	58–68 (0·03)	1·4372 (24·8°)	1·080 (26°)	38·7	[272]
$CH_3PO(OCH = CH_2)_2$	64–65 (8)	1·4394	1·1097	27	[120]
$ClCH_2PO(OCH = CH_2)_2$	66–67 (1)	1·4636	1·2458	32	[120]
$C_2H_5PO(OCH = CH_2)_2$	60–61 (5–5·5)	1·4409	1·0707	30	[120]
$C_6H_5PO(OCH = CH_2)_2$	110–111 (1·5–2) \newline 174 (3)	1·5144 \newline 1·5258	1·1589	10 \newline 61·5	[120] \newline [156]*
$C_2H_5P \begin{smallmatrix} OCH = CCl_2 \\ OCH_2CH = CH_2 \end{smallmatrix}$ \; $\parallel O$	76–78 (0·5)	1·4710	1·2623		[269]

* See footnote on p. 50

TABLE 42. ESTERS AND SUBSTITUTED AMIDO-ACID CHLORIDES OF ALKYLPHOSPHONIC ACIDS WITH β,γ-AND OTHER UNSATURATED ALCOHOLS

Formula	b. p., °C (mm)	n_D^{25}	d_{25}^{25}	Yield (%)	Reference
$(CH_3)_2P(O)OCH_2CH = CH_2$	97·5–98·5 (14)	1·4456 (22°)		65	[273]
$(C_4H_9)_2P(O)OCH_2CH = CH_2$	95 (1)				[183]
$(C_8H_{17})_2P(O)OCH_2CH = CH_2$	134 (0·5)				[183]
$C_6H_5CH_2P\begin{cases}OCH_2CH = CH_2 \\ OCH_2CH_2Cl\end{cases}$ (‖O)	175–177 (2)	1·5210 (20°)	1·2061 (20°)		[91]
$(CH_3)_2P(O)[OCH_2C(CH_3) = CH_2]$	103–104 (13·5)	1·4507 (20°)		90	[273]
$(CH_3)_2P(O)OCH_2CH = CHCH_2$	108 (11)	1·4543 (21°)		78	[273]
$CH_3PO(OCH_2CH = CH_2)_2$	101–102 (10–12)	1·4475 (18°)	1·0663 (18°)	86	[180]
$ClCH_2PO(OCH_2CH = CH_2)_2$	94–98 (1)	1·4674	1·1902		[274]
$CCl_3PO(OCH_2CH = CH_2)_2$	{ 136–138 (10) 118 (10·5)	1·4552 1·478	1·1719*	90	[182] [173]
$O[CH_2PO(OCH_2CH = CH_2)_2]_2$	107 (1)	1·4761			[275]
$C_2H_5PO(OCH_2CH = CH_2)_2$	73–78 (0·5)	1·4470	0·9963	65·8	[186]
$C_3H_7PO(OCH_2CH = CH_2)_2$	91 (1)	1·4472	1·021	63·3	[186]
iso-$C_3H_7PO(OCH_2CH = CH_2)_2$	52 (0·5)	1·4459	1·0166	60·8	[186]
$ClCH_2CHClCH_2PO(OCH_2CH = CH_2)_2$	137–140 (2)	1·4709 (20°)	1·2810 (20°)	7	[84]
$C_4H_9PO(OCH_2CH = CH_2)_2$	75–81 (0·5)	1·4478	1·002	74	[186]
iso-$C_4H_9PO(OCH_2CH = CH_2)_2$	65–67 (0·5)	1·4456	1·005	79·2	[186]
cyclo-$C_6H_{11}PO(OCH_2CH = CH_2)_2$	119·5–119·7 (2)	1·4760	1·0548	55·7	[188]
$C_6H_5CH_2PO(OCH_2CH = CH_2)_2$	173–175 (9)	1·5114	1·0970+		[101]
$(CH_3)_3C—CH_2CH(CH_3)CH_2—$ $—PO(OCH_2CH = CH_2)_2$	92 (0·5)	1·4439	0·9641	84	[186]
$(C_6H_5)_3CPO(OCH_3CH = CH_2)_2$	229·5–230+			45	[111]
3-$NO_2C_6H_4CH—PO(OCH_2CH = CH_2)_2$ (|) 3-$CH_3C_6H_4NH$				53·7	[128]
$C_6H_5NH—CHPO(OCH_2CH = CH_2)_2$ (|) 4-$(CH_3)_2NC_6H_4$				59·5	[128]
$CH_3PO[OCH_2C(CH_3) = CH_2]_2$	95 (1)	1·4491	1·024	69·5	[186]
$C_2H_5PO[OCH_2C(CH_3) = CH_2]_2$	93–95 (1)	1·4502	1·006	76·8	[186]
$C_3H_7PO[OCH_2C(CH_3) = CH_2]_2$	107–112 (1–2)	1·4512	0·9903	84	[186]
iso-$C_3H_7PO[OCH_2C(CH_3) = CH_2]_2$	106–108 (2)	1·4490	0·990	60	[186]
$C_4H_7PO[OCH_2C(CH_3) = CH_2]_2$	104–106 (1)	1·4519	0·9789	85·4	[186]
cyclo-$C_6H_{11}PO[OCH_2C(CH_3) = CH_2]_2$	94–98 (0·5)	1·4738	1·027	73	[186]
$C_6H_5CH_2PO[OCH_2C(CH_3) = CH_2]_2$	158–163 (2)	1·5053	1·0630		[186]

TABLE 42 — *(contd.)*

Formula	b.p., °C (mm)	n_D^{25}	d_{25}^{25}	Yield (%)	Reference
$2\text{-}C_8H_{17}PO[OCH_2C(CH_3) = CH_2]_2$	125 (0·5)	1·4543	0·947	59·5	[186]
$CH_3PO[OCH(CH_3)CH_2CH = CH_2]_2$	134–135 (17)	1·4462 (20°)	0·9837		[116]
$CCl_3P \underset{\underset{O}{\parallel}}{\overset{N\,=\,CH(CH\,=\,CH-)_2N\diagdown\genfrac{}{}{0pt}{}{CH_3}{C_6H_5}}{\diagdown Cl}} \cdot HCl$	155·5–157 ∓ (with decomposition)			76	[276]
$CCl_3P \underset{\underset{O}{\parallel}}{\overset{N\,=\,CH(CH\,=\,CH-)_2N\diagdown\genfrac{}{}{0pt}{}{CH_3}{C_6H_4Cl}}{\diagdown Cl}} \cdot HCl$	184–185 ∓ (with decomposition)			85	[276]
$(CH_3)_2P(O)OCH_2C \equiv CH$	89–89·5 (2·5)	1·4608 (22°)		75	[273]
$(CH_3)_2P(O)OCH_2C \equiv CCH_3$	81–81·5 (2·5)	1·4334 (22°)		80	[273]

* d_0^0.　　　 + d_0^{20}.　　　∓ Melting point.

TABLE 43. ESTERS OF HYDROXY- AND KETO-ALKYLPHOSPHONIC AND BENZOYLPHOSPHONIC ACIDS WITH β,γ-UNSATURATED ALCOHOLS

Formula	b.p., °C (mm)	n_D^{20}	d_4^{20}	Yield (%)	Reference
$RPO(OCH_2CH = CH_2)_2$ $\quad$ R					
CH_3CHOH-	151 (10)	1·4565	1·1187	63·5	[190]
C_2H_5CHOH-	129–130 (1)	1·4600	1·0961	49·4	[191]
C_3H_7CHOH-	163–164 (10)	1·4552	1·0769	31·6	[190]
$(CH_3)_2COH-$	132 (12)	1·4500	1·0907	38·8	[190]
$\genfrac{}{}{0pt}{}{CH_2-CH_2}{CH_2-CH_2}\!\!>\!\!COH-$	165–167 (1)	1·4740	1·1253	45·7	[190]
$CH_2\!\!<\!\!\genfrac{}{}{0pt}{}{CH_2-CH_2}{CH_2-CH_2}\!\!>\!\!COH-$	56·5–57*			67·7	[190]
$CH_3COP\underset{\underset{O}{\parallel}}{\diagup}\genfrac{}{}{0pt}{}{OCH_2CH=CH_2}{OCH_2CH_2Cl}$	139–142 (8)	1·4660	1·2530+		[91]
$CH_3COP\underset{\underset{O}{\parallel}}{\diagup}\genfrac{}{}{0pt}{}{OCH_2CH=CH_2}{OCH_2CH_2Br}$	125–129·5 (2–2·5)	1·4740	1·4348+		[91]
$C_6H_5COPO(OCH_2CH = CH_2)_2$ (undistilled)		1·5335	1·1726+		[101]

These substances were not completely pure

* Melting point.　　　 + d_0^{20}.

TABLE 44. ESTERS OF ARYLPHOSPHONIC ACIDS WITH
β,γ-UNSATURATED ALCOHOLS

Formula	b.p., °C (mm)	n_D^{25}	d_{25}^{25}	Yield (%)	References
$\begin{array}{c}CH_3\\ \\C_6H_5\end{array}{>}P(O)OCH_2CH = CH_2$	112–113 (1)	1·5208 (20°)	1·1110 (20°)		[105]
$\begin{array}{c}CH_3\\ \\4\text{-}ClC_6H_4\end{array}{>}P(O)OCH_2CH = CH_2$	129–130 (2)	1·5308 (20°)	1·1960 (20°)		[105]
$\begin{array}{c}C_2H_5\\ \\C_6H_5\end{array}{>}P(O)OCH_2CH = CH_2$	124–125 (3)	1·5155 (20°)	1·0854 (20°)		[105]
$\begin{array}{c}C_4H_9\\ \\C_6H_5\end{array}{>}P(O)OCH_2CH = CH_2$	113 (0·15)				[183]
$C_6H_5PO(OCH_2CH = CH_2)_2$	128 (1)	1·5128	1·1097	81·6	[184]
$C_6H_5PS(OCH_2CH = CH_2)_2$	126–129 (1)	1·5508	1·115	64·3	[186]
$4\text{-}ClC_6H_4PO(OCH_2CH = CH_2)_2$	136–139 (2)	1·5208		40	[184]
$4\text{-}CH_3C_6H_4PO(OCH_2CH = CH_2)_2$	134–136 (1)	1·5120	1·089	55·6	[184]
$C_6H_5PO(NHCH_2CH = CH_2)_2$	m. p. 88–89°			55·3	[186]
$C_6H_5PO[OCH_2C(CH_3) = CH_2]_2$	140–143 (2–3)	1·5057	1·0728	53·5	[184]
$4\text{-}ClC_6H_4PO[OCH_2C(CH_3) = CH_2]_2$	137–140 (1)	1·5162	1·145	53·8	[184]
$4\text{-}CH_3C_6H_4PO[OCH_2C(CH_3) = CH_2]_2$	146–149 (1)	1·5070	1·057	67·2	[184]

TABLE 45. ESTERS OF ALKOXYCARBONYLALKYLPHOSPHONIC ACIDS
OF THE TYPE $RO_2C—R'—PO(OCH_2CH = CH_2)_2$,
WHERE R AND R' ARE SATURATED (OR R' IS ABSENT)

Formula	b.p., °C (mm)	n_D^{20}	d_4^{20}	Yield (%)	Reference
R					
$C_2H_5OOC—$	123–126 (3)	1·4490	1·1204		[248]
	153–154 (12)	1·4469	1·1213	32·3	[123]
$CH_3OOCCH_2—$	128–129 (3)	1·4578	1·1472		[105]
	155·5–156·5 (8)	1·4514	1·1198	30	[123]
$C_2H_5OOCCH_2—$	118 (0·5)			90	[173]
iso-$C_3H_7OOCCH_2—$	150–151 (5)	1·4545	1·0983		[105]
$C_4H_9OOCCH_2—$	142–143 (1·5)	1·4552	1·0801		[105]
iso-$C_4H_9OOCCH_2—$	130–131 (1)	1·4560	1·0850		[105]
$C_4H_9OOCCH—$ $\;\;\;\;\;\;\;\;\;|$ $C_4H_9OOCCH_2$	185 (0·7)	1·4680	1·0954		[251]
$CH_3OOCCH(CH_3)CH_2—$	143–144 (8)	1·4395	1·0753	67·3	[128]
$C_4H_9OOCCH(CH_3)CH_2—$	176–177 (8)	1·4582	1·0573	65·0	[128]
$C_2H_5OOCCH_2CH(C_6H_5)—$	201–201·5 (8)	1·4960	1·1180	67·3	[128]
$CH_3OOCCH_2CH(COOCH_3)—$	185 (8)	1·4300	1·1120	62·3	[128]

Esters of unsaturated organophosphorus acids and unsaturated alcohols

The simplest example of such an ester is diallyl allylphosphonate, which is obtained by the isomerization of triallyl phosphite [111]. Other esters of phosphonic acids containing double bonds in both the acid and alcohol parts of the molecule have been synthesized by means of the Arbusov rearrangement [105]; by the reaction of acid chlorides of unsaturated phosphonic acids with allyl alcohol in the presence of pyridine [63–65, 186]; and also by the reaction of β-chloroethylphosphonic dichloride with acetaldehyde and triethylamine [120].

Diallyl allylphosphonate $CH_2 = CHCH_2PO(OCH_2CH = CH_2)_2$ [111]

$$P(OCH_2CH = CH_2)_3 \xrightarrow{CH_2=CHCH_2I} CH_2 = CHCH_2PO(OCH_2CH = CH_2)_2$$

A mixture of triallyl phosphite (9·8 g) and allyl iodide (4·6 g) (molar proportions, 2·22:1) was placed inside a thick-walled glass tube which was joined in the middle with a piece of glass capillary tubing. The liquid level was adjusted so that it was in the capillary, and the tube was sealed and allowed to stand at room temperature for 24 hr, during which time the liquid level in the capillary dropped. The tube was then immersed in water and heated at 80–90° for 3 hr; during this time the liquid level dropped about 4·5–5·0 cm; since further heating did not lead to any more change in the liquid level the reaction was then complete. When the tube was opened there was no gas pressure inside. Allyl iodide (5 g) was distilled from the reaction mixture and then the remaining liquid *in vacuo*. Two fractions were obtained: (i) b.p. 118–120·8°/8·5–9 mm (1·20 g) and (ii) 120·8–122·1°/8·5–9 mm (7·98 g).

The second fraction was redistilled to give pure diallyl allylphosphonate (7·9 g, 81%), b.p. 120–121°/8·5 mm, n_D^{20} 1·4618, d_0^{20} 1·0046. It was a colourless liquid, very soluble in alcohol, ether, petroleum ether, benzene, chloroform and other organic solvents. Unlike the esters of phosphoric acid, it was soluble in water. Since it was a derivative of pentavalent phosphorus it did not react with cuprous halides.

The properties of esters of unsaturated organophosphorus acids and unsaturated alcohols are recorded in Table 46 (see p. 74).

As a conclusion to this short account of the methods of synthesis of unsaturated esters of acids of phosphorus, a survey will be made of some special reactions by which the vinyl esters of these acids may be prepared.

TABLE 46. ESTERS OF UNSATURATED PHOSPHONIC AND CARBOXYALKYLPHOSPHONIC ACIDS WITH UNSATURATED ALCOHOLS

Formula	b. p., °C (mm)	n_D^{20}	d_4^{20}	Yield (%)	Reference
$CH_2 = CHPO(OCH = CH_2)_2$	49–50 (1·5–2)	1·4530	1·1020	10	[120]
$RPO(OCH_2CH = CH_2)_2$					
R					
$C_2H_5OCH = CH—$	112 (1)	1·4698	1·0792	56	[63]
$C_2H_5SCH = CH—$	134 (1)	1·5120	1·1119		[42]
$CH_3OC_2H_4OCH = CH—$	160 (2)	1·4789	1·1082	80	[68]
$C_2H_5OC_2H_4OCH = CH—$	138·5 (2)	1·4702	1·0854	47	[68]
$C_4H_9OC_2H_4OCH = CH—$	152 (1)	1·4860	1·0530	71	[68]
$C_3H_7OCH = CH—$	123 (1)	1·4675	1·0557		[63]
iso-$C_3H_7OCH = CH—$	120 (2)	1·4651	1·0448	54	[64]
$C_4H_9OCH = CH—$	139·5 (2)	1·4651	1·0442	50	[63]
$C_4H_9SCH = CH—$	146 (1)	1·5049	1·0800		[42]
iso-$C_4H_9OCH = CH—$	130 (1)	1·4643	1·0417		[64]
iso-$C_5H_{11}OCH = CH—$	137 (1)	1·4645	1·0335		[64]
$C_6H_{13}OCH = CH—$	151 (1)	1·4650	1·0178		[63]
$C_6H_5OCH = CH—$	153 (2)	1·5220	1·1330		[65]
$(CH_3)_2C = CH—$	87–91 (0·5)	1·4670	1·0485	69·0	[186]
$(CH_3)_3CCH_2C(CH_3) = CH—$	124–125 (2)	1·4660	0·9795	87·5	[186]
$C_6H_5CH = CH—$	159 (2)	1·5445	1·1076	56	[70]
	(a)*	1·5445	1·0996	70·0	[186]
$C_6H_5CCl = CH—$	164–165 (1)	1·5504	1·920	53	[71]
⬡ (indene)	169 (1)	1·5514	1·1354	61	[72]
$CH_2 = CHCH_2$⟩$P(O)OCH_2CH = CH_2$ / C_6H_5	131–132 (2)	1·5280	1·097≠		[105]
$CH_2 = CHCH_2$⟩$P(O)OCH_2CH = CH_2$ / 4-ClC_6H_4	148–149 (2)	1·5338	1·1203		[105]
$RPO(OCH_2CH = CH_2)_2$					
R					
$CH_2 = CHCH_2—$	120–122 (8)	1·4618	1·0046≠	80	[111]
$CH_2 = CHCH[N(C_2H_5)_2]—$	84 (0·5)			48	[277]
$CH_2 = CHCO—$	Polymerizes on distillation				[101]
$CH_2 = CHCHClCH_2—$	135 (2)	1·4832	1·1476	60	[43]
$CH_2 = C(CH_3)CHClCH_2—$	143–144 (2)	1·4870	1·1137	52	[44]
$CH_2 = CHOOCCH_2—$	107–108 (2)	1·4576	1·0512		[105]
$CH_2 = CHCH_2OOCCH_2—$	165–166 (9)	1·4711	1·0967 F		[105]
$CH_2 = CHCH = CH—$	98–100 (2)	1·4872	1·0541	81	[43]
$CH_2 = C(CH_3)CH = CH—$	124–125 (2)	1·4936	1·0490	86	[44]
$(CH_3)_2C = CHPO[OCH_2C(CH_3) = CH_2]_2$	108–115 (2)	1·4668	1·0091	64·3	[186]
$(CH_3)_3CCH_2C(CH_3) = CHPO—[OCH_2C(CH_3) = CH_2]_2$	121–125 (1)	1·4668	0·9638	82·8	[186]
$C_6H_5CH = CHPO[OCH_2C(CH_3) = CH_2]_2$	(b)	1·5360	1·0692	77·4	[186]

(a) * — Distilled from a Khimen still (bath temperature 130–140°/0·007 mm).

(b) + — Distilled from a Khimen still (bath temperature 135–142°/0·003 mm) at one drop every 2–3 sec.

≠ d_0^{20}.

A DISCUSSION OF SOME REACTIONS WHICH LEAD TO THE FORMATION OF VINYL ESTERS OF ACIDS OF PHOSPHORUS

An examination of the reactions which lead to vinyl esters of acids of phosphorus would be expected to include the large number of reactions by which most unsaturated organophosphorus compounds are made.

In the formation of such compounds the unsaturation may either be present in the starting materials used in the reaction (allyl alcohol, diallyl hydrogen phosphite, allyl halides, acid halides of unsaturated acids of phosphorus, etc.) or it may be introduced as a result of a simple transformation which does not alter the basic molecular skeleton. However, in the production of vinyl esters of acids of phosphorus (besides the synthesis of these substances by Upson* [156] by the dehydrochlorination of the corresponding β-chloroethyl ester; and the reaction of acetylene with the acids of phosphorus**[177]) more complex transformations of the molecules take place, and we will now examine these in detail.

The following methods of obtaining vinyl esters of acids of phosphorus will be considered: (a) the reaction of esters of acids of trivalent phosphorus with α-halogenocarbonyl compounds; (b) the dehydrochlorination of dialkyl esters of β,β-dichloro-α-hydroxy- and β,β,β-trichloro-α-hydroxy-ethylphosphonic acids; and (c) the reaction of acid chlorides of acids of phosphorus with acetaldehyde and triethylamine.

The reaction of esters of trivalent phosphorus with α-halogenocarbonyl compounds

From the time of discovery of the Arbusov rearrangement, almost half a century of chemical experiments carried out all over the world has established that a large number of reactions of many types of halogen-containing compounds with esters of acids of trivalent phosphorus invariably lead to esters of acids of pentavalent phosphorus or to tertiary phosphine oxides, and at the same time to the formation of a C—P bond. However, studies on the reactions of α-halogenocarbonyl compounds with trialkyl phosphites began to give results which disagreed with the firmly held opinion that such reactions could only take place via the Arbusov rearrangement.

Thus in 1946, Razumov and Petrov [193] in trying to prepare diethyl acetonylphosphonate by the reaction of bromoacetone with triethyl phosphite, obtained two products instead of one: these had different properties and physical constants but the same elementary composition (according to the phosphorus analyses) as the desired diethyl acetonylphosphonate. A number of

---

* See footnote on p. 50
** The soundness of this method has not yet been confirmed.

different substances were clearly obtained by B. A. Arbusov and his co-workers [194] from the reactions of triethyl phosphite with α- and γ-bromoacetoacetic ester. There was also considerable surprise when Arbusov and Alimov [195] claimed that diethyl a,a-dichloro-β-oxo-ethylphosphonate $[(C_2H_5O)_2P-$

$$\overset{\|}{O}$$

$-CCl_2CHO]$ was formed simply by mixing chloral with triethyl phosphite. This reaction was accompanied by a great evolution of heat, whereas the Arbusov rearrangement with esters of phosphorous acid generally requires the components to be heated. However, analyses of all these products agreed with those calculated for the expected products of the Arbusov rearrangement, and this, together with the qualitative reactions which demonstrated the presence of carbonyl groups, led the previously mentioned authors, and also other investigators [196–198] to the conclusion that they had obtained the usual Arbusov rearrangement products, but in two tautomeric or isomeric forms. It is interesting to note that this view was still accepted for a time even after the true products of this reaction had been established [199].

In 1952 Perkow and his co-workers [158] discovered that the reaction of α-halogenocarbonyl compounds with trialkyl phosphites did not take the same course as the Arbusov rearrangement. These authors showed that the reaction of chloral and bromal with triethyl phosphite led not to the diethyl a,a-dihalogeno-β-oxo-ethylphosphonates, but to the unsaturated isomers of these compounds, namely to the diethyl 2,2-dihalogenovinyl phosphates, $(C_2H_5O)_2PO(OCH = CX_2)$, where $X = Cl$ or Br.

This discovery aroused considerable interest and soon a number of workers [159–171] were investigating the limits of application of the reaction, its peculiarities and mechanism, and a body of results was obtained. The most important work, of course, was that directed to the obtaining of precise information about the structures of the compounds produced. Besides analytical results, which enabled empirical formulae to be derived, other results established that these compounds possessed double bonds (bromination, chlorination and infra-red spectroscopy), but not carbonyl group (negative carbonyl group reactions, no carbonyl absorption in the infra-red). Vinylic or halogenovinylic groups joined to phosphorus via oxygen were also shown to be present (transesterification with alkoxides gave known trialkyl phosphates or dialkyl esters of arylphosphonic acids). Certain reactions characteristic of aldehyde groups, such as the deposition of metallic silver from Tollens reagent by the product of the chloral-triethyl phosphite reaction, or the slow formation of glyoxal bis-2,4-dinitrophenylhydrazone by treatment of the same product with a strongly acidic solution of 2,4-dinitrophenylhydrazine, were accounted for by the hydrolysis of diethyl 2,2-dichlorovinyl phosphate with the formation of dichloroacetaldehyde or glyoxal.

From the great volume of experimental results, it can be stated that very many esters of phosphorous, phosphoramidous, alkylphosphonous and dialkylphosphinous acids react with carbonyl compounds containing from one to three halogen atoms in the a-position to give esters of phosphoric, phosphoramidic, alkylphosphonic and dialkylphosphinic acids, respectively, containing one vinyl (or halogeno-vinyl or dihalogeno-vinyl) group.

Whether these vinyl esters or the products of the usual Arbusov rearrangement form (both reactions occasionally occur together) depends on a number of factors: the temperature conditions, the nature and type of the halogen atoms, the molecular structures of the starting materials of etc.

The reactions of a-halogenocarbonyl compounds with esters of acids of trivalent phosphorus can, therefore, be summarized by the following general scheme:

$$
\begin{array}{c}
\underset{R''}{\overset{R'}{\diagdown}}P{-}OR''' + \overset{X}{\underset{Z}{\overset{|}{\underset{|}{C}}}}Y{-}COR
\;\begin{cases}
\nearrow\; \underset{R''}{\overset{R'}{\diagdown}}P{-}\overset{\overset{Z}{|}}{\underset{\underset{O}{\parallel}}{C}}Y{-}COR + R'''X \\[4ex]
\searrow\; \underset{R''}{\overset{R'}{\diagdown}}P{-}\underset{\underset{O}{\parallel}}{O}CR = CYZ + R'''X
\end{cases}
$$

It has been shown that increasing the temperature leads to the normal Arbusov rearrangement and lowering to the anomalous reaction. Reducing the electronegativity of the halogen (from chlorine to iodine) has the same effect as increasing the temperature, and vice versa. Some reactions can take only one path, however. For example, the reactions of triethyl phosphite with chloral, bromal, a-chloroacetoacetic ester and a number of other compounds lead to only unsaturated esters of phosphorus acids.

Tertiary phosphines and aromatic phosphites usually do not react with a-halogenocarbonyl compounds, but mixed alkyl aryl phosphites do at moderate temperatures to give the corresponding vinyl phosphates. Phosphites with tertiary alkyl groups (such as tri-*tert*-butyl phosphite) react with a-halogenocarbonyl compounds in the same way as they do with alkyl halides, that is, to give olefins. Allen and Johnson [169], in a short communication, have shown that although phosphorotrithioites do not give dichlorovinyl phosphorodithioates with chloral, there is spectral evidence to show that a vinylic ester is present among the products of the reaction of triethyl phosphorodithioite with chloral.

The reactivity of the halogenocarbonyl compounds decreases in the order: aldehydes, ketones, esters; and in any one of these classes with a decreasing number of halogens.

With reference to the mechanism of this reaction, Perkow [160] has suggested that triethyl phosphite and chloral first form an intermediate of the usual Arbusov type or an ester-aldehyde isomer of it, together with the simultaneous elimination of ethyl chloride. This intermediate then ionizes and the ions instantly rearrange and re-combine to give dichlorovinyl diethyl phosphate:

$$(C_2H_5O)_3P + CCl_3CHO \nearrow \begin{array}{c} (C_2H_5O)_2POCCl_2CHO \longrightarrow \\ or \\ (C_2H_5O)_2PCCl_2CHO \longrightarrow \\ \underset{O}{\overset{\parallel}{}} \end{array}$$

$$\longrightarrow (C_2H_5O)_2P-O^- + \left([CCl_2CHO]^+ \longrightarrow \left[CCl_2 = C \overset{H}{\underset{O}{\diagdown}} \right]^+ \right)$$

$$\longrightarrow (C_2H_5O)_2\underset{\downarrow O}{P^-} + \left([CCl_2CHO]^+ \longrightarrow \left[CCl_2 = C \overset{H}{\underset{O}{\diagdown}} \right]^+ \right) \nearrow \underset{O}{\overset{(C_2H_5O)_2POCH = CCl_2}{\parallel}}$$

However, this hypothesis has not been seriously considered and has been criticized on physical grounds.

Another view has been presented by Allen and Johnson [169]: they suggested that the lone pair of electrons on the phosphorus of the ester of the acid of trivalent phosphorus attacks the electrophilic carbon of the carbonyl group (similar views have been proposed by Karasch and Bengelsdorf [171]) or — and this is less likely — the carbonyl oxygen atom, which has been rendered less nucleophilic by the halogen in the a-position. The intermediate compound which forms looses alkyl halide and gives the vinyl ester:

$$\underset{B}{\overset{A}{\diagup}} P: + O = \underset{X}{\overset{R'}{\underset{|}{C}}} - \underset{|}{\overset{Y}{C}} - Z \longrightarrow \left[\underset{B}{\overset{A}{\diagup}} P - O - \underset{|}{\overset{R'}{C}} = C \overset{Y}{\underset{Z}{\diagdown}} \right]^+ \quad [X]^-$$

$$\underset{B}{\overset{A}{\diagup}} \underset{O}{\overset{OR}{\underset{\diagdown}{P}}} - \underset{X}{\overset{R'}{\underset{|}{C}}} - \underset{|}{\overset{Y}{C}} - Z \longrightarrow \underset{B}{\overset{A}{\diagup}} \underset{O}{\overset{\parallel}{P}} - O - \overset{R'}{\underset{|}{C}} = C - Z + RX$$

Kabachnik and Rossiiskaya [200], who studied the reaction of phosgene, chloroacetyl chloride and trichloroacetyl chloride with trialkyl phosphites, came to the conclusion that the initial stage of the Perkow reaction proceeded according to the mechanism advanced by Allen and Johnson [169], that is, via an epoxy-compound. Then, according to Kabachnik and Rossiiskaya, scission of a series of single bonds occured:

$$(RO)_2\overset{O}{\underset{\underset{R}{\overset{|}{O}}}{P}} - CH - CCl_2 - Cl \longrightarrow (RO)_2POCH = CCl_2 + RCl$$

An examination of the mechanistic proposals for the reaction of α-halo-genocarbonyl compounds with trialkyl phosphites suggests that this reaction does not follow the same path as the Arbusov rearrangement and is only "anomalous" in the sense that the two processes lead to different products. In both cases reaction commences with the linking of the halogen-containing compound to the ester of the trivalent phosphorus acid (by the donation of the lone pair of electrons on the phosphorus); however, the halogen does not appear to be absolutely necessary, and it only facilitates the addition by polarizing the molecule. Indeed, it has been shown that trialkyl phosphites can react with aldehydes, [201] anhydrides, [202] lactones, [203, 204] disulphides, [205] etc., to form esters of acids of pentavalent phosphorus by a route which must obviously be akin to an Arbusov-type rearrangement.

In a molecule highly polarized by the presence of a particular link, the reaction centre can be transferred and the degree of this transfer depends on the reactants and the reaction conditions, in the manner outlined above: the reaction then, depending on these factors, passes through either the Arbusov rearrangement or the "anomalous" path.

The dehydrochlorination of esters of β,β-dichloro-α-hydroxy- and β,β,β-trichloro-α-hydroxy-ethylphosphonic acids

Studies on the dimethyl ester of β,β,β-trichloro-α-hydroxyethylphosphonic acid were carried out by a number of workers [174—176] at almost the same time: in particular, the action of caustic alkali on this ester was studied. As was to be expected, all the investigators obtained one and the same dehydrochlorination product, the structure of which, however, was completely unexpected.

On the basis of the experimental results which were obtained by chemical and physical methods, this dehydrochlorination product might have had any of the following structures:

$$(CH_3O)_2P-C(OH) = CCl_2 \qquad (I)$$
$$\underset{O}{\overset{\|}{}}$$

$$(CH_3O)_2P-C-CHCl_2 \qquad (II)$$
$$\underset{O\ \ O}{\overset{\|\ \ \|}{}}$$

$$(CH_3O)_2P-CHOH-CCl_3 \xrightarrow{-HCl}$$

$$(CH_3O)_2P-CH-CCl_2 \qquad (III)$$
$$\underset{O\ \ \ \ \ O}{\overset{\|\ \ \ \ \diagdown\diagup}{}}$$

$$(CH_3O)_2P-O-CH = CCl_2 \qquad (IV)$$
$$\underset{O}{\overset{\|}{}}$$

The details of this reaction were studied by Bartel and his co-workers, [174] who investigated the dehydrochlorination of a whole series of esters of β,β,β-trichloro-α-hydroxyethylphosphonic acid as well as the methyl ester, [175 176]. It is important to note that the methyl ester of this acid differs in certain properties from the other esters (see below). This can lead to misconceptions about the structures of the dehydrochlorination products.

These workers showed that the substance did not have structure (I), since it did not have an active hydrogen atom or a hydroxyl group (negative Zerewittinoff reaction, negative acetylation reaction, and by infra-red spectroscopy). They also ruled out structure (II) because the substance did not possess a carbonyl group (no reaction — except by the methyl ester — with 2,4-dinitrophenylhydrazine or with semicarbazone hydrochloride). Also, the compound with structure (II) was prepared by the method of Kabachnik and Rossiiskaya [206] and was shown to be different from the substance under investigation.

Therefore, in the structural determination of these dehydrochlorination products it only remained to decide between the epoxy-compounds of type (III) and the dialkyl dihalogenovinyl phosphates of type (IV). The epoxide structure can be ruled out because the substances add a molecule of chlorine without liberating hydrogen chloride. Structure (IV) was completely confirmed because, as well as the chemical and spectroscopic evidence indicating the double bonds, these dehydrochlorination products were identical (according to their physical constants and biological action) with the dialkyl dihalogenovinyl phosphates which had been synthesized earlier by Perkow and his coworkers by the reaction of a-halogenocarbonyl compounds with trialkyl phosphites.

As was noted above, the dehydrochlorination product of dimethyl β,β,β-trichloro-a-hydroxyethylphosphonate (as distinct from the other esters) forms an osazone, thus suggesting that it contains a carbonyl group, and hence does not possess structure (IV). This inconsistancy is, however, resolvable. It is known that compounds containing methoxy-groups are often less stable to hydrolysis than compounds containing other alkoxy-groups. Clearly, if the hydrolysis of dichlorovinyl dimethyl phosphate proceeds easily, then dichlorovinyl alcohol will form and will promptly isomerize into dichloroacetaldehyde which can then form an osazone.

It is essential to point out that the yields of esters by this method are, as a rule, considerably lower than those from the Perkow reaction. A mechanism for the reaction was not proposed by either Bartel or the other investigators. By taking into account the suggestions of Kabachnik and Rossiiskaya [200] (see p. 78), it is plausible to suppose that the process passes through an intermediate epoxy-compound, followed by the scission of a series of single bonds:

$$(RO_2P-CH-CCl_3 \xrightarrow{OH-} (RO)_2PCH-CCl_3 \longrightarrow$$

$$\longrightarrow (RO)_2 P-CH-CCl_2-Cl \longrightarrow (RO)_2POCH = CCl_2 + Cl^-$$

The reaction of acid chlorides of acids of phosphorus with acetaldehyde and triethylamine

This reaction is an extension of the reaction of halides of trivalent phosphorus with aldehydes. Kabachnik and Shepeleva, [20–22, 24] during work on the synthesis of acid chlorides of a-chloroalkylphosphonic acids by the reaction of trivalent phosphorus halides with aldehydes ($PCl_3 + RCHO \rightarrow \rightarrow RCHCl \cdot POCl_2$), found that the first step (which went in the cold) of this reaction was the formation of a 1-chloroalkyl ester of a phosphorous acid ($> P{-}Cl + RCHO \rightarrow > P{-}OCHCl{-}R$), which underwent the final transformation on being heated. The formation of the ester products by the linking of the aldehyde to the trivalent phosphorus halide was confirmed by Faizullin and Trifonov's method [207] of physicochemical analysis. By introducing a strong organic base (triethylamine) into the aldehyde/phosphorus halide systems, Gefter and Kabachnik [120, 192] obtained a range of vinyl esters of phosphonic, phosphinic and phosphorous acids, as well as trivinyl phosphate, all by the following general scheme:

$$\begin{array}{l} R \\ \diagdown \\ \diagup P{-}Cl + CH_3CHO + N(C_2H_5)_3 \longrightarrow \\ R' \\ \quad \| \\ \quad O \end{array} \qquad \begin{array}{l} R \\ \diagdown \\ \diagup P{-}O{-}CH = CH_2 + N(C_2H_5)_3 \cdot HCl \\ R' \\ \quad \| \\ \quad O \end{array}$$

The yields in this reaction are small. The authors have varied the reaction conditions widely and have been unable to increase the yields of vinyl esters of acids of phosphorus above about 30–35% of the theoretical. The mechanism of formation of the phosphorus vinyl esters by this reaction was not investigated by the authors. It is plausible to suppose, however, that the initially formed 1-chloro-ester forms a complex with triethylamine (when trimethylamine was used, such complexes were isolated) which decomposes into the vinyl ester of the corresponding acid of phosphorus, triethylamine hydrochloride and other products.

Sladkov and Petrov, [208] who accomplished an analogous reaction in the carbon field, suggest that the aldehyde first isomerizes into the corresponding vinyl alcohol, which then reacts with the acid chloride. This suggestion seems extremely unlikely in view of the small tendency of acetaldehyde to enolize.

THE PROPERTIES OF UNSATURATED ESTERS OF ACIDS OF PHOSPHORUS

One of the most important properties of esters of trivalent phosphorus acids is their ease of conversion, under the influence of a wide variety of halogen-containing compounds (alkyl, acyl, esters, ethers, etc.) into compounds of pentavalent phosphorus. Thus, from esters of phosphorous, phosphinous or phosphonous acids, various esters of phosphonic or carboxyalkylphosphonic acids, etc., are formed, depending on the structures of the starting compounds. These interesting reactions were discovered at the beginning of this century by A. Ye. Arbusov [86] and they carry his name.

The general scheme of the Arbusov rearrangement is:

$$\begin{matrix} A \\ \diagdown \\ \diagup \\ B \end{matrix} P{-}OR + R'X \longrightarrow B{-}P \begin{matrix} A \\ \diagup \\ \diagdown \\ R' \end{matrix} \begin{matrix} O{+}R \\ \\ X \end{matrix} \longrightarrow \begin{matrix} A \\ \diagdown \\ B{-}P = O + RX \\ \diagup \\ R' \end{matrix}$$

where A and B are alkyl or aryl groups linked with phosphorus directly or through oxygen (or sulphur), and X = halogen. Trivalent phosphorus, on account of the lone pair of electrons, joins quite easily to alkyl or acyl halides, etc., and passes into the pentavalent state. The products of joining are unstable when A and B = R, RO or Ar, but are quite stable when A and B = ArO. (It is interesting to note that a range of substances of both types have been obtained in an analytically pure state. [209–212]) The first type of substance decomposes spontaneously at room temperature, whereas the second only does so at high temperatures or under the influence of hydroxyl-containing compounds. The decompositions lead to esters of pentavalent phosphorus acids or to tertiary phosphine oxides and also to alkyl (aryl) halides which are formed from the halogen of the original halides and the alkyl (aryl) groups originally linked to phosphorus through oxygen (see the scheme on above).

The theoretical and experimental study of the Arbusov rearrangement was initiated by A. Ye. Arbusov himself and his school and has been continued by other chemists both in the U. S. S. R. and abroad. Of all the work carried out over many years in the field of the Arbusov rearrangement, attention is drawn to the article by B. A. Arbusov [213] and to the thesis of Nesterov [214]. By means of the Arbusov rearrangement, which has justly been called "A highway in the field of synthesis of organophosphorus compounds" by A. N. Nesmeyanov, a vast number of esters (included a number of unsaturated ones) of alkyl- and carboxyalkyl-phosphonic acids have been prepared.

The ability of esters of trivalent phosphorus to undergo the Arbusov rearrangement is usually enhanced when the esters are unsaturated. The investigations of Zoroastrova [111] and Kamai [180] showed that as far as speed of rearrangement was concerned, triallyl phosphite was the fastest of the trialkyl phosphites, except possibly for trimethyl phosphite. It is interesting to note that although a-substituted allyl phosphites react easily with methyl iodide and carbon tetrachloride with the liberation of the corresponding alkyl halides, the products of these reactions are syrupy liquids which cannot be distilled without decomposition even under 1 mm pressure. The corresponding butenyl compounds, however, react with methyl iodide without any complications to give the usual Arbusov rearrangement products.

Diallyl arylphosphonites rearrange to some extent even during distillation *in vacuo* [105]:

$$ArP(OCH_2CH = CH_2)_2 \longrightarrow \begin{matrix} Ar \\ \diagdown \\ \diagup \\ CH_2 = CHCH_2 \end{matrix} \underset{\underset{O}{\parallel}}{P}OCH_2CH = CH_2$$

The allyl and thio-allyl esters of diphenylphosphinous acid cannot, as a rule, be obtained in a pure state because they isomerize completely on distillation and even on standing in the cold (albeit slowly) into the oxide and sulphide of allyldiphenylphosphine [178]:

$$(C_6H_5)_2P-X-CH_2CH=CH_2 \longrightarrow \overset{(C_6H_5)_2}{\underset{CH_2=CHCH_2}{\diagdown}} P = X$$

where X = oxygen or sulphur.

The properties of allyl esters of glycol hydrogen phosphites are interesting in that in undergoing the Arbusov rearrangement, the five-membered rings in these substances are broken, whereas the six-membered are unaffected [91]:

$$\begin{array}{c} CH_2-O \\ | \quad\quad\quad \diagdown \\ CH_2-O \end{array} P-O-CH_2CH=CH_2 + RCl \longrightarrow R-P \begin{array}{c} \diagup OCH_2CH=CH_2 \\ \underset{O}{\overset{\|}{}} \diagdown OCH_2CH_2Cl \end{array}$$

where R = allyl or benzyl;

$$\begin{array}{c} CH_2-O \\ | \\ CH_2 \\ | \\ CH_2-O \end{array} \diagup P-O-CH_2-CH=CH_2 + RX \longrightarrow R-P \begin{array}{c} \diagup O-CH_2 \\ \underset{O}{\overset{\|}{}} \diagdown \underset{O-CH_2}{\overset{CH_2}{\underset{|}{}}} \end{array} + CH_2=CH-CH_2X$$

where RX = allyl iodide, benzyl chloride or trityl bromide.

The allyl esters of glycol hydrogen phosphites with seven-membered rings are so unstable that all attempts to distill them at 1–2 mm pressure led to explosions which could not be prevented.

The formation of esters of unsaturated phosphonic acids by the Arbusov and Michaelis–Becker reactions has been studied in detail by Soviet investigators. They were concerned with the influence of the structures of the halide and the phosphorus ester on the course and result of the reactions, and also with the mechanism of these processes.

Pudovik and other investigators from the school of A. Ye. Arbusov [93–98] have studied the reactions of salts of dialkyl hydrogen phosphites with various allylic-type halides. According to these authors, changing the conditions can cause these reactions to take different paths and lead to different results. In the presence of a great excess of either the dialkyl hydrogen phosphite or the solvent, a double decomposition reaction occurs in which primary halides react in the normal way, while secondary halides undergo an allylic rearrangement:

$$\begin{array}{c} R'CH=CH-CH_2X \\ \\ R'CHX-CH=CH_2 \end{array} \xrightarrow{\text{NaPO (OR)}_2} R'CH=CH-CH_2-PO(OR)_2 + NaX$$

However, when these reactions were carried out without an excess of reagent and with a small quantity of solvent, they did not stop with the formation of the esters of the allylphosphonic acid, but continued and a second molecule of dialkyl hydrogen phosphite was added:

6*

$$R'CH = CH-CH_2PO(OR)_2 \xrightarrow[\text{NaPO (OR)}_2]{\text{HPO (OR)}_2} R'CH-CH_2-CH_2PO(OR)_2 \qquad (I)$$
$$PO(OR)_2$$

$$R'CH_2-CH = CHPO(OR)_2 \xrightarrow[\text{NaPO (OR)}_2]{\text{HPO (OR)}_2} R'CH_2-CH-CH_2PO(OR)_2 \qquad (II)$$
$$PO(OR)_2$$

The 1,2-bisdialkoxyphosphinyl derivatives (compounds of type II) were obtained almost exclusively. The authors suggested that these compounds formed as a result of the preliminary isomerization of the allylphosphonate esters into the thermodynamically more stable a,β-unsaturated phosphonates (cf. I, II), which then added a molecule of dialkyl hydrogen phosphite.

The reaction of allylic halide isomers with phosphite esters, just as with sodium dialkyl phosphites, leads to the formation of esters of β,γ-unsaturated phosphonic acids [95, 96]; the primary halides, however, react much more easily than the secondary.

The Arbusov rearrangement under the influence of unsaturated halogen compounds having the halogen on the double bond is, as would be expected, difficult or even impossible [215, 126].

It is interesting to note, however, that β-bromo-a-methylstyrene undergoes a normal rearrangement with triethyl phosphite:

$$C_6H_5-C = CHBr + P(OC_2H_5)_3 \longrightarrow C_6H_5-C = CHPO(OC_2H_5)_2$$
$$CH_3 \qquad\qquad\qquad\qquad\qquad\qquad CH_3$$

whereas β-bromostyrene (although only under forcing conditions) gives diethyl ethylphosphonate. [215]

In a study of the reaction of 2-chloro-2-methylbut-3-yne with the methyl, ethyl and butyl esters of phosphorous acid, Pudovik [103] found that besides an Arbusov rearrangement, a complex acetylene–allene rearrangement took place which led to, initially, as the first product of the reaction, an ester of dimethylallenylphosphonic acid:

$$(CH_3)_2C-C \equiv CH \longrightarrow [(CH_3)_2C = C = CHCl] \xrightarrow{P(OR)_3} (CH_3)_2C = C = CHP(OR)_3 \longrightarrow$$
$$Cl \qquad\qquad\qquad\qquad\qquad\qquad\qquad\qquad\qquad\qquad\qquad Cl$$
$$\longrightarrow (CH_3)_2C = C = CH-PO(OR)_2 + RCl$$

The greater part of this ester during the course of the reaction easily added another molecule of trialkyl phosphite:

$$(CH_3)_2C = C = CH-PO(OR)_2 + P(OR)_3 \longrightarrow \left[(CH_3)_2C = C-CH=P(OR)_2 \right] \longrightarrow$$
$$+ P(OR)_3 \quad O^-$$
$$PO(OR)_2$$
$$\longrightarrow (CH_3)_2C = C-CHPO(OR)_2$$
$$R$$

and then the adduct rearranged, as shown in the scheme, to give 3,4-bis(dialkoxyphosphinyl)-2-methyl-pent-2-ene, -hex-2-ene, or -oct-2-ene (in each case the first and second products have both been isolated).

Besides the Arbusov rearrangement, which is one important way of converting derivatives of trivalent phosphorus acids into derivatives of pentavalent phosphorus acids, such conversions can be accomplished by adding to the trivalent phosphorus derivatives, oxygen, sulphur and sometimes halogens or alkyl halides (to aryl phosphites), etc. Unsaturated esters of phosphorous, phosphonous and phosphinous acids undergo such reactions very easily [5, 91, 111, 139, 146].

We will now consider the properties of unsaturated esters of phosphorus acids which are determined by the double bonds present in their molecules.

These compounds add halogens and hydrogen halides with varying degrees of ease, and also decolourize bromine water and permanganate solution. A number of interesting investigations into the properties of esters of vinylphosphonic acid have been made by Pudovik and his co-workers and also by some foreign investigators.

It has been shown that various nucleophilic reagents are capable of adding to the double bonds of these compounds quite easily [217–223]. Thus the dialkyl hydrogen phosphites react with diethyl vinylphosphonate in the presence of alkali metal alkoxides to give bis (dialkoxyphosphinyl)ethanes:

$$CH_2 = CHPO(OC_2H_5)_2 + HPO(OR)_2 \xrightarrow{\text{RONa}} (RO)_2\underset{\underset{O}{\|}}{P}-CH_2CH_2-\underset{\underset{O}{\|}}{P}(OR)_2$$

In a similar way ammonia, amines, benzyl cyanide, hydrogen sulphide, mercaptans, acetoacetates, cyanoacetates, malonic esters and their homologues (that is, compounds having reactive hydrogen atoms) all can be added to vinylphosphonate esters. These reactions usually take place in the presence of sodium ethoxide, but sometimes (for example, in the cases of dimethylamine and piperidine) without catalysts.

These reactions, which Pudovik has called phosphonoethylation reactions, permit the group $- \underset{\underset{O}{\|}}{(C_2H_5O)_2P} -$ to be easily simply introduced into a wide variety of compounds [217. 219–224]

The general scheme of the phosphonoethylation reaction is:

$$R'H + CH_2 = CH—PO(OC_2H_5)_2 \longrightarrow R'CH_2CH_2PO(OC_2H_5)_2$$

where

$$R' = (RO)_2\underset{\underset{O}{\|}}{P}—NH_2—, \ RN_2—, C_5H_{10}N)—, \ HS—, \ —CH(CO_2C_2H_5)_2$$

and other radicals (see above).

Besides this, Pudovik and Imayev [219] and certain foreign chemists [225, 226] have found that vinylphosphonate esters can participate in the diene synthesis as dienophile components, although they are less reactive [219] than a,β-unsaturated aldehydes, ketones, nitriles and esters of carbon acids. By such a reaction, phosphonate esters are formed in which the dialkoxyphosphinyl-group is linked to a cyclohexene (or bicycloheptene) ring; for example:

$$
\begin{array}{c}
CH_3 \\
| \\
CH \\
CH \diagup \quad \diagdown \\
| \qquad CH\!-\!PO(OR)_2 \\
CH \qquad \| \\
\diagdown CH_2 \qquad CH_2
\end{array}
+
\longrightarrow
\begin{array}{c}
CH_3 \\
| \\
CH \\
CH \diagup \quad \diagdown \quad CH\!-\!PO\,(OR)_2 \\
\| \qquad \qquad | \\
CH \qquad \qquad CH_2 \\
\diagdown CH_2 \diagup
\end{array}
$$

UNSATURATED PHOSPHINES, THEIR OXIDES AND SULPHIDES, TETRACHLOROPHORANES AND PHOSPHONIUM SALTS

Unsaturated trialkyl- (and alkylaryl-)phosphines

Unsaturated phosphines have been obtained by Jones et al. [278] and by Mayer et al. [279] by the action of the corresponding alkenyl magnesium halides on phosphorus trichloride or arylphosphonous dichlorides. For example:

$$3CH_2 = CH\!-\!CH_2MgBr + PCl_3 \longrightarrow (CH_2 = CH\!-\!CH_2)_3P + 3MgBrCl$$

In this way tertiary phosphines of the general formula R_3P and R_2PR', where R = vinyl, allyl or methallyl, and R' = aryl, have been prepared. Interesting compounds of this type with acetylenic links and with one or two phosphino groups have been prepared by Hartmann and his co-workers by the reaction of diphenylphosphinous chloride with bromo-acetylene [280] or acetylene(dimagnesium bromide) [281]:

$$2(C_6H_5)_2PCl + BrMg\!-\!C \equiv C\!-\!MgBr \longrightarrow [(C_6H_5)_2P\!-\!C \equiv]_2 + 2MgBrCl$$

Unsaturated tertiary phosphines are usually liquids which are stable in the absence of air at 200–250°, and at higher temperatures in vacuo [bis-(diphenylphosphino)-acetylene decomposes fairly easily, however]. They add oxygen, psuphur and alkyl halides easily to form unsaturated oxides, sulphides and qhosphonium salts. Unsaturated tertiary phosphines also form complexes with luinones, carbon disulphide and mercuric chloride.

The properties of unsaturated phosphines are recorded in Table 47.

TABLE 47. UNSATURATED TERTIARY PHOSPHINES

Formula	b. p., °C (mm)	n_D^{25}	d_4^{25}	Yield (%)	Reference
$(CH_2 = CH)_3P$	117;–110*			18	[279]
$(CH_2 = CH)_2PC_6H_5$	55 (0·5)				[279]
$(CH_2 = CHCH_2)_2PR$					
R					
—C_6H_5	127 (14)	1·5670	0·9693		[278]
—C_6H_4Br-4	186 (37)		1·2783		[278]
—$C_6H_4OCH_3$-4	162 (15)	1·5705	1·0189		[278]
—$C_6H_4OC_6H_5$-4	238 (15)	1·6040	1·0847		[278]
—$C_6H_4CH_3$-4	138 (14)	1·5545	0·9651		[278]
—$C_6H_3(CH_3)_2$-2,5	144 (13)	1·5540	0·9584		[278]
—$C_6H_4C_2H_5$-4	145 (10)	1·5545	0·9484		[278]
—$C_6H_4C_3H_7$-iso-4	153 (11)	1·5435	0·9361		[278]

TABLE 47 — (contd.)

Formula	b. p., °C(mm)	n_D^{20}	d_4^{20}	Yield (%)	Reference
R					
$[CH_2 = C(CH_3)CH_2]_2PR$					
—C_6H_5	148 (13)	1·5485	0·9484		[278]
—C_6H_4Br-4	189 (18)	1·5752	1·2094		[278]
—$C_6H_4OCH_3$-4	192 (20)	1·5513	0·9948		[278]
—$C_6H_4CH_3$-4	168 (23)	1·5465	0·9426		[278]
—$C_6H_3(CH_3)_2$-2,5	166 (16)	1·5450	0·9402		[278]
—$C_6H_4C_2H_5$-4	178 (20)	1·5435	0·9360		[278]
—$C_6H_4C_3H_7$-iso-4	182·5 (19)	1·5350	0·9279		[278]
$(CH_2 = CHCH_2)_3P$	69 (13)				[278]
$[CH_2 = C(CH_3)CH_2]_3P$	112 (15)				[278]
$(C_6H_5)_2PC \equiv CH$	oil				[280]
$[(C_6H_5)_2PC \equiv]_2$	198 (3×10^{-5}) with slight decomposition 85·5—86*)				[281]

*Melting point.

Oxides and sulphides of unsaturated tertiary phosphines

Representatives of this class of compounds have been synthesized by the addition of oxygen or sulphur to unsaturated tertiary phosphines: $R_3P + \frac{1}{2}O_2 \rightarrow R_3PO$ [278, 281]; by the reaction of alkenyl magnesium halides with phosphoryl chloride: $3RMgX + POCl_3 \rightarrow R_3PO$ [278]; by the thermal decomposition of hydroxides (or esters) of alkenylarylphosphonium compounds:

$$\underset{R_3 /\!/}{\overset{R^{\nearrow}}{\diagdown}} P—OH \longrightarrow \underset{R_2 /\!/}{\overset{R^{\nearrow}}{\diagdown}} PO; \ (282)$$

and by the Arbusov rearrangement with esters of diarylphosphinous acids [178].

A few years ago a new method of obtaining oxides and sulphides of unsaturated cyclic tertiary phosphines was patented: it involved the reaction of aryl- or alkyl-phosphonous dichlorides with dienes, followed by hydrolysis (or treatment with hydrogen sulphide) of the reaction product [283, 284]; for example:

$$RPCl_2 + CH_2 = CH—CH = CH_2 \longrightarrow \underset{RPCl_2}{\overset{CH = CH}{\diagdown}} \overset{CH_2 \quad CH_2}{\underset{}{}} \xrightarrow{H_2O} \underset{RPO}{\overset{CH = CH}{\diagdown}} \overset{CH_2 \quad CH_2}{\underset{}{}}$$

The oxides and sulphides of unsaturated tertiary phosphines are liquid or crystalline substances, which are generally resistant to chemical agents and stable at high temperatures. However, if a triple bond is present in the molecule (for example, in the case of the dioxide or disulphide of bis-(diphenylphosphino) acetylene) then the action of alkali cleaves the phosphorus–oxygen bond to give acetylene [281].

The properties of the oxides and sulphides of unsaturated phosphines are shown in Table 48.

TABLE 48. OXIDES AND SULPHIDES OF UNSATURATED TERTIARY PHOSPHINES

Formula	b. p., °C (mm)	$n_D^{23.5}$	Yield (%)	Reference
$[C_6H_5COCH = C(C_6H_5)]P(C_6H_5)_2$ (with $\|$ O below)	143*		80	[285]
$[4\text{-}ClC_6H_4COCH = C(C_6H_5)]P(C_6H_5)_2$ (with $\|$ O below)	151*		100	[285]
$CH_2 = CHCH_2P(C_6H_5)_2$ (with $\|$ O below)	200–202 (2); 94–95*			[178]
$CH_2 = CHCH_2P(C_6H_4C_6H_5\text{-}4)_2$ (with $\|$ O below)	192–193*			[282]
$(CH_2 = CHCH_2)_3PO$	98 (0·5); 15–17*		26	[173]
$[CH_2 = C(CH_3)CH_2]PO$	132*			[278]
$CH_3C = CH$ $H_2C \quad CH_2$ C_2H_5PO	116–117 (0·6)	1·5049	59	[283]
Mixture of $CH_3C=CH$ $H_2C \quad CH_2$ $C_6H_{13}CHClCH_2PO$ and $CH_3C=CH$ $H_2C \quad CH_2$ $C_6H_{13}CH=CHPO$	165–167 (0·2)		9–10	[283]
$HC = CH$ $H_2C \quad CH_2$ C_6H_5PO	139–142 (0·2); 153–155 (0·5); 67–75*		61 29	[283]
$ClC = CH$ $H_2C \quad CH_2$ C_6H_5PO	158–164 (0·1)		37	[283]
$BrC = CH$ $H_2C \quad CH_2$ C_6H_5PO	160–164 (0·5)		53	[283]
$CH = CH$ $CH_3CH \quad CH_2$ C_6H_5PO	160–180 (1)		12·2	[283]

TABLE 48 — (contd.)

Formula	b. p., °C (mm)	$n_D^{23.5}$	Yield (%)	Reference
CH₃C═══CH H₂C CH₂ C₆H₅PO	164–183 (1)		91·5	[283]
CH₃C═══CH H₂C CH₂ 2-and-4-BrC₆H₄PO (mixture)	180–183 (0·7)		37	[283]
CH₃C═══CH H₂C CH₂ 4-CH₃OC₆H₄PO	210–212 (0·7)	1·5754	22	[283]
CH₃C═══CH H₂C CH₂ 2-and 4-C₂H₅C₆H₄PO (mixture)	165–170 (0·3)	1·5684	60	[283]
CH₃C═══CH H₂C CH₂ 1-and 2-C₁₀H₇PO (mixture)	215–230 (0·5)		54	[283]
HC═══CCH₃ CH₃CH CH₂ C₆H₅PO	202–208 (8)		50	[283]
CH₃C═══CCH₃ H₂C CH₂ C₆H₅PO	173–175 (0·3)		80	[283]
(CH₃)₂C = CHC₂H₄C═══CH H₂C CH₂ C₆H₅PO	192–193 (0·2)	1·5592	38	[283]

Formula structures in the table:

- $CH_3C{=\!=\!=}CH$ / H_2C CH_2 / C_6H_5PO
- $CH_3C{=\!=\!=}CH$ / H_2C CH_2 / $2\text{-and-}4\text{-}BrC_6H_4PO$ (mixture)
- $CH_3C{=\!=\!=}CH$ / H_2C CH_2 / $4\text{-}CH_3OC_6H_4PO$
- $CH_3C{=\!=\!=}CH$ / H_2C CH_2 / $2\text{-and }4\text{-}C_2H_5C_6H_4PO$ (mixture)
- $CH_3C{=\!=\!=}CH$ / H_2C CH_2 / $1\text{-and }2\text{-}C_{10}H_7PO$ (mixture)
- $HC{=\!=\!=}CCH_3$ / CH_3CH CH_2 / C_6H_5PO
- $CH_3C{=\!=\!=}CCH_3$ / H_2C CH_2 / C_6H_5PO
- $(CH_3)_2C = CHC_2H_4C{=\!=\!=}CH$ / H_2C CH_2 / C_6H_5PO

TABLE 48 — (contd.)

Formula	b. p., °C (mm)	$n_D^{23.5}$	Yield (%)	Reference
(structure: cyclic with $(CH_2)_4$, $(CH_2)_4$, $C=C$, CH, CH, C_6H_5PO)	210–220 (0·5)		25	[283]
(structure: $HC=CH$, C_6H_5CH, CH_2, C_6H_5PO)	224–226 (0·9); 96—98*		37·6	[283]
(structure: $C_6H_5C=CH$, H_2C, CH_2, C_2H_5PO)	235–240 (0·2); 125*		82	[283]
$\left[\equiv CP(C_6H_5)_2\right]_2$ with $\underset{O}{\overset{\|}{}}$	164*		87	[281]
(structure: $CH_3C=CH$, H_2C, CH_2, C_6H_5PS)	173–175 (1); 69–70*		80	[284]
$CH_2=CHCH_2P(C_6H_5)_2$ with $\underset{S}{\overset{\|}{}}$	184–185 (1); 49–50*			[178]
$\left[\equiv CP(C_6H_5)_2\right]_2$ with $\underset{S}{\overset{\|}{}}$	186*		75	[281]

* Melting point.

Unsaturated tetrachlorophosphoranes and phosphonium salts

There is little reported on the unsaturated tetrachlorophosphoranes: they have been prepared by the action of phosphorus pentachloride on unsaturated hydrocarbons [2, 12] (see the scheme on p. 18). Unsaturated phosphonium salts are well known, however.

Hofmann [286], in the middle of the last century, obtained triethylvinylphosphonium bromide by the thermal dehydrochlorination of the corresponding β-bromoethyl compound:

$$BrCH_2CH_2P(C_2H_5)_3Br \xrightarrow{200°} CH_2=CHP(C_2H_5)_3Br + HBr$$

However, this method is not generally applicable: a large number of alkylarylphosphonium halides of general formula,

$$
\left.
\begin{array}{l}
R^{I} \\
R^{II} \\
R^{III} \\
R^{IV}
\end{array}
\right\rangle P{-}X
$$

where at least one of the radicals is unsaturated, have been prepared by various authors by the addition of alkyl halides to tertiary phosphines [278, 281, 282, 286–290].

Unsaturated phosphonium salts are hard crystalline substances which decompose at elevated temperatures into tertiary phosphines and alkyl halides. They also easily form complexes with heavy metal salts (for example, with the iodides of mercury and cadmium) and with organic acids.

The properties of unsaturated tetrachlorophosphoranes and unsaturated phosphonium salts are recorded in Table 49.

TABLE 49 UNSATURATED ALKYL- AND ARYL-TETRACHLOROPHOSPHOR-
ANES AND PHOSPHONIUM SALTS

Formula	m. p. (°C)	Reference
$(CH_3)_2C = CHCHClCH_2PCl_4$	109–109·5	[2]
⟨indene⟩—PCl_4	Hard yellow substance	[12]
$CH_2 = CHP(C_2H_5)_3Br$	Crystalline	[286]
$CH_3C(OC_2H_5) = CHP(C_6H_5)_3I$	163–165	[291]
$C_6H_5C(OC_2H_5) = CHP(C_6H_5)_3I$	176–178	[291]
$(CH_2 = CH)_3P(CH_3)I$	198–200*	[279]
$(CH_2 = CH)_3P(C_2H_5)I$	327–328*	[279]
$(CH_2 = CH)_4PBr$	105–140*	[279]
$CH_2 = CHCH_2P(C_2H_5)_3I$	needles	[286]
$CH_2 = CHCH_2P(CH_2CH_2CN)_3Cl$	135–136	[292]
$CH_2 = CHCH_2P\left[\begin{array}{l}C_2H_5 \\ C_4H_9 \\ CH_2C_6H_5\end{array}\right] Br$	87–89	[290]
$CH_2 = CHCH_2P\left[\begin{array}{l}C_3H_7 \\ C_4H_9 \\ CH_2C_6H_5\end{array}\right] Br$	Syrup	[290]
$CH_2 = CHCH_2P\left[\begin{array}{l}(CH_3)_2 \\ C_6H_5\end{array}\right] Br$	113–114	[288]
$CH_2 = CHCH_2P\left[\begin{array}{l}(C_2H_5)_2 \\ C_6H_5\end{array}\right] Br$	152–153	[288]
$CH_2 = CHCH_2P\left[\begin{array}{l}CH_3 \\ (C_6H_5)_2\end{array}\right] Br$	161	[288]

TABLE 49 — (contd.)

Formula	m. p., (°C)	Reference
$CH_2 = CHCH_2P\begin{bmatrix} CH_3 \\ C_6H_5 \\ C_6H_4CH_3\text{-}4 \end{bmatrix} I$	175–177	[287]
$CH_2 = CHCH_2P(C_6H_4C_6H_5\text{-}4)_3Br$	195–196	[282]
$\left[CH_2 = C(CH_3)CH_2 \right]_2 P \begin{bmatrix} CH_3 \\ C_6H_5 \end{bmatrix} I$	188	[278]
$\left[CH_2 = C(CH_2)CH_2 \right]_2 P \begin{bmatrix} CH_3 \\ C_6H_4Br\text{-}4 \end{bmatrix} I$	174	[278]
$\left[CH_2 = C(CH_3)CH_2 \right]_2 P \begin{bmatrix} CH_3 \\ C_6H_4OCH_3\text{-}4 \end{bmatrix} I$	134·5	[278]
$\left[CH_2 = C(CH_3(CH_2 \right]_2 P \begin{bmatrix} CH_3 \\ C_6H_4CH_3\text{-}4 \end{bmatrix} I$	94	[278]
$\left[CH_2 = C(CH_3)CH_2 \right]_2 P \begin{bmatrix} CH_3 \\ C_6H_3(CH_3)_2\text{-}2,5 \end{bmatrix} I$	161	[278]
$\left[CH_2 = C(CH_3)CH_2 \right]_2 P \begin{bmatrix} CH_3 \\ C_6H_4C_2H_5\text{-}4 \end{bmatrix} I$	153	[278]
$(CH_2 = CHCH_2)_3P(CH_3)I$	Melts with decomposition	[278]
$[CH_2 = C(CH_3)CH_2]_3 \ P(CH_3)I$	151	[278]
$\begin{bmatrix} (C_6H_5)_2PC \equiv CP(C_6H_5)_2 \\ \quad\quad\quad \mid \\ \quad\quad\quad CH_3 \end{bmatrix} I^+$	156	[281]
$\begin{bmatrix} (C_6H_5)_2PC \equiv CP(C_6H_5)_2 \\ \quad\quad\quad \mid \\ \quad\quad\quad C_2H_5 \end{bmatrix} I^{\ddagger}$	128	[281]

* Temperature of decomposition.
+ Yield 90%.
‡ Yield 84%.

CHAPTER II

SATURATED ORGANOPHOSPHORUS COMPOUNDS
DIHYDROXY-COMPOUNDS

BESIDES the large numbers of unsaturated organophosphorus compounds which were described in the last chapter, of great importance for the preparation of organophosphorus polymers are those substances which contain two or more functional groups (acid chlorides, amides, etc.) and also aliphatic and aromatic diols. The presence of the functional groups in these compounds permits them to be used (preferably by means of the polycondensation reaction) for the preparation of high molecular weight compounds containing phosphorus in the main chain.

DI-ACID CHLORIDES OF SOME SATURATED ACIDS OF PHOSPHORUS

These di-acid chlorides are starting materials for the preparation of heterochain high molecular weight compounds. The di-acid chlorides of substituted phosphonic, phosphoric and phosphonous acids have the following general formulae: $RPOCl_2$ and $R'PCl_2$, where R = alkyl, aryl, alkoxy or aryloxy, and R' = alkyl or aryl.

Alkyl phosphorodichloridates $ROPOCl_2$

The general method for the preparation of alkyl phosphorodichloridates is the reaction between alcohols and phosphoryl chloride in a mole to mole ratio [2]:

$$ROH + POCl_3 \longrightarrow ROPOCl_2 + HCl$$

This reaction usually takes place on mixing, but it is sometimes carried out *in vacuo*, or with a stream of gas passing through the reaction mixture to remove the hydrogen chloride. Vacuum distillation then gives the pure alkyl phosphorodichloridate. When the molecular weight of the alcohol is increased, the reaction becomes more sluggish, the yields decrease and decomposition may occur during the vacuum distillation.

For the synthesis of the di-acid chloride of 2-chloroethyl dihydrogen phosphate another method was used: ethylene phosphorochloridite was treated with chlorine [293]. The five-membered ring opened thus:

The di-acid chlorides of the alkyl phosphoric acids are colourless liquids with a specific gravity greater than unity and a sharp smell; they also fume in air. They react violently with water to give the alkyl phosphoric acids, although with increasing molecular weight their reactivity decreases.

The properties of the alkyl phosphorodichloridates are recorded in Table 50.

TABLE 50. ALKYL PHOSPHORODICHLORIDATES $ROPOCl_2$

R	b. p., °C (mm)	n_D^{20}	d_4^{20}	Yield %	Reference
CH_3-	62–64 (15)				[294]
C_2H_5-	56–61 (9–10)	1·4347	1·3813		[295]
	64–65 (10)		1·353		[296]
	63 (19)				[297]
$ClCH_2CH_2-$	71·5 (2)	1·4960	1·5527		[293]
C_4H_9-	90 (17);	1·4453	1·2711		[298]
	85 (13)	(11°)	(11°)		
			1·2560*		[299]
$C_6H_{13}-$			1·1868		[299]
$C_4H_9CH(C_2H_5)CH_2-$			1·1320		[299]
$C_8H_{17}-$			1·1248		[299]
$(CH_3)_2CH(CH_2)_5-$			1·1329		[299]
$C_9H_{19}-$			1·1067		[299]
$C_{10}H_{21}-$			1·0924		[299]
$C_{12}H_{25}-$			1·0594		[299]
$C_{13}H_{27}-$			1·0613		[299]
$C_{14}H_{29}-$			1·0556		[299]
$C_{18}H_{37}-$			0·9995		[299]

* d_4^{25}.

Aryl phosphorodichloridates $ArOPOCl_2$

The aryl phosphorodichloridates are usually prepared by the reaction of mono-hydroxyphenols with phosphoryl chloride [2]. This reaction is considerably slower than in the aliphatic series. The equimolecular mixture of the corresponding phenol and phosphoryl chloride must be stirred and heated on an oil bath for a period of several hours, usually in the presence of small quantities of catalysts [2, 300, 301] — sodium chloride, potassium chloride, magnesium chloride, iron filings, etc. To ensure removal of the hydrogen chloride an inert gas is sometimes passed through the mixture. Vacuum distillation affords the pure aryl phosphorodichloridates: these are colourless high-boiling liquids or crystalline solids which fume slightly in air.

Di-acid chlorides with nuclear trichloromethyl groups are prepared by the treatment of hydroxy-aromatic carboxylic acids with phosphorus pentachloride:

$$HO_2C-Ar-OH + PCl_5 \longrightarrow [Cl-CO-Ar-O-POCl_2] \xrightarrow{PCl_5} CCl_3-Ar-OPOCl_2$$

Phenyl phosphorodichloridate $C_6H_5OPOCl_2$ [302]

$$C_6H_5OH + POCl_3 \longrightarrow C_6H_5OPOCl_2 + HCl$$

A round-bottomed flask, fitted with a reflux condenser and a drying tube, was charged with phenol (104·5 g, 1·1 mole) and phosphoryl chloride (170·6 g, 1·1 mole) and the mixture was refluxed for 10 hr. The reaction mass obtained was distilled *in vacuo* and a fraction b. p. 97–103/2 mm was collected. Redistillation gave the acid chloride (136 g, 57·7%), b.p. 103–104°/2 mm, as a colourless liquid, n_D^{20} 1·5216, d_4^{20} 1·4145.

The properties of aryl phosphorodichloridates are recorded in Table 51.

Alkylphosphonous dichlorides $RPCl_2$

The general method of preparation of alkylphosphonous dichlorides is by the reaction of phosphorus trichloride with organometallic compounds: such as dialkylmercurials [287, 321] (in sealed tubes), dialkyl cadmiums [322] tetraethyl-lead [323], trialkyl-aluminiums [324, 325] (in the last three cases at the boiling-points of the reaction mixtures). It is interesting to note that while phosphorus trichloride does not react with tetraethyltin, phosphorus tribromide and tri-iodide give the corresponding alkylphosphonous dihalides [326]. The general reaction scheme is:

$$PX_3 + R_nMe \longrightarrow RPX_2 + R_{n-1}MeX,$$

where R = alkyl; X = halogen; and Me = metal.

Chloroalkylphosphonous dichlorides have been synthesized by Yakubovich, Ginsburg and Makarov [327, 328] by the reaction of phosphorus trichloride with diazomethane and diazoethane at −50° to −70°; and by Karasch and his co-workers [329] by the addition of phosphorus trichloride to octene. Certain alkylphosphonous dihalides have been obtained by the treatment of the corresponding alkyltetrahalogenophosphoranes with phosphorus [5, 45, 330, 331]; by the halogenation of aliphatic phosphines [332]; and by the treatment of complexes (formed from alkyl chlorides, phosphorus trichloride and aluminium trichloride [47, 48]) with aluminium, sodium or phosphorus [333].

Alkylphosphonous dichlorides are liquids heavier than water with a sharp disagreeable smell and are soluble in many organic solvents. They react violently with water and alcohols. With increasing molecular weight their chemical reactivity decreases.

Ethylphosphonous dichloride $C_2H_5PCl_2$ [323]

$$(C_2H_5)_4Pb + 3PCl_3 \longrightarrow 3C_2H_5PCl_2 + PbCl_2 + C_2H_5Cl$$

A 500 ml four-necked flask equipped with a stirrer, reflux condenser, dropping funnel and a gas inlet tube was charged with phosphorus trichloride

TABLE 51. ARYL PHOSPHORODICHLORIDATES $ArOPOCl_2$

Ar	b. p., °C (mm)	n_D^{20}	d_4^{20}	Yield (%)	Reference
C_6H_5—	103–104 (2)	1·5216	1·4145	57·7	[302]
	105–108 (8)	1·5320	1·4207	86·7	[302a]
$2\text{-}ClC_6H_4$	123–125 (7)	1·5372	1·5232	77	[302a]
$4\text{-}ClC_6H_4$—	127–130 (7)	1·5380	1·5236	79·5	[302]
$2,4\text{-}Cl_2C_6H_3$—	160 (15)	1·554		75	[303]
$2,4,6\text{-}Cl_3C_6H_2$—	121 (0·4)				[303]
	75–76*				
$2,4\text{-}Br_2C_6H_3$—	147 (1·5)	1·588 (22°)			[303]
$2\text{-}CH_3OC_6H_4$—	178–180 (30)				[304]
$2\text{-}C_6H_5OC_6H_4$ —	195–198 (11)				[305]
$2,4\text{-}Cl(C_6H_5O)C_6H_3$—	216–219 (11)				[305]
$2\text{-}CH_3C_6H_4$—	127 (15)				[306]
$4\text{-}CH_3C_6H_4$—	255				[307]
$3,4\text{-}(CH_3)ClC_6H_3$—	95 (0·1)				[308]
$2,4,6\text{-}(CH_3)Cl_2C_6H_2$—	168–170 (10);				[303]
	56–57*	1·62019			
$2\text{-}CCl_3C_6H_4$—	178—179 (11)				[309]
$3\text{-}CCl_3C_6H_4$—	178 (11)				[309]
$2,4\text{-}(CCl_3)ClC_6H_3$—	197 (15);				[310]
	59–60*				
$2,4,6\text{-}(CCl_3)Cl_2C_6H_2$—	102–104*				[311]
$2,4,6\text{-}(CCl_3)Br_2C_6H_2$—	129–130*				[312]
$2,4,6\text{-}(CCl_6)I_2C_6H_2$—	126*				[313]
$2,4\text{-}(CCl_3)CH_3C_6H_3$—	199·4–199·8 (13);				[314]
	80*				
$2,5\text{-}[(CH_3)_2CH]CH_3C_6H_3$—	246–249 (300)		1·244		[315]
$2,5,6\text{-}[(CH_3)_2CH](CH_3)ClC_6H_2$—	168 (12)				[308]
$4\text{-}(CH_3)_3CC_6H_4$—	141–143 (4)	1·5136	1·2472	87·3	[302a]
$2,6\text{-}(CH_3)C_3H_7COC_6H_3$—	167 (0·2)		1·259+		[308]
$2,4\text{-}(CH_3)C_4H_9C_6H_3$—.	128–133 (0·4)				[308]
$4\text{-tert } C_5H_{11}C_6H_4$—	174 (10)				[316]
$2,4\text{-}(CH_3)C_5H_{11}(iso)C_6H_3$—	125–133 (0·3)				[308]
$2,4\text{-}(CH_3)C_6H_{13}C_6H_3$—	140–145 (0·15)				[308]
$2,5,6\text{-}[CH_3)_2CH](CH_3)C_4H_9C_6H_2$—	138–141 (0·2)				[308]
$4\text{-iso } C_8H_{17}C_6H_4$—	192–195 (10)				[316]
$2\text{-}C_6H_5C_6H_4$—	228 (47)				[306]
$3\text{-}C_6H_5C_6H_4$—	218–221 (9)				[317]
$4\text{-}C_6H_5C_6H_4$—	211–223 (12–13);				[318]
	83*				
$4\text{-}C_6H_5C(CH_3)_2C_6H_4$—	167–170 (2)	1·5670	1·2653	71·5	[302a]
$1\text{-}C_{10}H_7$—	198–200 (20)				[319]
$2\text{-}C_{10}H_7$—	204–205 (20);				[319]
	39*				
$2\text{-}CCl_3C_{10}H_6$	115*				[320]

* Melting point.

$+\ d_4^{25}$

(137·4 g, 1 mole). Tetraethyl-lead*(100 g, 0·3 mole) was added gradually, with stirring, from the dropping funnel while nitrogen was passed through the flask. The mixture was gradually heated to boiling and was refluxed at 110° for about 30 hr (after about 2 hr lead chloride began to precipitate) until the liquid stopped dripping from the condenser. The ethylphosphonous dichloride (116–126 g, 89–96%) was then distilled, b. p. 113–116°, from the flask.

Methylphosphonous dichloride CH_3PCl_2 [333]

$$3CH_3Cl + 3PCl_3 + 3AlCl_3 \longrightarrow 3CH_3PCl_4 \cdot AlCl_3 \xrightarrow{2Al+5KCl} 3CH_3PCl_2 + 5AlCl_3KCl$$

A mixture of aluminium dust (2·7 g) and freshly heated potassium chloride (23·2 g) (the reagent 1) was prepared. A flask was then charged with tetrachloromethylphosphorane/aluminium chloride complex** (50 g) and the reagent 1 (2·59 g). The substances were mixed well, the mixture was cautiously melted and the remaining quantity of the reagent 1 was gradually added while the reaction mass was cautiously heated. The reaction proceeded with a considerable evolution of heat. The methylphosphonous dichloride (13·2 g, 72%) was then distilled from the flask, b. p. 81–82°. n_D^{20} 1·4960, d_4^{20} 1·3039.

The properties of alkylphosphonous dichlorides are recorded in Table 52.

TABLE 52. ALKYLPHOSPHONOUS DICHLORIDES $RPCl_2$

R	b.p., °C(mm)	n_D^{25}	d_4^{27}	Yield (%)	Reference
CH_3—	81–82 (760)	1·4960 (20°)	1·3039 (20°)	72	[333]
$ClCH_2$—	80–81 (140)	1·5247 (20°)	1·5289 (20°)	40	[328]
CCl_3—	82–83 (7); m. p. 50–52° (with decomposition)				[330]
C_2H_5—	⎰ 112 ⎱ 114–117	1·4930	1·2600 1·2952 (19°)	61·5 89–96*	[325] [321]
CH_3CHCl—	63·5–64·5 (50)	1·5090 (20°)	1·4232 (20°)	35	[328]
C_3H_7—	⎰ 134·5 ⎱ 140—142	1·4842	1·1664 1·1771 (19°)	44	[322] [321]
iso-C_3H_7—	130 (745)	1·4880 (20°)	1·1922+	43·1	[325]

* Tetraethyl-lead is extremely toxic and hence the work must be done under good ventilation conditions.

+ The preparation of the complex was not described, but the authors obviously followed the method of Kinnear and Perren: [48] in the present case this would involve the mixing of methyl chloride (12 g), phosphorus trichloride (21·3 g) and aluminium chloride (20·8 g), shaking the mixture in a closed system for 64 hr, and then distilling off the excess of methyl chloride.

TABLE 52 — (contd.)

R	b.p., °C(mm)	n_D^{25}	d_4^{27}	Yield (%)	Refer-ence
C_4H_9-	160	1·4838	1·1341	47	[322]
iso-C_4H_9-	59–60 (50); 148–149 (740) 48·5–49 (12)	1·4818 (20°) 1·4719	1·1268+ 1·1720	17·6 26	[325] [334]
$C_5H_{11}-$	184		1·0997	40	[322]
iso-$C_5H_{11}-$	180–183	1·4815	1·1024 (23°)		[321]
$C_6H_{13}-$	208			41	[322]
$C_7H_{15}-$	228·5	1·4800	1·0653	42	[322]
$C_8H_{17}-$	247	1·4788	1·0636	33	[322]
$C_3H_6CHClCH_2-$	85–88 (0·5)	1·4778	1·0433		[329]

* Yield according to (289).
+ d_4^{20}.

Arylphosphonous dichlorides $ArPCl_2$

Arylphosphonous dichlorides can be prepared by the following methods:

(1) by the reaction of diarylmercurials with phosphorus trichloride in sealed tubes at a temperature of about 200° [2, 321]:

$$Ar_2Hg + PCl_3 \longrightarrow ArPCl_2 + ArHgCl$$

(This method is very suitable for preparing small quantities of arylphosphonous dichlorides.)

(2) By the reaction of aromatic hydrocarbons with phosphorus trichloride in the gas phase

$$ArH + PCl_3 \longrightarrow ArPCl_2 + HCl$$

In this method, which was first described by Michaelis [335–337], a mixture of the reactants is vapourized from a reservoir and passed through a glass or porcelain tube packed with a catalyst of the alumina type and heated to the required temperature. The products of the reaction, together with unchanged starting material, are condensed, returned to the reservoir and recycled. Different apparatuses and catalysts have been used from time to time, but the principle of the method has remained largely as described here [287, 288, 335–340]. In this process, as well as the arylphosphonous dichlorides, fair quantities of white phosphorus and polyphosphines, which are spontaneously inflammable in air, are formed. The whole process is hence carried out in a stream of inert gas and, before distillation, the reaction products are heated in a sealed tube at 200° for several hours or are refluxed in an inert gas atmosphere.

Disadvantages of this process are the bulky apparatus required and the danger of fire and explosion.

(3) By the reaction of aromatic hydrocarbons with phosphorus trichloride in the presence of aluminium chloride:

$$RH + PCl_3 \xrightarrow{AlCl_3} RPCl_2 + HCl$$

This method, which was also first discovered by Michaelis [335–337], was at first of little value because of the slowness of the reaction and the poor yields. However, later developments of this reaction have radically improved it. It has been shown that the ratios of the reaction components have a great effect on the yields of the corresponding dichlorides. An increase in the quantity of aluminium chloride (from $0\cdot2$ mole to 1 mole, with 1 mole of benzene) increases the reaction rate (twelve times faster than under the conditions given by Michaelis) and the amount of product; at the same time, however, the isolation of the arylphosphonous dichloride is made more difficult because it forms a strong complex with the aluminium chloride. It has been established that the optimum ratios of the components are; hydrocarbon: PCl_3 : $AlCl_3 =$ $= 1 : 3 : 1$, and that the optimum reaction time is 3–8 hr. The yields of arylphosphonous dichlorides, which in the earlier experiments did not exceed 20–25% [341], have been greatly increased in this way.

A further improvement in the process was accomplished by complexing the aluminium chloride (at the end of the experiment) with various reagents (H_2O, $POCl_3$, C_5H_5N) [342–345].

(4) Finally, a method has been described for obtaining phenylphosphonous dichloride by the thermal decomposition of trichlorodiphenylphosphorane:

$$(C_6H_5)_2PCl_3 \longrightarrow C_6H_5PCl_2 + C_6H_5Cl$$

Only the second and third methods can, of course, be employed industrially for the synthesis of arylphosphonous dichlorides, and of these the third is much the safer and the apparatus is easier to make.

Arylphosphonous dichlorides are heavy, colourless, transparent liquids, often with a sharp unpleasant smell (except for phenylphosphonous dichloride and its near homologues), which are soluble in a range of organic solvents, and which react violently with water and alcohols. With increased nuclear substitution, the reactivity of the arylphosphonous dichlorides decreases.

Phenylphosphonous dichloride $C_6H_5PCl_2$*

$$C_6H_6 + 3PCl_3 + AlCl_3 \longrightarrow C_6H_5PCl_2 \cdot AlCl_3 + 2PCl_3 + HCl$$
$$\Big| \ C_5H_5N$$
$$\longrightarrow C_6H_5PCl_2 + AlCl_3 \cdot C_5H_5N$$

A large stainless steel vessel of capacity 10 l. which could be immersed in a bath heated by a liquid, was fitted with a stirrer with a hole in it through which the system could be evacuated, a thermometer and a reflux condenser

---

* This method is based on one given by the author in a note [345].

with a large cooling surface and a wide interior tube. The following components
were added successively to it:

Benzene	1130 g (1300 ml)	molar ratio of
phosphorus trichloride	5900 g (4000 ml)	components
aluminium chloride	1800 g	— 1 : 3 ; 1

The aluminium chloride gradually dissolved exothermically and the temperature of the reaction mixture rose to 35–45°.

After the exothermic reaction had stopped the vessel was immersed in
the heating bath and stirring was commenced. At a bath temperature of about
50–55° (45–50° in the vessel) hydrogen chloride began to be evolved at a rate
depending on the temperature. (The degree of heating is determined by the
capacity of the condenser, which must not become choked.) The mixture was
heated for 3·5–4 hr (a longer reaction time can lead to the formation of some
diphenylphosphinous chloride). After this time the temperature was raised
from 50–55° to 65–70°. More hydrogen chloride was evolved and was absorbed in an aqueous or an alkali solution. When the hydrogen chloride evolution
had ceased, the reaction mixture was cooled to 40° and the unreacted excess
of phosphorus trichloride was distilled by reducing the pressure through 150
mm to 50 mm, finally raising the bath temperature to 50–55°. The distilled
phosphorus trichloride (2100–2300 ml) can be redistilled and used again in
the reaction.

The reaction mixture was then cooled to room temperature and pyridine
(1110 g, 1133 ml) (to complex with the aluminium chloride catalyst) was added
over a period of 4–5 hr (molar ratio of $AlCl_3 : C_5H_5N = 1 : 1$).

The reaction of the pyridine with the aluminium chloride was carried
out with stirring and exterior cooling so that the reaction temperature did
not exceed 45–50°. The complex, $AlCl_3 : C_5H_5N$, which formed on standing,
was a solid, although in the presence of phenylphosphonous dichloride it
became liquid at 60–70°. The reflux condenser was then turned to the distillation position and the reaction mixture was distilled to give a very volatile
fraction (unchanged pyridine and residual phosphorus trichloride), b.p.
70–85° (bath temperature)/30–40 mm, and then phenylphosphonous dichloride,
b.p. 90–155° (bath temperature)/1–3 mm.

[Notes: (1) For the final distillation it is essential to use tubing of a
sufficiently large bore so that blockages are not caused by the small amounts
of pyridine hydrochloride (m. p. +82°) which distill with the first fractions of
phenylphosphonous dichloride.

(2) The distillation must be conducted cautiously, preferably in an
atmosphere of an inert gas, because oxygen and phenylphosphonous
dichloride can form explosive mixtures.]

The yield of technical grade phenylphosphonous dichloride was 2000–
2100 g (77–80%), n_D^{20} 1·5850–1·6000: by using distilled starting materials
and working in glass apparatus, the yield increases to 85–92%.

TABLE 53. ARYLPHOSPHONOUS DICHLORIDES ArPCl$_2$

Ar	b. p., °C (mm)	n_D^{25}	d_4^{25}	Yield (%)	Reference
C$_6$H$_5$—	58–59 (0·8–1)	1·5952–1·5960 (20°)	1·3191	85–92	[345]
	68–70 (1)	1·5962	1·3173	78	[343]
4·ClC$_6$H$_4$—	253–255		1·425 (17°)		[336, 337]
4·BrC$_6$H$_4$	271–272		1·6895 (15°)		[336, 337]
	135–136 (14)				[278]
4·CH$_3$OC$_6$H$_4$—	153 (21); 140 (11)		1·3468+		[346]
4·C$_2$H$_5$OCH$_4$—	266				[336, 337]
4·C$_6$H$_5$OC$_6$H$_4$—	200 (12)		1·3122		[278]
4·(CH$_2$)$_2$NC$_6$H$_4$—	250 (120); 66*				[347]
4·(C$_2$H$_5$)NC$_6$H$_4$—	undistillable oil				[347]
4-$\begin{cases} CH_3 \\ C_6H_5CH_2 \end{cases}NC_6H_4$—	,,				[347]
4-$\begin{cases} C_2H_5 \\ C_6H_5CH_2 \end{cases}NC_6H_4$—	,,				[347]
					[347]
4-$\begin{cases} CH_3 \\ C_6H_5 \end{cases}NC_6H_4$—	oil decomposing at 200°				[347]
CH$_3$C$_6$H$_4$— ‡	107–110 (10)	1·5865	1·2661	66	[343]
2,4-Cl(CH$_3$)C$_6$H$_3$—	265–266		1·373 (22°)		[348]
2,5-(CH$_3$)$_2$C$_6$H$_3$—	133 (16)				[278]
C$_2$H$_5$C$_6$H$_4$— ‡	122–125 (10)	1·5776	1·2266	69	[343]
2,4,5-(CH$_3$)$_3$C$_6$H$_2$—	280		1·2356		[336, 337]
2,46-(CH$_3$)$_3$C$_6$H$_2$—	273–275		1·205 (15°)		[336, 337]
C$_3$H$_7$C$_6$H$_4$— ‡	127–131 (5)	1·5658	1·1905	47	[343]
iso-C$_3$H$_7$C$_6$H$_4$— ‡	129–132 (10)	1·5677	1·1917	64	[343]
iso-C$_4$H$_9$C$_6$H$_4$— ‡	116—119 (1)	1·5591	1·1611	39	[343]
sec.-C$_4$H$_9$C$_6$H$_4$— ‡	116–120 (1·5)	1·5644	1·1840	23	[323]
sec. -C$_5$H$_{11}$C$_6$H$_4$— ‡	128–131 (1)	1·5541	1·1437	22	[343]
C$_6$H$_{13}$C$_6$H$_4$— ‡	146–149 (1·5)	1·5478	1·1157	50	[343]
(C$_6$H$_5$)$_3$CC$_6$H$_4$— ‡	138–140*	Decomposes at 240°			[349]
1-C$_{10}$H$_7$	180 (10); 58–59*				[350]
2-C$_{10}$H$_7$	180 (9–10); 50–60*				[350]

* Melting point.

+ d^{15}.

‡ Mainly *para*-isomer.

Phenylphosphonous dichloride is colourless liquid with a sharp, very unpleasant smell: it causes headache and nausea. In air it gives off hydrogen chloride fumes. It reacts violently with water. Vacuum distillation of the technical grade material gives 95–97% yields of pure phenylphosphonous dichloride, b. p. 58–59°/0·8–1 mm, n_D^{20} 1·5952–1·5960, d_4^{20} 1·3191.

Di-acid chlorides of alkyl- and aryl-phosphonic acids
(alkyl- and aryl-phosphonic dichlorides)

The main methods of obtaining alkylphosphonic dichlorides are the following: the reaction of alkyl chlorides with phosphorus trichloride and aluminium chloride, followed by cautious hydrolysis of the complex which forms (the work of Clay [47], and Kinnear and Perren [48] is discussed on p. 19; details of such a reaction are given on p. 20); the reaction of alkylphosphonic acids or their esters with phosphorus pentachloride [2, 351]:

$$RPO(OH)_2 + 2PCl_5 \longrightarrow RPOCl_2 + 2POCl_3 + 2HCl$$

and

$$RPO(OR')_2 + 2PCl_5 \longrightarrow RPOCl_2 + 2POCl_3 + 2R'Cl$$

the reaction of alkyltetrachlorophosphoranes with sulphur dioxide gas [2]:

$$RPCl_4 + SO_2 \longrightarrow RPOCl_2 + SOCl_2$$

and finally, the reaction of aliphatic hydrocarbons with phosphorus trichloride and oxygen (the work of Soborovskii, Zinov'ev and Englin [49, 50], and Clayton and Jensen [51] is discussed on p. 19; details of such a reaction are given on p. 20).

A simple method of preparing di-acid chlorides of α-chloroalkylphosphonic acids has been discovered by Kabachnik and Shepeleva [20, 21, 24]: it involves the reaction of phosphorus trichloride with aldehydes under pressure at 200–250°:

$$RCHO + PCl_3 \longrightarrow RCHCl \cdot POCl_2$$

Arylphosphonic dichlorides are prepared in similar ways to the alkyl analogues, that is, by the reaction of arylphosphonic acids with phosphorus pentachloride [2]; by the treatment of aryltetrachlorophosphoranes with sulphur dioxide gas [2]; and also by the oxidation of arylphosphonous dichlorides with chlorine and phosphorus pentoxide [184]:

$$3ArPCl_2 + 3Cl_2 + P_2O_5 \longrightarrow 3ArPOCl_2 + 2POCl_3$$

The direct oxidation of arylphosphonous dichlorides with oxygen from the air,

$$ArPCl_2 + \tfrac{1}{2}O_2 \longrightarrow ArPOCl_2$$

is extremely dangerous, since very slight impurities in the reaction system may cause powerful explosions [335].

Finally, it is possible in certain cases to obtain arylphosphonic dichlorides by the partial hydrolysis of aryltetrachlorophosphoranes [87, 335].

The di-acid chlorides of the alkyl- (aryl-) phosphonic acids are either colourless, transparent liquids heavier than water, or crystalline solids: they are soluble in a range of organic solvents. The lower members fume in air, are easily hydrolysed and react with alcohols. With increasing molecular weight this reactivity decreases.

Chloromethylphosphonic dichloride $ClCH_2POCl_2$ [21]

$$PCl_3 + CH_2O \longrightarrow ClCH_2POCl_2$$

Paraformaldehyde (5 g, 0·167 mole) and phosphorus trichloride (35 g, 0·250 mole) were heated together in a sealed tube for 10 hr at 235–245°. Phosphorus trichloride was first distilled from the reaction mixture at slightly reduced pressure, and then the residue was distilled *in vacuo*. After two distillations the di-acid chloride (17·1 g, 61%), b. p. 84–85°/13 mm, n_D^{20} 1·4990, was obtained. The undistillable residue amounted to 4·1 g.

For the preparation of large quantities of chloromethylphosphonic dichloride the experiment was carried out in an autoclave under the same conditions. By using 1 mole of paraformaldehyde and 1·5 mole of phosphorus trichloride, 0·6 mole of the di-acid chloride was obtained. In this way, the compound can be prepared in any desired quantity.

Chloromethylphosphonic dichloride is a colourless, mobile liquid which fumes slightly in air; it is insoluble in water, but reacts violently with it with the evolution of heat. It has b. p. 87–88°/15 mm, 84–85°/13 mm, 78–79°/10 mm, 52–53°/2 mm; n_D^{20} 1·4978; d_4^{20} 1·6361.

Phenylphosphonic dichloride $C_6H_5POCl_2$ [184]

$$3C_6H_5PCl_2 + 3Cl_2 + P_2O_5 \longrightarrow 3C_6H_5POCl_2 + 2POCl_3$$

A four-necked 3 l. flask, fitted with a reflux condenser with a calcium chloride drying tube, stirrer, thermometer and inlet tube for the passage of chlorine, was charged with phenylphosphonous dichloride (1611 g, 9 mole). Finely ground phosphorus pentoxide (511 g, 3·6 mole) was then added and chlorine was passed, with stirring, into the liquid mixture which formed.

In the resulting exothermic reaction, the temperature initially rose to 150°. However, the dripping of phosphoryl chloride from the condenser soon lowered the liquid temperature to about 130°. The chlorine was passed at such a rate as to ensure a steady refluxing of the phosphoryl chloride. After 4 hr the temperature began to drop, indicating that the reaction had finished. The passage of chlorine was stopped and the reaction mixture was fractionated.

After the removal of the greater part of the phosphoryl chloride at atmospheric pressure, the phenylphosphonic dichloride (1550 g, 88·4%), was distilled *in vacuo*, b. p. 137–138°/15 mm, 258°/760 mm, 104°/4 mm; n_D^{20} 1·5581; d_4^{20} 1·197.

Phenylphosphonic dichloride $C_6H_5POCl_2$*

$$C_6H_5PCl_2 + Cl_2 \longrightarrow C_6H_5PCl_4 \xrightarrow{SO_2} C_6H_5POCl_2 + SOCl_2$$

The apparatus for the synthesis of phenylphosphonic dichloride was a four-necked 4 l. flask fitted with a reflux condenser with a calcium chloride drying tube, stirrer, thermometer and a T-piece; gas could be passed through the side tube of the T-piece, and a glass rod fitted through a sleeve of pressure tubing (lubricated with glycerine) was inserted through the upper tube.

The flask was charged with phenylphosphonous dichloride (1720 g) and carbon tetrachloride (1400 ml). The gas inlet tube was adjusted so that it was just above the surface of the liquid, and dry chlorine was passed, with efficient stirring, into the system for 6–8 hr. By exterior cooling (ice-salt mixture) the reaction temperature was kept in the range 10–20°. The tetrachlorophenylphosphorane separated out as it formed in yellow-white crystals. The vertical part of the T-piece was periodically freed from crystals with the glass rod. After the exothermic reaction had ceased, chlorine was passed for a further 5–10 min, and then the end of the gas inlet tube was pushed below the surface of the semi-liquid mass and dry sulphur dioxide gas was passed into the system (also with stirring and exterior cooling) until the crystals had completely dissolved and the reaction mixture had changed into a homogenous liquid. This was distilled to give a very volatile fraction (SO_2, $SOCl_2$, SO_2Cl_2, CCl_4), and then the residue was distilled *in vacuo* to give phenylphosphonic dichloride (1620–1650 g, 88–90%), b.p. 83–84°/1 mm, n_D^{20} 1.5578, d_4^{20} 1.1977

The properties of alkyl- and aryl-phosphonic dichlorides are recorded in Tables 54 and 55.

---

* This method is based on one given by the author in a note [345].

TABLE 54. ALKYLPHOSPHONIC DICHLORIDES $RPOCl_2$

R	b. p., °C (mm)	n_D^{20}	d_4^{20}	Yield (%)	Reference
CH_3—	162; 33*			68	[48]
$ClCH_2$—	77–78 (10)	1·4978	1·6361	60; 85+	[21]
$CHCl_2$—	79 (9)			63	[48]
CCl_3—	156*			85	[48]
C_2H_5—	45–46 (3)	1·4661	1·3678	82+	[352]
CH_3CHCl—	71–72 (6)	1·4911	1·5134	14–16; 75+	[21]
$ClCH_2CH_2$—	68 (2)	1·4977 (16°)	1·5430 (16°)	70	[351]
	86·5–87 (2)	1·4998	1·5446		[50]
CH_3CCl_2—	147–150*				[48]
CCl_3CH_2	65–66 (1)			20	[48]
C_3H_7—	88–90 (50)		1·3088		[321]
iso-C_3H_7—	82–84 (50)		1·3018	90+	[321]
$ClCH_2CH(CH_3)$—	190—218				[37]
C_3H_6Cl— (from propane)	85–87 (6)	1·4930	1·4615		[50]
Mixture of $ClCH_2CH(CN)$– and $CNCH_2CHCl$—	99–101 (2)	1·4783	1·5721	16·6	[227]
$ClCH_2CH(COOCH_3)$—	124 (8)	1·4745	1·5238	69·5	[227]
C_4H_9— (from isobutane)	55–57 (2)	1·4660	1·2639		[50]
iso-C_4H_9—	104–108 (50)		1·2333		[321]
$C_2H_5CH(CH_3)$—	57 (2)			93	[48]
$(CH_3)_3C$—	110 (25); 123* (sublimes)			92+	[47]
C_3H_7CHCl—	84 (25)	1·5010	1·3236		[328]
	107 (13)	1·4885	1·3598	10	[21]
$ClCH_2CH(C_2H_5)$—	116–123 (18)			53·5	[37]
C_4H_8Cl—(from butane)	85–87 (5)	1·4900	1·3950		[50]
C_4H_8Cl— (from isobutane)	78–80 (4)				[50]
C_5H_{11}— (from n-pentane)	67–69 (2)	1·4694	1·2180		[50]
iso-C_5H_{11}—	122–125 (55)		1·1883		[321]
C_5H_{11}— (from 2-methylbutane)	64–65 (2)	1·4708	1·2246		[50]
iso-C_4H_9CHCl—	106–109 (12)				[353]
$ClCH_2(CH_2)_2CH(CH_3)$—	112–123 (1)			15	[48]
$ClCH_2CH(C_3H_7)$—	130–132 (20); 39–42*				[37]
C_6H_{11}— (from cyclohexane)	93–94 (2); 39–40*			82+	[50]
C_6H_{13}—(from n-hexane)	82–84 (3)				[50]
C_6H_{13}—(from 2,3-dimethylbutane)	75–76 (2)	1·4715	1·1733		[50]
C_6H_{13}— (from 3-methylpentane)	110–120 (16–18)				[51]

TABLE 54 — *(contd.)*

R	b. p., °C (mm)	n_D^{20}	d_4^{20}	Yield (%)	Reference
C_7H_{15}— (from n-pentane)	96–98 (2)	1·4830	1·1852		[50]
C_8H_{17}— (from 2,3,4-trimethyl-pentane)	81–82 (2)				[50]
$C_{16}H_{33}$—	165 (1)	1·4707	1·1329	60	[48]
$C_6H_5CH_2$—	130 (2); 57·5*			62	[48]
C_6H_5CHCl—	124–126 (2), 60–61*	1·5666 (40°)	1·4534 (40°)	62	[21]
$C_6H_5CCl_2$—	114–120 (2)				
$4-ClC_6H_4CHCl$—	144–144·5 (1·5); 58–60·5*			10 40	[48] [21]
$3-NO_2C_6H_4CHCl$—	116 (1); 62·5–64·5*			3–7	[21]
$4-CH_3C_6H_4CHCl$—	129·5–130·5 (0·5); 52–54*			35	[21]

* Melting point.
⁺ Yield according to Ref. (48).

TABLE 55. ARYLPHOSPHONIC DICHLORIDES ArPOCl₂

Ar	b. p., °C (mm)	n_D^{25}	d_4^{25}	Yield (%)	Reference
C_6H_5—	137–138 15), 104 (4)	1·5581	1·197	88·4	[184]
$4-ClC_6H_4$—	121–123 (3)	1·5743	1·302	88	[185]
$4-BrC_6H_4$—	290–291				[336, 337]
$4-CH_3OC_6H_4$—	173 (12–15)				[336, 337]
$4-C_2H_5OC_6H_4$—	oil				[336, 337]
$2-CH_3C_6H_4$—	273		1·3877 (18·5)		[336, 337]
$3-CH_3C_6H_4$—	275		1·3533 (18)		[336, 337]
$4-CH_3C_6H_4$—	142 (11)	1·5542	1·154	91·7	[184]
$2,5-(CH_3)_2C_6H_3$—	280–281		1·31 (18)		[354]
$4-C_2H_5C_6H_4$—	294		1·29 (16)		[336, 337]
$2,4,5-(CH_3)_3C_6H_2$—	307–308; 63*				[336, 337]
$2,4,6-(CH_3)_3C_6H_2$—	>360; 92–93*				[336, 337]
$4(?)-iso-C_3H_7C_6H_4$—	183 (35); 35*				[336, 337]
$4(?)-C_6H_5CH_2C_6H_4$—	261 (20)		1·207		[336, 337]
$1-C_{10}H_7$—	208 (20); 60*				[350]

* Melting point.

SOME COMPOUNDS CONTAINING TWO HYDROXYL-GROUPS (DI-FUNCTIONAL ALCOHOLS AND PHENOLS)

Both these classes of compound are well known. Hence, we will give only a brief account of them and a table of compounds.

Of the huge number of substituted glycols which could be used for the synthesis of high molecular weight phosphorus-containing compounds, greatest interest lies in the di-primary saturated glycols, and to a lesser extent in the primary–secondary and di-secondary compounds. The methods of preparation of glycols and di-functional phenols and their properties have been widely described in the literature and they will not be detailed in this book.

We will, however, make special mention of the 4,4′-dihydroxydiarylalkanes which, although they received little attention in the literature in the past, have recently aroused some interest [355, 356]. Their general formula is:

$$HO \bigcirc R \bigcirc OH$$

where R is alkyl or cycloalkyl; the phenyl rings can contain various substituents. These compounds are easily prepared by the condensation of phenols with ketones or aldehydes (with the latter the yields are, as a rule, low and the purification of the products is very difficult), usually in the presence of sulphuric acid (or less often hydrochloric) and catalytic quantities of sulphur dichloride, hydrogen sulphide, mercaptans or other sulphur containing compounds.

$$RR''-C = O + 2HO \bigcirc \xrightarrow{-H_2O} HO \bigcirc - \underset{\underset{R''}{|}}{\overset{\overset{R'}{|}}{C}} - \bigcirc -OH$$

The dihydroxydiarylalkanes are solid substances which are purified by recrystallisation or distillation *in vacuo*. They decompose at about 270–280°. Of greatest value is 2,2-bis-(4,4′-dihydroxydiphenyl)propane, which can be made from acetone and phenol in yields of 86–90%.

The properties of di-functional alcohols and phenols, and also dihydroxydiarylalkanes are shown in Tables 56–58.

TABLE 56. SOME GLYCOLS

Formula	b. p., °C (mm)	n_D^{20}	d_4^{20}	Reference
$HOCH_2CH_2OH$	197·2	1·4319	1·114	[357]
$CH_3CHOHCH_2OH$	188–189	1·4328	1·040	[357]
$HO(CH_2)_3OH$	214·7	1·4396	1·053	[357]
$C_2H_5CHOHCH_2OH$	192–194	1·439 (18°)	1·006 (17°)	[357]
$CH_3(CHOH)_2CH_3$ (meso-form)	184; 34·4*	1·4375	1·048	[357]
$CH_3CHOHCH_2CH_2OH$	206·5	1·4424	1·006	[357]
$HO(CH_2)_4OH$	230; 19*	1·4461	1·020	[357]
$HOCH_2C \equiv CCH_2OH$	238; 58*			[357]

TABLE 56. — *(contd.)*

Formula	b. p., °C (mm)	n_D^{20}	d_2^{40}	Reference
HO(CH₂)₆OH	250; 42*			[3]
HO(CH₂)₇OH	262; 22·5*			[3]
HO(CH₂)₈OH	172 (20); 63*			[3]
HO(CH₂)₁₀OH	179 (15); 72–73*			[3]
HO(CH₂CH₂O)₂H	244·8	1·4475	1·118	[3]
HO(CH₂CH₂O)₃H	290		1·125	[3]
HO(CH₂CH₂O)₄H	327–328		1·125	[3]

* Melting point.

TABLE 57. DI-FUNCTIONAL PHENOLS (3)

Names	b. p., °C (mm)	m. p., °C
Catechol*	240–245	104–105
Resorcinol⁺	276·5	108; 110·7
Hydroquinone‡	285 (730)	170·3
2,3-Dihydroxytoluene	238–240 (with decomposition)	168
2,4-Dihydroxytoluene	267–270	104–105
2,5-Dihydroxytolune		124–125
2,6-Dihydroxytoluene	264	116
3,4-Dihydroxytoluene	252	65
3,5-Dihydroxy-*o*-xylene		136–137
3,6-Dihydroxy-*o*-xylene		221 (with decomposition)
2,4-Dihydroxy-*m*-xylene		149–150
2,5-Dihydroxy-*p*-xylene		213
2,6-Dihydroxy-*p*-xylene	277–280	163
2,5-Dihydroxydiphenyl		96–98
3,4-Dihydroxydiphenyl	360	136–137
2,2′-Dihydroxydiphenyl	325–326	103–109
2,4′-Dihydroxydiphenyl	324	160–161
3,3′-Dihydroxydiphenyl	247	123
4,4′-Dihydroxydiphenyl		270–272
1,2-Dihydroxynaphthalene		103
1,3-Dihydroxynaphthalene		124–125
1,4-Dihydroxynaphthalene		173–176
1,5-Dihydroxynaphthalene		258–260 (with decomposition)
1,6-Dihydroxynaphthalene		137–138
1,7-Dihydroxynaphthalene		178
1,8-Dihydroxynaphthalene		140
2,3-Dihydroxynaphthalene		159–160
2,6-Dihydroxynaphthalene		216–218
2,7-Dihydroxynaphthalene		190
Dihydroxy-2,2′-dinaphthyl (HOC₁₀H₆)₂		218
a,a′-Dihydroxydinaphthyl		300

* d^4 1·344.
+ d^{15} 1·272.
‡ d^{15} 1·332.

TABLE 58. DIHYDROXYDIARYLALKANES

Formula	b. p., °C (mm)	m. p., °C	Yield (%)	Reference
$CH_2\left(-\langle\bigcirc\rangle-OH\right)_2$		158 (148)		[3]
$CH_3CH\left(-\langle\bigcirc\rangle-OH\right)_2$		122·9		[358]
$CCl_3CH\left(-\langle\bigcirc\rangle-OH\right)_2$		202		[359]
$(CH_3)_2C\left(-\langle\bigcirc\rangle-OH\right)_2$	241–243 (10)	154–155	80–82	[355]
$(CH_3)_2C\left(-\langle\bigcirc\rangle\substack{Cl\\Cl}-OH\right)_2$		127–128		[356]
$C_2H_5C(CH_3)\left[-\langle\bigcirc\rangle-OH\right]_2$	242–245 (7)	125	82–85	[355]
$HO-\langle\bigcirc\rangle\substack{CH_3}-C(CH_3)_2-\langle\bigcirc\rangle-OH$		113–115		[356]
iso-$C_4H_9CH\left(-\langle\bigcirc\rangle-OH\right)_2$		155		[356]
$(C_2H_5)_2C\left(-\langle\bigcirc\rangle-OH\right)_2$	254–256 (10)	201	55–60	[355]
$(CH_3)_2C\left(-\langle\bigcirc\rangle\substack{CH_3}-OH\right)_2$	244–246 (10)	136–137	80–84	[355]
$\langle\bigcirc\rangle C\left(-\langle\bigcirc\rangle-OH\right)_2$		186–187		[360]
$C_2H_5C(CH_3)\left[-\langle\bigcirc\rangle\substack{CH_3}-OH\right]_2$	253–255 (10)	145–146	47–53	[355]
$\langle\bigcirc\rangle\substack{CH_3}C\left(-\langle\bigcirc\rangle-OH\right)_2$		236–240		[360]
$CH_3-\langle\bigcirc\rangle C\left(-\langle\bigcirc\rangle-OH\right)_2$		178		[360]
$C_6H_{13}CH\left(-\langle\bigcirc\rangle-OH\right)_2$		103		[358]
$C_5H_{11}C(CH_3)\left[-\langle\bigcirc\rangle-OH\right]_2$		97–99		[361]
$(C_3H_7)_2C\left(-\langle\bigcirc\rangle-OH\right)_2$		155		[362]

TABLE 58 — (contd.)

Formula	b. p., °C (mm)	m. p., °C	Yield (%)	Reference
$(CH_3)_2C\left(-\underset{}{\bigcirc}\overset{C_2H_5}{-}OH\right)_2$	199–200 (1·5)			[356]
$\bigcirc C\left(-\underset{}{\bigcirc}\overset{CH_3}{-}OH\right)_2$		187		[360]
$C_6H_{13}C(CH_3)\left[-\underset{}{\bigcirc}-OH\right]_2$		83·5		[362]
$C_7H_{15}C(CH_3)\left[-\underset{}{\bigcirc}-OH\right]_2$		80–83		[356]
$(CH_3)_2C\left(-\underset{}{\bigcirc}\overset{C_3H_7\text{-iso}}{-}OH\right)_2$	186–195 (0·6)			[356]
$C_{10}H_{16}\left(-\underset{}{\bigcirc}-OH\right)_2$ (Decalin-β,β)		180–181		[356]
$\bigcirc C\left(-\underset{}{\bigcirc}\overset{C_3H_7\text{-}i}{-}OH\right)_2$		109·5–111·5		[360]
$(CH_3)_2C\left(-\underset{}{\bigcirc}\overset{C_6H_5}{-}OH\right)_2$		99–100		[361]
$(CH_3)_2C\left(-\underset{}{\bigcirc}\overset{C_6H_{11}\text{-cyclo}}{-}OH\right)_2$		145·5		[356]
$C_6H_5CH\left(-\underset{}{\bigcirc}-OH\right)_2$		160–161		[363]
$C_6H_5C(CH_3)\left[-\underset{}{\bigcirc}-OH\right]_2$		187–188		[364]
$C_6H_5C(C_2H_5)-\left[-\underset{}{\bigcirc}-OH\right]_2$		180		[361]

DI- AND TRI-CARBOXYLIC ACIDS (AND THEIR ESTERS) CONTAINING PHOSPHINYL GROUPS

There is very little known about this class of compounds. Michaelis [365] and also Morgan and Herr [366] have synthesized such acids via organomagnesium compounds and alkyl-(aryl-)ditolyl- or tritolyl-phosphine oxides, followed by oxidation of the methyl groups to carboxyl:

$$RP\left(-\langle\ \rangle CH_3\right)_2 \xrightarrow{KMnO_4} RP\left(-\langle\ \rangle COOH\right)_2$$

where R = alkyl or aryl.

Kolesnikov, Korshak and Zubanov [367, 368] have obtained compounds of this type by oxidation of the high molecular weight compounds which are formed by the reaction of arylphosphonous dichlorides with 1,2-diphenylethane in the presence of aluminium chloride.

All the di- and tri-carboxylic acids which contain phosphinyl-groups are crystalline substances with high melting-points. Also, in general, like the tertiary phosphine oxides, they are very resistant to chemical reagents and high temperatures.

As starting materials for high molecular weight compounds, the acids are not of as much interest as the esters, usually the methyl compounds, since these react easily with glycols. These esters are also solids, but with lower melting points than the acids themselves.

The properties of the described compounds are recorded in Table 59.

TABLE 59. CARBOXYARYL- AND ALKOXYCARBONYLARYL-PHOSPHINE OXIDES

Formula	m. p., °C	Yield (%)	Reference
$CH_3PO\left(-\langle\ \rangle-COOH\right)_2$	285	88	[366]
$CH_3PO\left(-\langle\ \rangle-COOCH_3\right)_2$	255·5	82	[366]
$C_2H_5PO\left(-\langle\ \rangle-COOH\right)_2$	265	82	[366]
$C_2H_5PO\left(-\langle\ \rangle-COOCH_3\right)_2$	162		[366]
$C_6H_5PO\left(-\langle\ \rangle-COOH\right)_2$	307–310; 304–306; 306–308		[367]
$C_6H_5PO\left(-\langle\ \rangle-COOCH_3\right)_2$	165–166 146–147		[366] [367]
$4\text{-}ClC_6H_4PO\left(-\langle\ \rangle-COOH\right)_2$	75–76		[367]
$PO\left(-\langle\ \rangle-COOH\right)_3$	323–330		[366]
$PO\left(-\langle\ \rangle-COOCH_3\right)_2$	123–125		[366]

PHOSPHORUS-CONTAINING DI- AND TRI-ISOCYANATES

These little-known organophosphorus compounds have been made by the reaction of acid chlorides of phosphorous, phosphoric, phosphonous and phosphonic acids with silver cyanate [369–372] in an inert solvent (benzene, acetonitrile) according to the following general scheme:

$$\text{>P—X} \quad \text{AgCNO} \longrightarrow \text{AgX} + \text{>PNCO}$$

$$\left(\text{or } \underset{O}{\overset{\|}{\text{>P—X}}} \right) \qquad\qquad \left(\text{or } \underset{O}{\overset{\|}{\text{>P—NCO}}} \right)$$

The yields are, as a rule, not high (from trace amounts to 50%). The properties of phosphorus-containing di- and tri-isocyanates are recorded in Table 60.

TABLE 60. ISOCYANATES AND ISOTHIOCYANATES OF PHOSPHOROUS, PHOSPHORIC, ALKYL- AND ARYL-PHOSPHONOUS AND PHOSPHONIC ACIDS

Formula	b. p., °C (mm)	n_D^{20}	d_4^{20}	Yield (%)	Reference
$C_6H_5P(NCO)_2$	118–122 (3)				[372]
$ClCH_2PO(NCO)_2$	80–82 (0·9)				[372]
$C_2H_5PO(NCO)_2$	58–59 (0·7)			48	[372]
iso-$C_3H_7PO(NCO)_2$	60–61 (1)				[372]
$C_{16}H_{33}PO(NCO)_2$	Viscous oil				[372]
$C_6H_5CH_2PO(NCO)_2$	145 (1–2)				[372]
$C_6H_5PO(NCO)_2$	Polymerizes on distillation				[372]
$P(NCO)_3$	169·3; 2*	1·5352	1·439		[369]
$PO(NCO)_3$ (On heating for 5 hr at 156°, isomerizes into $PO(OCN)_3$; at 120° for 20 hr this isomerization only proceeds by about 2%	193; 5*	1·4804	1·570	11	[370]
$PO(NCS)_3$	215				[371]

* Melting point.

TETRAKIS-(HYDROXYMETHYL)PHOSPHONIUM CHLORIDE (THPC) AND TRIS-(HYDROXYMETHYL)PHOSPHINE OXIDE (THPO)

Tetrakis-(hydroxymethyl)phosphonium chloride was first described by Hofmann [373], who later also determined its structure [374]. THPC is easily synthesized and in good yield by the reaction of phosphine, hydrogen chloride and formaldehyde [375]:

$$PH_3 + 4CH_2O + HCl \longrightarrow P(CH_2OH)_4Cl$$

It is a crystalline compound, soluble in water and the lower alcohols but insoluble in most organic solvents. The structure of THPC (owing to the presence of the four hydroxymethyl groups) renders it particularly suitable as a starting material for the preparation of high molecular weight phosphorus-containing compounds. There are, in fact already reports in the literature on its use in this field.

Tetrakis-(hydroxymethyl)phosphonium chloride
$P(CH_2OH)_4Cl$ (THPC) [375]

$$PH_3 + 4CH_2O + HCl \longrightarrow P(CH_2OH)_4Cl$$

(a) The apparatus for the synthesis of THPC consisted of two phosphine generators, fitted with safety water-seal pressure releases, and a reactor. Each generator consisted of a 2 l. filter-flask closed with a rubber stopper with two holes. Through one was brought a tube for passing nitrogen, and the other was connected to the safety water-seal pressure release, the level of water in which could be varied from 0 to 15in. (37·5 cm). The side arm of each flask was connected to a 5 l. reactor which was closed with a wooden lid. There were four openings in this lid, and through two of them tubes (for passing gas), which were fitted to bubble-plates, were inserted almost to the bottom of the reactor; a high-speed stirrer and a tube open to the atmosphere were fitted through the other two openings.

(b) Reagents: (1) nitrogen. (2) A formaldehyde–hydrochloric acid solution, which was made up in the molar ratio $CH_2O : HCl = 4·2 : 1$, prepared by mixing a 37% aqueous solution of formaldehyde and a 35% solution of hydrochloric acid. (3) Aluminium phosphide prepared thus: 100 g portions of a mixture [from powdered aluminium (528 g) and red phosphorus (352 g)] were placed on an asbestos mat and ignited (in a good fume hood) with a match. A weight of 880 g of crude aluminium phosphide was obtained in all. (4) Phosphine prepared by adding aluminium phosphide to water.*

(c) The preparation of THPC. During the introduction of the phosphine the experiment was conducted in a good fume-hood. The reaction temperature was kept at 10–25° (phosphine is liable to inflame spontaneously at 80°, and even at 50° it has been known to explode). Water was poured into the generators (1600 ml in each) and into the water-seal pressure releases, and the aqueous formaldehyde (2100 g of 37%)/hydrochloric acid (660 g of 35%) mixture was put into the reactor. The system was stirred and blown out with nitrogen for 10 min. The nitrogen stream was then stopped and aluminium phosphide (5 g)

---

* Recently, a safer, more convenient and more easily controlled method of obtaining phosphine has been proposed — the adding of water to a suspension of aluminium phosphide in a dry solvent [Ye. V. Kuznetsov, R. K. Valentdinov and P. M. Zavlin, *Avt. svid. (U. S. S. R. Pat.)* 125551; *Byull. Isobr. (Bulletin of Inventions)*, No. 2, (1960).]

was introduced into each generator. After about 1 hr a further amount of
phosphide (15 g) was added and this operation was repeated at hourly inter-
vals until approximately all the phosphide (880 g) had been used. The reactor
was opened 2 hr after the last addition and the solution was poured into large
evaporating basins. The volatile components were evaporated, with stirring,
at 70–75°, until crystals began to form, when the whole mass was transferred
to a desiccator where it was allowed to cool to room temperature over granu-
lar caustic soda. The whole mass crystallized completely to give tetrakis-
(hydroxymethyl)phosphonium chloride (THPC) (1135 g, 95% pure; 90%
yield, based on the formaldehyde and hydrogen chloride used), m. p. 145°,
raised to 151° on recrystallization from acetic acid. At 25° the absorption of
phosphine and its reaction with the other components took place rapidly until
about 85–90% of the starting materials had been converted into THPC. At this
point the reaction was broken off in order to avoid the possibility of escape of
unreacted phosphine at about the end of the reaction. The time of breaking
off the reaction was determined by evaporating trial solutions and weighing
the crystalline residues from them.

The THPC produced can be converted into tris(hydroxymethyl)phos-
phine oxide, by the thermal decomposition of THPC, and also by the action
of alkaline or acidic reagents on THPC [374].

DIALKYL HYDROGEN PHOSPHITES (DIALKYL PHOSPHOROUS ACIDS) HPO(OR)$_2$

The simplest method of obtaining dialkyl hydrogen phosphites involves
the reaction of a mole of phosphorus trichloride with three moles of an absolute
alcohol [88]:

$$PCl_3 + 3ROH \longrightarrow P(OR)_3 + 3HCl \longrightarrow \underset{Cl}{\overset{H}{\diagdown}} P(OR)_3 + 2HCl \longrightarrow$$

$$\longrightarrow HPO(OR)_2 + 2HCl + RCl$$

The yields of dialkyl hydrogen phosphites (particularly the lower members) can reach 90–93% when the reactions are conducted in low-boiling solvents (for example, in butane, methyl chloride, etc.) and when the hydrogen
chloride formed is carefully removed [376, 377].

Dialkyl hydrogen phosphites are colourless, transparent liquids soluble
in many organic solvents. The lower members of the class are soluble in water.
The hydrogen in these dialkyl hydrogen phosphites is very reactive, and it
can undergo a number of transformations (the replacement of the hydrogen
by chlorine, bromine, sodium; the addition of dialkyl hydrogen phosphites to
double bonds, etc.).

Dimethyl hydrogen phosphite $HPO(OCH_3)_2$ [376]

$$PCl_3 + 3CH_3OH \longrightarrow HPO(OCH_3)_2 + 2HCl + CH_3Cl$$

A solution of phosphorus trichloride (413 g) in butane (265 g) was gradually added over 2 hr to a solution of methyl alcohol (320 g) in butane (400 ml). The reaction was carried out with stirring and exterior cooling, so that the temperature of the mixture was kept at about 0°, and at the same time a liquid cooling mixture* was passed through the reflux condenser. The volatile reaction products were then evaporated and the residue was distilled *in vacuo* to give dimethyl hydrogen phosphite (300 g, 91%), b. p. 37–43°/6 mm.

The properties of dialkyl hydrogen phosphites are recorded in Table 61.

TABLE 61. SYMMETRIC AND UNSYMMETRIC, UNSUBSTITUTED, SUBSTITUTED AND RING-CONTAINING DIALKYL HYDROGEN PHOSPHITES

Formula	b. p., °C (mm)	n_D^{20}	d_4^{20}	Yield (%)	Reference
$(CH_3O)_2PHO$	53 (7)	1·4036	1·1944		[378]
$\begin{array}{c}CH_3CH-O\\ \mid \quad\quad\ \ \rangle PHO\\ CH_2-O\end{array}$	96·5–97·5 (1)	1·4705		86	[379]
$(C_2H_5O)_2PHO$	76 (14)	1·4081	1·0756		[378]
$(ClCH_2CH_2O)_2PHO$	119–120(3·5–4	1·4708	1·4025	63	[380]
$\begin{array}{c}CH_3-CH-O\\ /\quad\quad\ \ \backslash\\ CH_2 \quad\quad PHO\\ \backslash\quad\quad /\\ CH_2-O\end{array}$	150–155 (10–11); 48–50*			40	[381]
	138–140 (3); 49–50*			51·2	[382]
$\begin{array}{c}CH_3OCH_2CH-O\\ \mid\quad\quad\quad\ \rangle PHO\\ CH_2O\end{array}$	156–158 (10)	1·4719			[383]
$\begin{array}{c}(CH_3)_2CO\\ \mid\quad\quad \rangle PHO\\ (CH_3)_2CO\end{array}$	106·5–108*				[384]
$(C_3H_7O)_2PHO$	87 (6)	1·4184	1·0179		[378]
$(iso\text{-}C_3H_7O)_2PHO$	80·5 (12)	1·4090	0·9963		[378]
$[(ClCH_2)_2CHO]_2PHO$	180 (2)				[385]
$(C_4H_9O)_2PHO$	122 (9)	1·4254	0·9850		[378]
$(iso\text{-}C_4H_9O)_2PHO$	105 (9)	1·4200	0·9766		[386]
$[CH_3CH(C_2H_5)O]_2PHO$	101 (12)				[387]

* If the reflux condenser is not specially cooled, as indicated above, then, although the yield of dimethyl hydrogen phosphite reaches 93%, the amount of solvent used is significantly greater on account of evaporation.

TABLE 61 — *(contd.)*

Formula	b. p., °C (mm)	n_D^{20}	d_4^{20}	Yield %	Reference
C_2H_5O $\;\;\;\;\;$>PHO $C_6H_{13}O$	104–105 (3·5)	1·4268	0·9883[+]		[388]
$[(CH_3)_3CO]_2PHO$	70–72 (10)	1·4168 (25°)	0·975 (25°)	51	[389]
$(iso\text{-}C_5H_{11}O)_2PHO$	133 (10)				[387]
$[C_2H_5CH(CH_3)CH_2O]PHO$	142 (15)				[387]
$[(C_2H_5)_2CHO]_2PHO$	72 (0·2)				[385]
C_2H_5O $\;\;\;\;\;$>PHO $C_8H_{17}O$	125–128·5 (4·5)	1·4312	0·9779[+]		[388]

	92–93*				[390]

$(RO)_2PHO$

R					
cyclo-C_6H_{11}	149–150 (1)	1·4800	1·0982	39	[391]
C_6H_{13}—	145–146 (2)	1·4325	0·9486		[386]
iso-$C_3H_7CH_2CH(CH_3)$—	81 (0·2)				[385]
C_7H_{15}—	166–167 (2)	1·4382	0·9363		[386]
C_8H_{17}—	190–191 (3)	1·4420	0·9286		[386]
2-C_8H_{17}—	138–140 (2)	1·4375 (18°)	0·9176 (18°)		[392]
C_9H_{19}—	174·5–175·5 (0·04)	1·4458	0·9212[+]		[388]
$C_{10}H_{21}$—	190–191 (0·04)	1·4502	0·9157		[388]
$C_{16}H_{33}$—	51–52*				[388]
C_2H_5OOC—$CH(CH_3)$—	135 (0·2)				[385]
C_2H_5OOC—$CH(C_6H_5)$—		1·5200			[392]

R					
$C_6H_5CH_2$—	165 (0·1); 17*				[393]
$C_6H_5CH_2CH_2$—	183–185 (0·05)	1·5465	1·1333		[388]
$(C_6H_5)_2CH$—	105* (rapid heating, decomp. at 60°)				[393]

* Melting point.

+ d_0^{20}.

‡ >C<⬡>is cyclohexylidene.

CYCLIC ESTERS OF SOME ACIDS OF PHOSPHORUS (CYCLIC ESTERS OF PHOSPHOROUS, PYROPHOSPHOROUS, PHOSPHORAMIDOUS, PHOSPHORODITHIOUS, PHOSPHOROTRITHIOUS, PHOSPHORIC, PHOSPHOROTHIONIC, PHOSPHOROAMIDOTHIONIC AND ALKYL- AND ARYL-PHOSPHONIC ACIDS)

A general method of obtaining cyclic esters of phosphorous, phosphoric, phosphoramidic and phosphorothionic acids, first discovered by A. Ye. Arbusov and his coworkers [394], is the reaction of the cyclic acid chlorides of these acids with alcohols or phenols in the presence of an organic base [381, 383, 394–396] or with dialkylamines [397]:

$$R \underset{O}{\overset{O}{\diamondsuit}} \underset{\overset{\|}{X}}{P-Cl} + R'OH + C_5H_5N \longrightarrow R \underset{O}{\overset{O}{\diamondsuit}} \underset{\overset{|}{X}}{P-OR'} + C_5H_5N \cdot HCl$$

where R = alkylene; R' = alkyl or aryl; X = O or S (with the phosphorous acids X is absent).

A special method for the synthesis of cyclic esters of phosphorous acids is the reaction, discovered by Menshutkin, of glycols with the corresponding acid chlorides (in the presence of organic bases [381, 383, 395, 398]) or with triaryl phosphites [142]:

$$HOROH + \begin{cases} R'OPCl_2 + C_5H_5N \longrightarrow \, 'R \underset{O}{\overset{O}{\diamondsuit}} POR' + C_5H_5N \cdot HCl \\ \\ P(OAr)_3 \longrightarrow \quad R \underset{O}{\overset{O}{\diamondsuit}} POAr + 2ArOH \end{cases}$$

The cyclic esters of alkyl- and aryl-phosphonic acids are obtained by the reaction of the di-acid chlorides of these acids with glycols; sometimes, the hydrogen chloride eliminated is taken up with an organic base [272, 399–401]. They can also be prepared by the Arbusov rearrangement of cyclic esters of phosphorous acid (provided that ring scission does not take place in the reaction) [381, 383].

The properties of cyclic esters of acids of phosphorus are recorded in Tables 62–68.

TABLE 62. CYCLIC ESTERS OF PHOSPHOROUS ACID OF THE TYPE $R'OP\begin{smallmatrix}O\\\\O\end{smallmatrix}R$, WHERE R AND R' ARE ALIPHATIC RADICALS

Formula	b. p., °C (mm)	n_D^{20}	d_0^{20}	Yield (%)	Reference
CH_3OP O—CH$_2$ / O—CH$_2$	55–56 (23)	1·4460	1·2159	49	[395]
CH_3OP O—CHCH$_3$ / O—CH$_2$	67–69 (25)	1·4354+	1·1374+	50	[396]
CH_3OP O—CH—CH$_2$OCH$_3$ / O—CH$_2$	77–78 (9)	1·4459	1·1798		[383]
CH_3OP O—CH—CH$_3$ \ CH$_2$ / O—CH$_2$	62 (13)	1·4420	1·1092	60	[381]
CH_3OP O—CH$_2$—CH$_2$ / O—CH$_2$—CH$_2$	54–55 (4·5–5)	1·4642	1·1640	3	[395]
CH_3OP O—C(CH$_3$)$_2$ / O—C(CH$_3$)$_2$	91–92·5 (48)	1·4417	1·0449	51·4	[384]
C—C * O O POCH$_3$	m. p. 55–56° (not recrystal-lized)				[390]
C_2H_5OP O—CH$_2$ / O—CH$_2$	51–51·5 (15)	1·4395	1·1317	56	[395]
C_2H_5OP O—CH—CH$_3$ / O—CH$_2$	70·5 (25)	1·4330+	1·0814+	76	[396]
C_2H_5OP O—CHCH$_2$OCH$_3$ / O—CH$_2$	84–85 (10)	1·4498	1·1415		[383]
C_2H_5OP O—CH—CH$_2$OC$_2$H$_5$ / O—CH$_2$	93–94 (7)	1·4401	1·0937		[383]
C_2H_5OP O—CH—CH$_3$ / O—CH—CH$_3$	77–77·6 (25)	1·4358+	1·0592+		[396]
C_2H_5OP O—CH$_2$ \ CH$_2$ / O—CH$_2$	77 (25)	1·4498+	1·1227+	86	[396]
C_2H_5OP O—CH—CH$_3$ \ CH$_2$ / O—CH$_2$	63–64 (8)	1·4410	1·0696	76·5	[381]
C_2H_5OP O—C(CH$_3$)$_2$ / O—C(CH$_3$)$_2$	75–76 (14)	1·4392	1·0136	46·7	[384]

TABLE 62 — *(contd.)*

Formula	b. p., °C (mm)	n_D^{20}	d_0^{20}	Yield (%)	Reference
(ring)C—C(ring) *, O O, POC_2H_5	163·5—165	1·4990	1·0871≠	25	[390]
$ClCH_2CH_2OP\big\langle\substack{O—CH_2 \\ O—CH_2}$	78·5—79·5 (6·5)	1·4755	1·3206	74	[395]
$C_3H_7OP\big\langle\substack{O—CH_2 \\ O—CH_2}$	64—66 (12)	1·4445	1·1026		[402]
$C_3H_7OP\big\langle\substack{O—CHCH_3 \\ O—CH_2}$	85·6—85·8 (25)	1·4357+	1·0540+	83	[396]
iso-$C_3H_7OP\big\langle\substack{O—CH_2 \\ O—CH_2}$	53·5—54 (10—10·5)	1·4348	1·0829		[402]
iso-$C_3H_7OP\big\langle\substack{O—CH—CH_3 \\ O—CH_2}$	70·3 (25)	1·4296+	1·0380+	70·3	[396]
$C_3H_7OP\big\langle\substack{O—C(CH_3)_2 \\ O—C(CH_3)_2}$	84·5—86 (11·5)	1·4406	0·9961	44·9	[384]
(ring)C—C(ring) *, O O, POC_3H_7	177—179 (11·5)	1·4970	1·0730≑	25·6	[390]
$C_4H_9OP\big\langle\substack{O—CH_2 \\ O—CH_2}$	71—72 (8·5)	1·4470	1·0819	44·3	[395]
$C_4H_9OP\big\langle\substack{O—CHCH_3 \\ O—CH_2}$	100—100·2 (25)	1·4380+	1·0307+	79	[396]
$C_4H_9OP\big\langle\substack{O—CH—CH_2Cl \\ O—CH_2}$	108·5—110 (8)	1·4601	1·1629		[383]
$C_4H_9OP\big\langle\substack{O—CHCH_2OCH_3 \\ O—CH_2}$	107—107·5 (9)	1·4450	1·0713		[383]
$C_4H_9OP\big\langle\substack{O—C(CH_3)_2 \\ O—C(CH_3)_2}$	105—106·5 (14·5)	1·4413+	0·9780+	66·5	[384]
$C_4H_9OP\big\langle$ O—CH—CH_3, CH_2, O—CH_2	75—76 (3·5—4)	1·4472	1·0252	54·1	[381]
$C_4H_9OP\big\langle\substack{O—CH_2—CH_2 \\ O—CH_2—CH_2}$	100—102 (9—10)	1·4540	1·0557	11	[395]

TABLE 62 — (contd.)

Formula	b. p., °C (mm)	n_D^{20}	d_0^{20}	Yield (%)	Reference
iso-C_4H_9OP ⟨O—CH_2 / O—CH_2⟩	87 (25)	1·4401⁺	1·0633⁺	73	[396]
iso-C_4H_9OP ⟨O—CH—CH_3 / O—CH_2⟩	91·1–91·3 (25)	1·4353⁺	1·0269⁺	76	[396]
CH_3CHOP(—C_2H_5) ⟨O—CH_2 / O—CH_2⟩	83 (25)	1·4410⁺	1·0765⁺	72	[396]
C_2H_5CH—OP(—CH_3) ⟨O—$CHCH_3$ / O—CH_2⟩	87·9–88·3 (25)	1·4331⁺	1·0249⁺	90	[396]
$(CH_3)_3$COP ⟨O—CH_2 / O—CH_2⟩	73·8 (25)	1·4368⁺	1·0593⁺	87	[396]
$(CH_3)_3$COP ⟨O—$CHCH_3$ / O—CH_2⟩	77·9–78·6 (25)	1·4307⁺	1·0170⁺	54	[396]
⬡C—C⬡* with O O / POC₄H₉	186–188 (12·8)	1·4948	1·0665	26·5	[390]
$C_6H_{13}OP$ ⟨O—CH—CH_3 / O—CH_2⟩	109·5–111 (15)	1·4465	1·0190	19	[379]
$C_7H_{15}OP$ ⟨O—CH—CH_3 / O—CH_2⟩	130–132 (16)	1·4468	0·9974	29	[379]
$C_8H_{17}OP$ ⟨O—CH—CH_3 / O—CH_2⟩	134–135 (10)	1·4470	0·9878	43	[379]
$C_6H_5CH_2OP$ ⟨O—CH_2 / O—CH_2⟩	120–120·5 (4)	1·5335	1·2122	50	[382]
$C_6H_5CH_2OP$ ⟨O—CH_2 / CH_2 / O—CH_2⟩	147–148 (13–14)	1·5270	1·1873	53	[382]
$C_6H_5CH_2OP$ ⟨O—CH—CH_3 / CH_2 / O—CH_2⟩	121·5–122 (2–3)	1·5170	1·1432	53·3	[382]

* ⟩C⬡ is cyclohexylidene.

⁺ At 25°.

‡ d_{20}^{20}.

TABLE 63. CYCLIC ESTERS OF PHOSPHOROUS ACID OF THE TYPE

$$ArOP\underset{O}{\overset{O}{<}}\rangle R,$$ WHERE R = ALIPHATIC RADICAL AND Ar = AROMATIC RADICAL

Formula	b. p., °C (mm)	n_D^{20}	d_4^{20}	Yield (%)	Reference
$C_6H_5OP\underset{O-CH_2}{\overset{O-CH_2}{<}}$	73 (0·3)	1·5342		46	[142]
$C_6H_5OP\underset{O-CH_2}{\overset{O-CHCH_3}{<}}$	121–121·5 (11)	1·5201	1·1820	52	[379]
$C_6H_5OP\underset{O-CH_2}{\overset{O-CHCH_2OCH_3}{<}}$	145·5–146 (7)	1·4768	1·2130		[383]
$C_6H_5OP\underset{O-CH_2}{\overset{O-CH_2}{<}}CH_2$	88 (0·9); 44–46+	1·5337		27	[142]
$C_6H_5OP\underset{O-CH_2-CH_2}{\overset{O-CH_2-CH_2}{<}}$	94 (0·3)	1·5361 (22°)		20	[142]
$C_6H_5OP\underset{O-CH_2-CH_2}{\overset{O-CH_2-CH_2}{<}}CH_2$	99 (0·0015)	1·5237 (17°)		13	[142]
$C_6H_5OP\underset{O-CH_2-CH_2}{\overset{O-CH=CH}{<}}CH_2(cis)$	68 (0·007)	1·5240		49	[142]
$C_6H_5OP\underset{O-CH_2-CH_2-CH_2}{\overset{O-CH=CH-CH_2(cis)}{<}}$	97 (0·04); 43–45+			37	[142]
$C_6H_5OP\underset{O-CH_2-CH_2-CH_2}{\overset{O-CH=CH-CH_2 (trans)}{<}}$	84 (0·0045)	1·5330 (37°)		29	[142]

* Yields based on unpurified products.
+ Melting point.

TABLE 64. CYCLIC ESTERS OF PYROPHOSPHORIC ACID (403)

Formula	b. p., °C (mm)	n_D^{20}	d_4^{20}	Yield (%)
$\left(\underset{CH_2O}{\overset{CH_2O}{|}}\right\rangle P-\right)_2 O$	100–101 (4)	1·4900	1·4293	40
$(C_2H_5O)_2POP\underset{O-CH_2}{\overset{O-CH_2}{<}}$	84–85 (2)	1·4557	1·1890	60
$(C_3H_7O)_2POP\underset{O-CH_2}{\overset{O-CH_2}{<}}$	93–94 (2)	1·4600	1·1446	51

TABLE 64. — *(contd.)*

Formula	b. p., °C (mm)	n_D^{20}	d_4^{20}	Yield (%)
$(\text{iso-}C_3H_7O)_2POP\langle\begin{smallmatrix}O-CH_2\\ \,\,\,\,\,\,\,\,\,\,\,\,\,\,\mid\\ O-CH_2\end{smallmatrix}$	90–91 (2)	1·4515	1·1392	47·4
$(C_4H_9O)_2POP\langle\begin{smallmatrix}O-CH_2\\ \,\,\,\,\,\,\,\,\,\,\,\,\,\,\mid\\ O-CH_2\end{smallmatrix}$	104–105 (1)	1·4626	1·136	10·2
$(C_2H_5O)_2POP\langle\begin{smallmatrix}O-CH-CH_3\\ \,\,\,\,\,\,\,\,\,\,\,\,\,\,\mid\\ O-CH_2\end{smallmatrix}$	73–74 (3)	1·4520	1·1493	68·1
$(C_3H_7O)_2POP\langle\begin{smallmatrix}O-CH-CH_3\\ \,\,\,\,\,\,\,\,\,\,\,\,\,\,\mid\\ O-CH_2\end{smallmatrix}$	110 (2)	1·4530	1·1090	38·46
$(\text{iso-}C_3H_7O)_2POP\langle\begin{smallmatrix}O-CH-CH_3\\ \,\,\,\,\,\,\,\,\,\,\,\,\,\,\mid\\ O-CH_2\end{smallmatrix}$	86–88 (3)	1·4530	1·1070	24·5
$(C_4H_9O)_2POP\langle\begin{smallmatrix}O-CH-CH_3\\ \,\,\,\,\,\,\,\,\,\,\,\,\,\,\mid\\ O-CH_2\end{smallmatrix}$	120–121 (3)	1·4550	1·080	19·6
$(C_2H_5O)_2POP\langle\begin{smallmatrix}O-CH-CH_2Cl\\ \,\,\,\,\,\,\,\,\,\,\,\,\,\,\mid\\ O-CH_2\end{smallmatrix}$	110 (1—2)	1·4660	1.2470	15
$(C_3H_7O)_2POP\langle\begin{smallmatrix}O-CH-CH_2Cl\\ \,\,\,\,\,\,\,\,\,\,\,\,\,\,\mid\\ O-CH_2\end{smallmatrix}$	125–129 (1–2)	1·4690	1·1990	20
$(C_4H_9O)_2POP\langle\begin{smallmatrix}O-CH-CH_2Cl\\ \,\,\,\,\,\,\,\,\,\,\,\,\,\,\mid\\ O-CH_2\end{smallmatrix}$	147–150 (3)	1·473	1·1986	23
$(C_2H_5O)_2POP\langle\begin{smallmatrix}O-CH-CH_3\\ \,\,\,\,\,\,\,\,\,\,\,\,CH_2\\ O-CH_2\end{smallmatrix}$	113–113·5 (5)	1·4563	1·1368	53·3
$(C_3H_7O)_2POP\langle\begin{smallmatrix}O-CH-CH_3\\ \,\,\,\,\,\,\,\,\,\,\,\,CH_2\\ O-CH_2\end{smallmatrix}$	110–111 (4)	1·4580	1·1001	56·4
$(\text{iso-}C_3H_7O)_2POP\langle\begin{smallmatrix}O-CH-CH_3\\ \,\,\,\,\,\,\,\,\,\,\,\,CH_2\\ O-CH_2\end{smallmatrix}$	98–102 (2)	1·4460	1·0645	32·7
$(C_4H_9O)_2POP\langle\begin{smallmatrix}O-CH-CH_3\\ \,\,\,\,\,\,\,\,\,\,\,\,CH_2\\ O-CH_2\end{smallmatrix}$	152–156 (7)	1·4580	1·0663	40·1
$\left(\begin{smallmatrix}CH_3-CHO\\ \,\,\,\,\,\,\,\,\,\,\,\,\mid\\ CH_2O\end{smallmatrix}\!\!>\!P-\right)_2 O$	82–83 (2–3)	1·4625	1·2772	44·5
$\left(\begin{smallmatrix}ClCH_2-CHO\\ \,\,\,\,\,\,\,\,\,\,\,\,\,\,\,\,\mid\\ CH_2O\end{smallmatrix}\!\!>\!P-\right)_2 O$	144–145 (3)	1·5130	1·5126	44
$\left(\begin{smallmatrix}CH_3-CHO\\ \,\,\,\,\,\,\,\,\,\,\,\,\mid\\ CH_2\\ \,\,\,\,\,\,\,\,\,\,\,\,\mid\\ CH_2O\end{smallmatrix}\!\!>\!P-\right)_2 O$	118–120 (2)	1·4745	1·2329	34·8

TABLE 65. CYCLIC ESTERS OF PHOSPHORAMIDOUS, PHOSPHORODITHIOUS AND PHOSPHOROTRITHIOUS ACIDS

Formula	b. p., °C (mm)	n_D^{20}	d_0^{20}	Yield (%)	Reference
$(CH_3)_2NP\big\langle\genfrac{}{}{0pt}{}{OCH_2}{OCH_2}$	61–62 (11)	1·4730	1·1285	73	[397]
$(C_2H_5)_2NP\big\langle\genfrac{}{}{0pt}{}{OCH_2}{OCH_2}$	66–67 (3·5)	1·4680	1·0639	65·9	[397]
$C_5H_{10}NP\big\langle\genfrac{}{}{0pt}{}{O—CH_2}{O—CH_2}$	89–90 (2·5–3)	1·5040	1·1454	68·5	[397]
$(C_2H_5)_2NP\big\langle\genfrac{}{}{0pt}{}{O—CH_2}{O—CH_2}\big\rangle CH_2$	102 (25)	1·4679 (25°)	1·0302 (25°)	86	[396]
$C_5H_{10}NP\big\langle\genfrac{}{}{0pt}{}{O—CH_2}{O—CH_2}\big\rangle CH_2$	96–97 (4)	1·5020	1·1173	65	[397]
$(C_2H_5)_2NP\big\langle\genfrac{}{}{0pt}{}{O—CH—CH_3}{O—CH—CH_3}$	110 (25)	1·4595 (25°)	1·0024 (25°)	89	[396]
$(CH_3)_2NP\big\langle\genfrac{}{}{0pt}{}{O—CH—CH_3}{O—CH_2}\big\rangle CH_2$	71 (13·5)	1·4650	1·0423	57·8	[397]
$(C_2H_5)_2NP\big\langle\genfrac{}{}{0pt}{}{O—CH—CH_3}{O—CH_2}\big\rangle CH_2$	69–70 (2)	1·4620	1·0050	55·3	[397]
$C_5H_{10}NP\big\langle\genfrac{}{}{0pt}{}{O—CH—CH_3}{O—CH_2}\big\rangle CH_2$	95–96 (3)	1·4930	1·0741	59·5	[397]
$C_6H_5NHP\big\langle\genfrac{}{}{0pt}{}{O—CH—CH_3}{O—CH_2}\big\rangle CH_2$	136–137 (2)	1·5558	1·1748	22·8	[397]
$\genfrac{}{}{0pt}{}{C_6H_5}{CH_3}NP\big\langle\genfrac{}{}{0pt}{}{O—CH—CH_3}{O—CH_2}\big\rangle CH_2$	133–134 (3)	1·5442	1·1382	22·6	[397]
$CH_3PO\big\langle\genfrac{}{}{0pt}{}{S—CH_2}{S—CH_2}$	97–98 (7·5)	1·6200	1·3426	59	[404]
$C_2H_5OP\big\langle\genfrac{}{}{0pt}{}{S—CH_2}{S—CH_2}$	95–98 (5)	1·5922	1·2629	57·3	[404]
$\Big[—CH_2SP\big\langle\genfrac{}{}{0pt}{}{S—CH_2}{S—CH_2}\Big]_2$	m. p. 130°				[404]

TABLE 66. CYCLIC ESTERS OF PHOSPHORIC ACID

Formula	b. p., °C (mm)	n_D^{20}	d_4^{20}	Yield (%)	Reference
CH_3OP O—CH—CH$_3$ / O—CH$_2$ ‖ O	114–118 (5)	1·4250	1·2734	33	[405]
C_2H_5OP O—CH—CH$_3$ / O—CH$_2$ ‖ O	105–108 (3)	1·4265	1·2095	34	[405]
C_3H_7OP O—CH—CH$_3$ / O—CH$_2$ ‖ O	116–118 (3)	1·4290	1·1623	34	[405]
C_4H_9OP O—CH—CH$_3$ / O—CH$_2$ ‖ O	127–130 (3)	1·4312	1·1211	32·2	[405]
iso-C_4H_9OP O—CH—CH$_3$ / O—CH$_2$ ‖ O	122–124 (3)	1·4310	1·1331	32·2	[405]
C_6H_5OP O—CH$_2$ / CH$_2$ / O—CH / CH$_3$ ‖ O		1·5163*	1·2507*		[405]
C_6H_5OP O—CH$_2$ / CH—C$_2$H$_5$ / O—CH / C$_3$H$_7$ ‖ O		1·5017*	1·1539*		[406]
4-ClC_6H_4OP O—CH$_2$ / CH$_2$ / O—CH / CH$_3$ ‖ O		1·5228*	1·3295*		[406]
$CH_3C_6H_4OP$ O—CH$_2$ / CHC$_2$H$_5$ / O—CH / C$_3$H$_7$ ‖ O		1·5019*	1·1298*		[406]
2-$C_{10}H_7OP$ O—CH$_2$ / CHC$_2$H$_5$ / O—CH / C$_3$H$_7$ ‖ O		1·5543*	1·1814*		[406]

* At 25°.

TABLE 67. CYCLIC ESTERS OF PHOSPHOROTHIONIC AND PHOSPHOROAMIDOTHIONIC ACIDS

Formula	b. p., °C (mm)	n_D^{20}	d_4^{20}	Yield (%)	Reference
$CH_3OP\begin{smallmatrix}O-CH-CH_3\\ \|\\ O-CH_2\end{smallmatrix}$ ‖S	121–123 (11)	1·4828	1·2639	41·8	[405]
$CH_3OP\begin{smallmatrix}O-CH-CH_2-OCH_3\\ \|\\ O-CH_2\end{smallmatrix}$ ‖S	111–112·5 (1·5)	1·4889	1·2877		[383]
$C_2H_5OP\begin{smallmatrix}O-CH_2\\ \|\\ O-CH_2\end{smallmatrix}$ ‖S	98–99 (3)	1·4849 (21°)	1·2737 (21°)	60	[407]
$C_2H_5OP\begin{smallmatrix}O-CH-CH_3\\ \|\\ O-CH_2\end{smallmatrix}$ ‖S	107–108 (6)	1·4770	1·2086	55	[405]
$C_2H_5OP\begin{smallmatrix}O-CH-CH_2-OCH_3\\ \|\\ O-CH_2\end{smallmatrix}$ ‖S	121·5–122 (2)	1·4790	1·2359		[383]
$C_3H_7OP\begin{smallmatrix}O-CH-CH_3\\ \|\\ O-CH_2\end{smallmatrix}$ ‖S	110–112 (5)	1·4741	1·1696	· 61	[405]
iso-$C_3H_7OP\begin{smallmatrix}O-CH-CH_3\\ \|\\ O-CH_2\end{smallmatrix}$ ‖S	104–106 (3)	1·4750	1·1734	38	[405]
$C_4H_9OP\begin{smallmatrix}O-CH-CH_3\\ \|\\ O-CH_2\end{smallmatrix}$ ‖S	114–116 (3)	1·4730	1·1435	52·4	[405]
o-$C_4H_9OP\begin{smallmatrix}O-CH-CH_3\\ \|\\ O-CH_2\end{smallmatrix}$ ‖S	112–115 (3)	1·4720	1·1386	38	[407]
$C_6H_{13}OP\begin{smallmatrix}O-CH-CH_3\\ \|\\ O-CH_2\end{smallmatrix}$ ‖S	118·5–119 (0·15)	1·4725	1·0891		[379]
C—C, O O, S = POCH₃	115·5–116·2⁺			72·7	[390]
C—C*, O O, S = POC₂H₅	65–66⁺				[390]

TABLE 67 — (contd.)

Formula	b. p., °C (mm)	n_D^{20}	d_4^{20}	Yield (%)	Reference
[cyclohexylidene C—C cyclohexylidene, O O, S = POC$_3$H$_7$] *	50–52+				[390]
$(C_2H_5)_2NP\begin{smallmatrix}O-CH_2\\ \| \\ O-CH_2\\ S\end{smallmatrix}$	133–134·5 (3)	1·5050	1·1825		[397]

* $\rangle C\langle$ is cyclohexylidene

melting point

TABLE 68. CYCLIC ESTERS OF ALKYL- AND ARYL-PHOSPHONIC ACIDS

Formula	b. p., °C (mm)	n_D^{20}	d_4^{20}	Yield (%)	Reference
$CH_3P\begin{smallmatrix}O-CH_2\\ \| \\ O-CH_2\\ O\end{smallmatrix}$	104–105 (3)	1·4470	1·3219	30	[401]
$CH_3P\begin{smallmatrix}O-(CH_2)_2\\ \\ O-(CH_2)_2\\ O\end{smallmatrix}O$	105–107 (3) (with decomposition)	1·4644	1·3250	13·9	[401]
$CH_3P\begin{smallmatrix}O-CH-CH_3\\ \| \\ O-CH_2\\ O\end{smallmatrix}$	137 (10)	1·4431	1·2381		[408]
$CH_3P\begin{smallmatrix}O-CH_2\\ \| \\ O-CH_2\\ O\end{smallmatrix}CH_3$	110–112 (3); 98–99*			60·5	[401]
$CH_3P\begin{smallmatrix}O-CH_2\quad CH_2\\ O-CH-\|\\ -CH_2\\ O\end{smallmatrix}$	97–99 (3); 67·5–69*	1·4623 On supercooled substance	1·226	42·4	[401]
$CH_3P\begin{smallmatrix}O-CH_2\\ \| \\ O-CH\\ O\quad CH_3\end{smallmatrix}CH_2$	71 (0·25); 40*			69·7	[272]
$CH_3P\begin{smallmatrix}O-CH-CH_3\\ \| \\ O-CH-CH_3\\ O\end{smallmatrix}$	93 (0·35); 43–45*			75·5	[399]
$CH_3P\begin{smallmatrix}O-CH_2-CH_2\\ \| \\ O-CH_2-CH_2\\ O\end{smallmatrix}CH_2$	118–120 (4) (with decomposition)	1·4652	1·1519	3–5	[401]
$CH_3P\begin{smallmatrix}CH_3\\ O-CH\\ \| \\ O-CH\\ O\quad CH_3\end{smallmatrix}CH_2$	99 (0·85)			87	[272]

TABLE 68 — (contd.)

Formula	b. p., °C (mm)	n_D^{20}	d_4^{20}	Yield (%)	Reference
CH_3P with $O-CH(CH_3)-CH_2$ and $O-CH(CH_3)-CH_2$, =O	73–76 (0·2)	1·4525 (25°)	1·105 (25°)	64·6	[399]
$ClCH_2P$ with $O-CH_2-CH_2$ and $O-CH_2-CH_2$, =O	118–119 (3) 67–68*			42	[401]
C_2H_5P with $O-CH-CH_3$ and $O-CH_2$, =O	143·5–144·5 (12)	1·4444	1·1941		[408]
C_2H_5P with $O-CH-OCH_3$ and $O-CH_2$, =O	140–141 (3)				[383]
CH_3COP with $O-CH(CH_3)-CH_2$ and $C-CH_3$, =O	142–143 (3·5–4)	1·4555	1·2574	47·3	[381]
C_4H_9P with $O-CH-CH_3$ and $O-CH_2$, =O	121·5–123 (0·22)	1·4482	1·1300		[408]
C_4H_9P with $O-CH_2-CH_2$ and $O-CH_2-CH_2$, =O	120–122 (5)	1·4627	1·1073	28·9	[401]
$C_6H_5CH_2P$ with $O-CH_2$ and $O-CH_2$, =O	123*			45·3	[382]
$C_6H_5CH_2P$ with $O-CH-CH_3$ and $O-CH_2$, =O	122–122·5*				[408]
$C_6H_5CH_2P$ with $O-CH-CH_2Cl$ and $O-CH_2$, =O	94–95*				[383]
$C_6H_5CH_2P$ with $O-CH-CH_2OCH_3$ and $O-CH_2$, =O	88–89*				[383]
$C_6H_5CH_2P$ with $O-CH-CH_2OC_2H_5$ and $O-CH_2$, =O	198–199 (2)				[383]
$C_6H_5CH_2P$ with $O-CH_2$ and $O-CH_2$ bridged by CH_2, =O	138*			30·3	[382]

TABLE 68 — *(contd.)*

Formula	b. p., °C (mm)	n_D^{20}	d_4^{20}	Yield (%)	Reference
$C_6H_5CH_2P$ $\begin{smallmatrix} O-CH-CH_3 \\ \\ O-CH_2 \end{smallmatrix}$ CH_2 $\parallel O$	120–121*			21	[381]
$C_6H_5CH_2P$ $\begin{smallmatrix} O-C(CH_3)_2 \\ \\ O-C(CH_3)_2 \end{smallmatrix}$ $\parallel O$	115–116·3*			90	[384]
C_6H_5COP $\begin{smallmatrix} O-C(CH_3)_2 \\ \\ O-C(CH_3)_2 \end{smallmatrix}$ CH_2 $\parallel O$	90–91*				[384]
$(C_6H_5)_3CP$ $\begin{smallmatrix} O-CH_2 \\ \\ O-CH_2 \end{smallmatrix}$ $\parallel O$	203–204*			27	[382]
$(C_6H_5)_3CP$ $\begin{smallmatrix} O-CH_2 \\ \\ O-CH_2 \end{smallmatrix}$ CH_2 $\parallel O$	228–229*			37	[382]
$(C_6H_5)_3CP$ $\begin{smallmatrix} O-CH-CH_3 \\ \\ O-CH_2 \end{smallmatrix}$ CH_2 $\parallel O$	192–193*				[381]
$(C_6H_5)_3CP$ $\begin{smallmatrix} O-C(CH_3)_2 \\ \\ O-C(CH_3)_2 \end{smallmatrix}$ $\parallel O$	231–231·5*				[384]
C_6H_5P $\begin{smallmatrix} O-CH_2 \\ \\ O-CH_2 \end{smallmatrix}$ $\parallel O$	119–122 (3); 58–59*			18·4	[401]
C_6H_5P $\begin{smallmatrix} O-CH_2 \\ \\ O-CH_2 \end{smallmatrix}$ CH_2 $\parallel O$	212–214 (7·5)			67	[409]
C_6H_5P $\begin{smallmatrix} O-CH_2-CH_2 \\ \\ O-CH_2-CH_2 \end{smallmatrix}$ $\parallel O$	125–127 (3) (with decomposition) 76–77·5°				[401]
C_6H_5P $\begin{smallmatrix} O-CH-CH_3 \\ \\ O-CH-CH_3 \end{smallmatrix}$ $\parallel O$	210–215 (15)			78·6	[409]

* Melting point.

SATURATED DI-ESTERS OF ALKYL- AND ARYL-PHOSPHONIC ACIDS RPO(OR')₂

Many (although not all) syntheses of unsaturated esters of phosphonic acids (cf. pp. 65–67, 73) can be applied to the synthesis of the analogous saturated compounds of general formula $RPO(OR')_2$, where R and R' are saturated alkyl or aryl radicals. The sole difference lies in that saturated starting materials are used: acid chlorides of phosphonic acids, alcohols, alkyl halides, etc. Although the methods of synthesis of this class of compound are of interest, as are the compounds themselves for the preparation of organophosphorus polymers, we will not discuss these syntheses since there has already been a detailed description of them in Kosolapoff's monograph [2].

AMIDES OF ACIDS OF PHOSPHORUS (DI- AND TRI-AMIDES, AND MONO-, DI- AND TRI-ETHYLENIMIDES OF PHOSPHOROUS, PHOSPHORIC, PHOSPHORAMIDIC, PHOSPHOROTHIONIC, PHOSPHORAMIDOTHIONIC, AND ALKYL- AND ARYL-PHOSPHONIC ACIDS)

As starting materials for the preparation of high molecular weight phosphorus-containing compounds, there is some interest in the numerous unsubstituted or monosubstituted (on the nitrogen atoms) di- and tri-amides of acids of phosphorus of general formula:

$$R-P\overset{\nearrow NHR'}{\underset{\parallel \ \searrow NHR''}{_X}} \quad \text{or} \quad X = P\overset{\nearrow NHR}{\underset{\searrow NHR''}{-NHR'}},$$

where X = O or S; and also in the compounds which contain from one to three ethylenimine rings, such as:

$$\overset{R\searrow}{\underset{R'\diagup \ _X}{P-N}}\overset{\diagup CH_2}{\underset{\diagdown CH_2}{\big|}}, \quad R-P-\left[N\overset{\diagup CH_2}{\underset{\diagdown CH_2}{\big|}}\right]_2 \quad \text{and} \quad X=\left[P-N\overset{\diagup CH_2}{\underset{\diagdown CH_2}{\big|}}\right]_3,$$

where X = O or S.

The methods of synthesis of such compounds and their properties were described earlier (see p. 24) in the examples of amides of unsaturated phosphonic acids.

Esters of acids of phosphorus, containing unsubstituted amino-groups, were obtained by Sokolovskii and Zavlin [410] by the reaction of the corresponding acid chlorides with alkanolamines: for example:

$$CH_3POCl_2 + 2HOCH_2CH_2NH_2 \longrightarrow CH_3PO(OCH_2CH_2NH_2 \cdot HCl)_2 \xrightarrow{2C_2H_5ONa}$$

$$\longrightarrow CH_3PO(OCH_2CH_2NH_2)_2 + 2NaCl + 2C_2H_5OH$$

The ethylenimide of dipropyl phosphoric acid $(C_3H_7O)_2P-N\overset{CH_2}{\underset{CH_2}{<}}$ [411]

$$(C_3H_7O)_2POCl + \underset{CH_2}{\overset{CH_2}{|}}\!\!>\!NH + N(C_2H_5)_3 \longrightarrow$$

$$\longrightarrow (C_3H_7O)_2PO\left[N\overset{CH_2}{\underset{CH_2}{<}}\right] + N(C_2H_5)_3 \cdot HCl$$

A solution of dipropyl phosphorochloridate $(31 \cdot 4$ g, $0 \cdot 157$ mole) in dry benzene (50 ml) was added dropwise to a solution of ethylenimine $(6 \cdot 75$ g, $0 \cdot 157$ mole) and triethylamine $(15 \cdot 8$ g, $0 \cdot 157$ mole) in dry benzene over 40 min at a temperature of from $-5°$ to $+5°$. After this the mixture was stirred for $1 \cdot 5$–2 hr at room temperature and then at 40–50° for 1 hr. After cooling to room temperature, the triethylamine hydrochloride was filtered off, twice washed with dry benzene, dried and weighed. Twenty grams of material (94%) were obtained. The benzene filtrate and washings were combined and distilled *in vacuo* to give, after two distillations, the pure ethylenimide of dipropyl phosphoric acid (25 g, 76%), b. p. 127–128°/10 mm, n_D^{20} $1 \cdot 4382$, d_4^{20} $1 \cdot 0584$.

The properties of di- and tri-amides, and mono-, di- and tri-ethylenimides of acids of phosphorus are recorded in Tables 69–78.

TABLE 69. DIAMIDES OF PHOSPHORIC ACID OF THE TYPE

$$ROP \begin{matrix} NHR' \\ \\ NHR'' \end{matrix}$$
$$\underset{O}{\|}$$

Formula	m. p., °C	Reference
$C_2H_5OPO(NH_2)_2$*	110	[412]
$C_6H_5OPO(NH_2)_2$+	185	[412]
4-tert.$C_5H_{11}C_6H_4OPO(NH_2)_2$	160	[413]
2-$C_6H_5C_6H_4OPO(NH_2)_2$	151	[413]
$C_2H_5OP\underset{\underset{O}{\|}}{<}\begin{matrix}NH_2\\NHC_6H_5\end{matrix}$	127	[413]
$C_2H_5OP\underset{\underset{O}{\|}}{<}\begin{matrix}NH_2\\NHC_6H_4CH_3\text{-}4\end{matrix}$	125	[413]
$C_6H_5OPO(NHCH_3)_2$	103–105	[414]
$C_2H_5OPO(NHC_3H_7)_2$	108	[414]
$C_2H_5OPO(NHC_4H_9\text{-iso})_2$	123	[414]
$C_6H_5OPO(NHC_6H_{11}\text{-cyclo})_2$	124–125	[415]
$C_6H_5OPO(NHCH_2C_6H_5)_2$	114	[414]
$C_2H_5OPO(NHC_6H_5)_2$	114	[414]
$[CH_2OPO(NHC_6H_5)_2]_2$	180	[415]
$C_6H_5OPO(NHC_6H_5)_2$	179–180	[414]
4-$ClC_6H_4OPO(NHC_6H_5)_2$	167–168	[414]
2-$C_6H_5OOCC_6H_4OPO(NHC_6H_5)_2$	174–175	[414]
4-$NO_2C_6H_4COOCH_2CHOHCH_2OPO(NHC_6H_5)_2$	220	[414]
2-$C_6H_4O_2[PO(NHC_6H_5)_2]_2$	192	[414]
$C_6H_5OPO(NHC_6H_3Cl_2\text{-}2,4)_2$	227	[414]
$CH_3OPO(NHC_6H_4OOCCH_3\text{-}2)_2$	174	[415]
$C_2H_5OP\underset{\underset{O}{\|}}{<}\begin{matrix}NHC_6H_5\\NHC_6H_4CH_3\text{-}4\end{matrix}$	116–117	[415]
$C_6H_5OP\underset{\underset{O}{\|}}{<}\begin{matrix}NHC_6H_5\\NHC_6H_4CH_3\text{-}4\end{matrix}$	136–137	[415]
$C_2H_5OPO(NHC_6H_4CH_3\text{-}2)_2$	115	[414]
$C_2H_5OPO(NHC_6H_4CH_3\text{-}4)_2$	108	[415]
$C_6H_5OPO(NHC_6H_4CH_3\text{-}2)_2$	157·5	[415]
$C_6H_5OPO(NHC_6H_4CH_3\text{-}4)_2$	147–148	[415]
2-$C_6H_5OOCC_6H_4OPO(NHC_6H_4CH_3\text{-}2)_2$	146	[415]
$C_6H_5OPO[NHC_6H_3(Br)CH_3\text{-}2,4]_2$	221	[415]

* Yield 93%.
+ Yield 96%.

9*

TABLE 70. ETHYLENIMIDES OF PHOSPHOROUS AND PHOSPHORIC ACIDS OF THE TYPE $(RO)_2PN\!\!<^{CH_2}_{CH_2}$, $(RO)_2P(O)N\!\!<^{CH_2}_{CH_2}$ AND $ROPO\left(N\!\!<^{CH_2}_{CH_2}\right)_2$

Formula	b. p., °C (mm)	n_D^{20}	d_4^{20}	Yield (%)	Reference
$(C_2H_5O)_2PN\!\!<^{CH_2}_{CH_2}$	57·5–58·5 (10)	1·4458	1·0070	63·5	[411]
$(RO)_2P(O)N\!\!<^{CH_2}_{CH_2}$					
R					
CH_3—	99·5–100 (10)	1·4375	1·2212	73·5	[411]
C_2H_5—	108·5 (9·5)	1·4362	1·1148	82	[411]
C_3H_7—	127–128 (10)	1·4382	1·0584	76	[411]
iso-C_3H_7—	112–113 (12)	1·4310	1·0439	74	[411]
C_4H_9—	146–147 (11)	1·4407	1·0260	87·5	[411]
iso-C_4H_9—	135·5–136 (10·5)	1·4367	1·0174	83	[411]
iso-C_5H_{11}—	155·5–156·5 (10·5)	1·4415	1·0004	81	[411]
$ROPO\left[N\!\!<^{CH_2}_{CH_2}\right]_2$					
R					
C_2H_5—	95–97 (1·3–1·4)			85	[416]
$ClCH_2CH_2$—	106–107 (0·8)			95	[416]
C_4H_9—	116–118 (1–1·2)			97	[416]
C_8H_{17}—	117–118 (0·2–0·24)				[417]
C_6H_5—	Undistillable oil			95	[416]
$(CH_3)_2C_6H_3$—	Undistillable oil			98	[416]
2-$C_{10}H_7$—	m. p. 69–70°			92–93	[416]

TABLE 71. PHOSPHORIC TRIAMIDES OF THE TYPE

$$\begin{array}{c} R \\ \\ R' \end{array} NP \begin{array}{c} NHR'' \\ \| \\ O \end{array} NHR'''$$

Formula	m. p., °C	Yield (%)	Reference
$(CH_3)_2NPO(NH_2)_2$	119	95	[412]
$(C_2H_5)_2NPO(NH_2)_2$	81	86	[412]
$C_4H_9NHPO(NH_2)_2$	110 (not sharp)	79	[412]
$RPO(NHC_6H_5)_2$			
R			
$(CH_3)_2N-$	196		[418]
C_2H_5NH-	147		[419]
$CHCl_2CONH-$	219–220		[419]
CCl_3CONH-	194–195		[419]
C_3H_7NH-	146		[419]
$(C_2H_5)_2N-$	150		[418]
iso-C_4H_9NH-	207		[419]
iso-$C_5H_{11}NH-$	117		[418]
$(C_3H_7)_2N-$	220		[418]
(iso-$C_4H_9)_2N-$	202		[418]
2,4-$Br_2C_6H_3NH-$	228		[419]
3-$NO_2-C_6H_4NH-$	177		[419]
4-$NO_2-C_6H_4NH-$	242		[419]
$\begin{array}{c} CH_3 \\ \\ C_6H_5 \end{array} N-$	192		[418]
2-$CH_3C_6H_4NH-$	175		[419]
4-$CH_3C_6H_4NH-$	168		[419]
$(C_6H_5)_2N-$	232		[418]

TABLE 72. DIETHYLENIMIDES OF PHOSPHORAMIDIC ACIDS

OF THE TYPE $\dfrac{R}{R'}{>}NPO\left(N{<}\dfrac{CH_2}{CH_2}\right)_2$. THE TRIETHYLENIMIDE

OF PHOSPHORIC ACID $PO\left(N{<}\dfrac{CH_2}{CH_2}\right)_3$ AND ITS DERIVATIVES

Formula	m. p., °C	Yield (%)	Reference
$RPO\left[N{<}\dfrac{CH_2}{CH_2}\right]_2$			
R			
$\dfrac{CH_2}{CH_2}{>}N-$	90–91 (0·3)*; 51·5	90–91	[420]
$(C_2H_5)_2N-$	98–100 (1)*	92	[420]
$CH_2{<}\dfrac{CH_2-CH_2}{CH_2-CH_2}{>}N-^+$	103–104 (0·4–0·5)*; 41–42	93–94	[421] [416]
$(C_4H_9)_2N-$	78–79		[422]
$(C_8H_{17})_2N-$	168 (0·3)*		[422]
C_6H_5NH-	141–143	78·2	[423]
$4\text{-}ClC_6H_4NH-$	171–172	65·3	[423]
$2,4\text{-}Cl_2C_6H_3NH-$	156–158	66·6	[423]
$2,4,6\text{-}Cl_3C_6H_2NH-$	161–163	65	[423]
$4\text{-}NO_2C_6H_4NH-$	168–170	72·3	[423]
$4\text{-}CH_3C_6H_4NH-$	132–134	95·4	[423]
$\dfrac{CH_3}{C_6H_5}{>}N-$	83·5–84		[416]
$\dfrac{C_2H_5}{C_6H_5}{>}N-$	86–87	85	[416]
$OP\left[N{<}\dfrac{CH_2}{CH-CH_3}\right]_3$	90–92 (0·15–0·3)*		[424]

* Boiling point, °C (mm).
+ n_D^{20} 1·5020.

TABLE 73. PHOSPHORIC TRIAMIDES OF THE TYPE $PO(NHR)_3$

R	m. p., °C	Yield (%)	Reference
H—	Decomposes at 150° with the evolution of ammonia (in high vacuum decomposition begins at 80°)	80 94	[425] [412]
—C_3H_7	Oil		[415]
—iso-C_4H_9	46–47		[415]
—iso-C_5H_{11}	uncrystallizable liquid		[415]
—cyclo-C_6H_{11}	245–246 (decomposes)	72	[426]
—$C_{12}H_{25}$	75		[415]
—$CH_2C_6H_5$	98–99 (decomposes); 250	42·2	[426]
—C_6H_5	211–214 (slightly decomp.)	82	[426]
—C_6H_4Cl-4	248–250		[427]
—C_6H_3Cl-4-NO_2-2(or-3)	249		[427]
—$C_6H_3Br_2$-2,4(?)	252–253		[427]
—$C_6H_4OC_2H_5$-4	172–173 (decomposes)	55·6	[426]
—$C_6H_3NO_2(OC_6H_5)$-2,4	126		[427]
—$C_6H_4CH_3$-2	229–230 (decomposes)	55	[426]
—$C_6H_4CH_3$-4	198–199 (slightly decomposed)	87·5	
	250		[426]
—$C_6H_3(Br)CH_3$-2*	253		[427]
—$C_6H_3(Br)CH_3$-2,4	268		[427]
—$C_6H_3(Br)CH_3$-4*	221; 222		[427]
—$C_6H_3(NO_2)CH_3$-4*	247		[427]
—$C_6H_3(CH_3)_2$-2,4	255; 198		[427]
—$C_6H_3(CH_3)_2$-2,5	247		[427]
—$C_6H_3(CH_3)_2$-3,4	183		[427]
—$C_6H_2(CH_3)$ 2,4,5	217		[427]
—$C_{10}H_7$-1	216		[427]
—$C_{10}H_7$-2	170		[427]

* The position of the bromo- and nitro-groups is not known.

TABLE 74. DIAMIDES OF PHOSPHOROTHIONIC ACIDS OF THE TYPE

$$ROP\overset{\displaystyle \nearrow NHR'}{\underset{\displaystyle \parallel \quad \searrow NHR''}{S}}$$

Formula	m. p., C°	n_D^{35}	d	Reference
$C_6H_5OPS(NH_2)_2$	119			[413]
$4\text{-}CH_3C_6H_4OPS(NH_2)_2$	84			[413]
$2\text{-}C_{10}H_7OPS(NH_2)_2$	176			[413]
$2,4,5\text{-}Cl_3C_6H_2OP\overset{\nearrow NH_2}{\underset{\parallel \searrow NHC_2H_5}{S}}$	87–93			[428]
$4\text{-}NO_2C_6H_4OP\overset{\nearrow NH_2}{\underset{\parallel \searrow NHC_2H_5}{S}}$		1·5039	1·15 (24°)	[429]
$2,4,5\text{-}Cl_3C_6H_2OP\overset{\nearrow NH_2}{\underset{\parallel \searrow NHC_3H_7\text{-iso}}{S}}$	60–73			[428]
$2,4,5\text{-}Cl_3C_6H_2OP\overset{\nearrow NHCH_3}{\underset{\parallel \searrow NHC_2H_5}{S}}$		1·5354	1·28 (30)	[428]
$2,4,6\text{-}Cl_3C_6H_2OP\overset{\nearrow NHCH_3}{\underset{\parallel \searrow NHC_2H_5}{S}}$		1·5432	1·31 (32)	[428]
$4\text{-}NO_2C_6H_4OP\overset{\nearrow NHCH_3}{\underset{\parallel \searrow NHC_2H_5}{S}}$		1·5000	1·01 (23)	[429]
$2,4,5\text{-}Cl_3C_6H_2OP\overset{\nearrow NH_2}{\underset{\parallel \searrow NHC_4H_9}{S}}$		1·5780 (29·5°)	1·364 (29)	[428]
$2,4,5\text{-}Cl_3C_6H_2OP\overset{\nearrow NHCH_3}{\underset{\parallel \searrow NHC_3H_7\text{-iso}}{S}}$		1·5049	1·17 (23)	[428]
$4\text{-}NO_2C_6H_4OP\overset{\nearrow NHCH_3}{\underset{\parallel \searrow NHC_3H_7\text{-iso}}{S}}$		1·5824	1·07 (25)	[429]
$2,4,5\text{-}Cl_3C_6H_2OPS(NHC_2H_5)_2$		1·5256	2·30 (23)	[428]
$2,4,5\text{-}Cl_3C_6H_2OP\overset{\nearrow NHC_2H_5}{\underset{\parallel \searrow NHC_4H_9}{S}}$		1·5610	1·22 (27)	[428]
$2,4,5\text{-}Cl_3C_6H_2OPS(NHC_3H_7)_2$		1·5642	1·348 (35)	[428]
$2,4,5\text{-}Cl_3C_6H_2OP\overset{\nearrow NHCH_3}{\underset{\parallel \searrow NH\text{-}C_6H_{11}\text{-cyclo}}{S}}$		1·5193	1·11 (23)	[428]

TABLE 74 — *(contd.)*

Formula	m. p., °C	n_D^{35}	d	Reference
4-NO$_2$C$_6$H$_4$OP$\overset{\text{NHCH}_3}{\underset{\underset{S}{\|}}{\diagdown\text{NHC}_6\text{H}_{11}\text{-cyclo}}}$		1·5441	1·101 (25)	[429]
2,4,5-Cl$_3$C$_6$H$_2$OP$\overset{\text{NHC}_2\text{H}_5}{\underset{\underset{S}{\|}}{\diagdown\text{NHC}_6\text{H}_{11}\text{-cyclo}}}$		1·5390	1·27 (30)	[428]
2,4,6-Cl$_3$C$_6$H$_2$OP$\overset{\text{NHC}_2\text{H}_5}{\underset{\underset{S}{\|}}{\diagdown\text{NHC}_6\text{H}_{11}\text{-cyclo}}}$		1·5360	1·26 (32)	[428]
2,3,4,6-Cl$_4$C$_6$HOP$\overset{\text{NHC}_2\text{H}_5}{\underset{\underset{S}{\|}}{\diagdown\text{NHC}_6\text{H}_{11}\text{-cyclo}}}$		1·5413	1·26 (26)	[428]
C$_6$Cl$_5$OP$\overset{\text{NHC}_2\text{H}_5}{\underset{\underset{S}{\|}}{\diagdown\text{NHC}_6\text{H}_{11}\text{-cyclo}}}$		1·5635	1·40 (27)	[428]
2,4,6-Br$_3$C$_6$H$_2$OP$\overset{\text{NHC}_2\text{H}_5}{\underset{\underset{S}{\|}}{\diagdown\text{NHC}_6\text{H}_{11}\text{-cyclo}}}$		1·5379	1·32 (26)	[428]
2,4,5-Cl$_3$C$_6$H$_2$OPS(NHC$_4$H$_9$)$_2$		1·5435	1·26 (80)	[428]
2,4,5-Cl$_3$C$_6$H$_2$OP$\overset{\text{NHC}_4\text{H}_9}{\underset{\underset{S}{\|}}{\diagdown\text{NHC}_6\text{H}_{11}\text{-cyclo}}}$		1·5148	1·13 (31)	[428]
2,4,5-Cl$_3$C$_6$H$_2$OP$\overset{\text{NH}_2}{\underset{\underset{S}{\|}}{\diagdown\text{NHC}_{12}\text{H}_{25}}}$		1·5405	1·32(24)	[428]
2,4,5-Cl$_3$C$_6$H$_3$OP$\overset{\text{NHC}_2\text{H}_5}{\underset{\underset{S}{\|}}{\diagdown\text{NHC}_{12}\text{H}_{25}}}$		1·5223	1·12 (27)	[428]
2,4,5-Cl$_3$C$_6$H$_2$OPS(NHC$_{12}$H$_{25}$)$_2$			1·41 (35)	[428]
2,4,5-Cl$_3$C$_6$H$_2$OP$\overset{\text{NHC}_2\text{H}_5}{\underset{\underset{S}{\|}}{\diagdown\text{NHCH}_2\text{C}_6\text{H}_5}}$	74–77	1·5652 (after solidi	1·24 (28) fication)	[428]
C$_6$H$_5$OPS(NHCH$_2$C$_6$H$_5$)$_2$	73			[414]
2-NO$_2$C$_6$H$_4$OP$\overset{\text{NH}_2}{\underset{\underset{S}{\|}}{\diagdown\text{NHC}_6\text{H}_5}}$	81–83			[429]
C$_6$H$_5$OPS(NHC$_6$H$_5$)$_2$	126			[414]

TABLE 75. DIAMIDES OF PHOSPHORAMIDOTHIONIC ACIDS OF THE TYPE

$$\begin{array}{c} R \\ \diagdown \\ R' \end{array} NP \underset{\underset{S}{\|}}{\overset{\diagup NHR''}{\diagdown NHR'''}} \quad \text{and} \quad (C_2H_5)NPS \left[N \diagup^{CH_2}_{CH_2} \right]_2$$

Formula	m. p., °C	Yield (%)	Reference
$(CH_3)_2NPS(NH_2)_2$	107	89	[412]
$(C_2H_5)_2NPS(NH_2)_2$	64	93	[412]
$C_4H_9NHPS(NH_2)_2$	54	90	[412]
$(C_2H_5)_2NP\left[N\diagup^{CH_2}_{CH_2}\right]_2$ $\underset{S}{\|}$	86–87 (0·8)*		[420]
$C_2H_5NHPS(NHC_4H_9)_2$	48·5		[419]
$(CH_3)_2NPS(NHC_6H_5)_2$	209–210		[418]
$C_2H_5NHPS(NHC_6H_5)_2$	106		[419]
$C_3H_7NHPS(NHC_6H_5)_2$	116		[419]
$(C_2H_5)_2NPS(NHC_6H_5)_2$	192		[418]
iso-$C_4H_9NHPS(NHC_6H_5)_2$	118		[418]
$C_5H_{10}NPS(NHC_6H_5)_2$	199		[418]
$(C_3H_7)_2NPS(NHC_6H_5)_2$	145		[418]
(iso-$C_5H_{11})_2NPS(NHC_6H_5)_2$	141		[418]
$\begin{array}{c}C_2H_5\\ \diagdown\\ C_6H_5\end{array}NPS(NHC_6H_5)_2$	140		[418]
$C_2H_5NHPS(NHC_6H_4CH_3\text{-}4)_2$	140		[419]
$(C_2H_5)_2NPS(NHC_6H_4CH_3\text{-}4)_2$	166–167		[418]
iso-$C_4H_9NHPS(NHC_6H_4CH_3\text{-}4)_2$	152		[419]
$C_5H_{10}NPS(NHC_6H_4CH_3\text{-}4)_2$	190		[418]
iso-$C_5H_{11}NHPS(NHC_6H_4CH_3\text{-}4)_2$	129		[419]
$\begin{array}{c}C_2H_5\\ \diagdown\\ C_6H_5\end{array}NPS(NHC_6H_4CH_3\text{-}4)_2$	158		[418]

* b. p., °C (mm).

TABLE 76. TRIAMIDES OF PHOSPHOROTHIONIC ACID OF THE TYPE

$$PS(NHR)_3$$

R	m. p., °C	Yield (%)	Reference
—H	Decomposes at 100° in high vacuum with the evolution of ammonia	90	[425]
		96	[412]
—C_2H_5	68		[415]
—C_3H_7	73–74	10	[431]
—C_4H_9	54		[432]
—iso-C_4H_9	78–78·5		[415]
—iso-C_5H_{11}	Uncrystallizable liquid		[415]
cyclo-C_6H_{11}	143·5–144	89·6	[426]
—$CH_2C_6H_5$	125–126	43	[431]
—C_6H_5	153–154	50	[431]
—$C_6H_4Cl\text{-}4$	225–226	97	[431]
—$C_6H_4OC_2H_5\text{-}4$	152		[427]
—$C_6H_4CH_3\text{-}2$	134·5		[427]
—$C_6H_4CH_3\text{-}4$	185–186		[427]
$PS\left[N\diagup^{CH_2}_{CH_2}\right]_3$	51·5		[430]

TABLE 77. DIAMIDES OF PHOSPHONIC ACIDS OF THE TYPE $RP\underset{\underset{O}{\|}}{\overset{NHR'}{\diagdown}}_{NHR''}$

Formula	m. p., °C	Yield (%)	Reference
$RPO(NH_2)_2$			
R			
CH_3—	128–129	73·5	[433]
C_2H_5—	180–185		[57]
C_4H_9—	170–175		[57]
C_6H_5—	189		[434]
$4\text{-}BrC_6H_4$—	202		[434]
$4\text{-}NH_2C_6H_4$—	224		[434]
$4\text{-}CH_3C_6H_4$—	209		[435]
$C_2H_5PO(NHCH_3)_2$	Oil		[57]
$RPO(NHC_6H_5)_2$			
R			
$ClCH_2CH_2$—	169–170		[434]
$BrCH_2CH_2$—	169–170		[434]
C_6H_5—	211·5	40·3	[436]
$4\text{-}CH_3OC_6H_4$—	210	18·1	[436]
$4\text{-}C_6H_5NHC_6H_4$—	242		[434]
$2\text{-}CH_3C_6H_4$—	234 230·5		[336] [436]
$4\text{-}CH_3C_6H_4$—	207·5–208·5	21·7	[436]
$2,4,5\text{-}(CH_3)_3C_6H_2$—	197		[435]
$(C_6H_5CH_2)_2CHC_6H_4$—	196		[435]
$C_6H_5P\underset{\underset{O}{\|}}{\overset{NHC_6H_5}{\diagdown}}_{NHC_6H_4CH_3\text{-}4}$	200		[434]
$4\text{-}CH_3C_6H_4P\underset{\underset{O}{\|}}{\overset{NHC_6H_5}{\diagdown}}_{NHC_6H_4CH_3\text{-}4}$	220		[435]
$C_6H_5PO(NHC_6H_4CH_3\text{-}4)_2$	221		[434]
$4\text{-}CH_3C_6H_4PO(NHC_6H_5CH_3\text{-}4)_2$	237		[435]

TABLE 78. DIETHYLENIMIDES OF PHOSPHONIC ACIDS OF THE TYPE

$$RPO\left[N\diagdown\begin{matrix}CH_2\\ |\\ CH_2\end{matrix}\right]_2$$

R	m. p., °C
C_2H_5-	76–80 (0·8)*
cyclo-$C_6H_{11}-$	64–66
C_6H_5-	75–76·5; 117–120 (0·2)*
4-ClC_6H_4-	Crystalline mass
4-$CH_3C_6H_4-$	56–57
2-$C_{10}H_7-$	93–94

* b. p., °C (mm).

PHOSPHONITRILIC CHLORIDES

The phosphonitrilic chlorides, which were discovered over a hundred years ago, were of only preparative interest for a long time.

In recent years, however, some interesting investigations have been made on these compounds, which show that from them can be obtained interesting and useful non-inflammable and thermally stable polymers with an inorganic skeleton which can be used as additives to lubricating oils, for improved high-temperature resistant products, etc.

It is known that the starting materials for the preparation of the poly-phosphonitrilic chlorides are the mixed trimers and tetramers of these compounds (the monomers and dimers have not been prepared). Because of this, and because the phosphonitrilic chlorides are converted into the high molecular weight forms in the same way as the low molecular weight forms are converted into one another, we shall defer a discussion of these compounds to the second part of this book ("High Molecular Weight Organophosphorus Compounds").

CHAPTER III

REFRACTIVITIES OF CERTAIN ATOMIC GROUPS IN ORGANOPHOSPHORUS COMPOUNDS

FINALLY, in this first section, we list the refractivities of some commonly encountered groups (for the yellow line of sodium) in organophosphorus compounds. The refractivities have been calculated from Eisenlohr's values (for carbon, hydrogen, oxygen, chlorine and double bonds) and also from the results

TABLE 79. ATOMIC REFRACTIVITES OF PHOSPHORUS

Environment of P atom	R_D	Reference
Esters and ester-acid halides of phosphorous acid	7·04	[437]
Esters and acid halides of alkylphosphonous acids	7·74	[438]
Esters and acid halides of dialkylphosphinous acids	8·44	[438]
Trialkylphosphines	9·14	[439]
	9·8–10	[439]
Dialkylarylphosphines		[439]
Esters and ester-acid halides of phosphoric acid	3·75	[437]
Esters and acid halides of alkylphosphonic acids	4·27	[437]
Esters and acid halides of dialkylphosphinic acids	{ 4·79	[440]
	{ 4·85	[441]

TABLE 79 (a) REFRACTIVITIES OF CERTAIN GROUPS

Group	R_D	Group	R_D
$CH_2<$	4·618	iso-C_4H_9—	19·572
CH_3—	5·718	sec-C_4H_9—	19·572
$CH_2 = CH$—	9·869	C_5H_{11}—	24·190
C_2H_5—	10·336	C_6H_{13}—	28·808
$CH_2 = CHCH_2$—	14·487	C_7H_{15}—	33·426
C_3H_7—	14·954	C_8H_{17}	38·044
iso-C_3H_7—	14·954	C_6H_5-(phenyl)	25·207
C_4H_9—	19·572	$CH_2 = CHO$—	11·512
		$CH_2 = CHCH_2O$—	16·130

TABLE 79 (a) — *(contd.)*

Group	Compounds	R_D
P—O— with O— above and O— below	Derivatives of phosphorous acids	11·969
—O, —O >P—Cl		16·662
—O—P< Cl Cl		21·355
—O—P< O, O, with ‖O	Derivatives of phosphoric acid	10·890
—O, —O >P—Cl, ‖O		15·583
—O—P< Cl, Cl, ‖O		20·276
$CH_2=CHCH_2OP<$ O— O— ‖O		25·377
$(CH_2=CHCH_2O)_2P(O)-$		39·864
$CH_2=CHOP<$ O— O— ‖O		20·759
—P< O— O— ‖O	Derivatives of alkyl- (and aryl-) phosphonic acids	9·767
—P< Cl Cl ‖O		19·153
$CH_2=CHP<$ O— O— ‖O		19·636
$CH_2=CHCH_2P<$ O— O— ‖O		24·254
$(CH_2=CHCH_2O)_2P-$ ‖O		38·741

TABLE 79 (a) — *(contd.)*

Group	Compounds	RD
$>\!\!P\!-\!O\!-\!$ $\parallel$ O	Derivatives of alkyl- (and aryl-) phosphonic acids	8·644
$>\!\!POCH\!=\!CH_2$ $\parallel$ O		18·513
$>\!\!POCH_2CH\!=\!CH_2$ $\parallel$ O		23·131

of Kabachnik [437], Razumov and Mukhacheva [438], Jones, Davies and Dyke [439], Kosolopoff and Watson [440], Kabachnik and Shepeleva [441] (for phosphorus and various organophosphorus compounds) (see Table 79 and 79*a*).

PART TWO

HIGH MOLECULAR WEIGHT ORGANOPHOSPHORUS COMPOUNDS

By means of the reactions of polymerization, copolymerization, polycondensation, poly-transesterification, etc., the organophosphorus monomers which were described in the first part of this book can be converted into organophosphorus high molecular weight compounds of various types.

Attempts to systematize the methods of synthesis and properties of these compounds run into certain difficulties.

As is well known, the reproduction of results is a much more complex problem in macromolecular chemistry than in the field of low molecular weight compounds. In our case this is made even more difficult because there are far fewer published results (which to a large extent are in patents) on the preparation and properties of organophosphorus polymers than on the thoroughly examined "completely organic" polymers, copolymers, polyesters, etc., where such results have also been frequently confirmed. Hence in this book we will often be discussing unclear, non-coincident and even contradictory results, which cannot always be critically appraised with any confidence.

In the chapters of this second part, it is to be noted that there are no detailed descriptions of the preparations of high molecular weight organophosphorus compounds (in distinction from the first part, where the preparation of many monomers was described in detail); the conditions under which these compounds have been prepared are, however, recorded in various Tables.

CHAPTER IV.

CARBON-CHAIN AND HETERO-CHAIN HIGH MOLECULAR WEIGHT COMPOUNDS CONTAINING PHOSPHORUS IN THE SIDE CHAINS

POLYMERS AND COPOLYMERS OF UNSATURATED ESTERS OF ACIDS OF PHOSPHORUS

Polymers and copolymers of allyl esters of acids of phosphorus

ONE of the most interesting and important properties of unsaturated esters of acids of phosphorus is their ability to be polymerized. This was first investigated in the 1940's by Toy and his colleagues (at the Victor Chemical Works), who studied, in particular, the polymerizing capacity of the allyl and methallyl esters of arylphosphonic acids: they showed that these substances, which are quite stable, are converted, by heating with peracidic materials, into transparent, heat-resistant, glass-like polymers which are insoluble in organic solvents [442–444].

There was great interest in high-quality artificial glass, and so, immediately after the publications of these investigators, intensive work began on this section of organophosphorus chemistry. For several years now a range of papers and patents have been published on the synthesis, polymerization and copolymerization of allyl and substituted allyl esters of various acids of phosphorus, and also on the properties and applications of the high molecular weight compounds derived from these esters.

The methods of synthesis of the starting materials have been described in the first part of this book. The examination of the polymerizing capacity of these esters has produced some very interesting, although far from complete or even incontestable, results. Recently, it has been shown that a whole range of esters of acids of phosphorus having one allylic group, either are incapable of being polymerized or, less usually, can only be converted into low molecular weight compounds, possibly dimers [101, 105, 186, 250]. An analogous picture is observed with other allyl derivatives: the weak polymerizing capacity of allyl acetate, for example, is well known [445].

Esters which contain two or more allyl groups usually polymerize easily to give cross-linked polymers [101, 105, 184–186, 250].

Toy, Brown and Cooper [184–186] have shown that the polymerizing capacity of allyl (and methallyl) esters of acids of phosphorus depends on the following factors:

(a) the proportion of substituents to phosphorus atoms;

(b) the electronic characteristics of these substituents;

(c) the presence or absence of inhibitor groups in the ester molecule.

In fact, in a range of polymers from diallyl esters of alkylphosphonic acids of the type $RPO(OCH_2CH = CH_2)_2$, where $R = H$, CH_3, C_2H_5, $n-C_3H_7$, iso-C_3H_7 or C_4H_9, only the first member of this series, which has least substituents on the phosphorus, forms a hard, glass-like polymer [186]. The other esters, as the size of the substituents on the phosphorus increases, polymerize into high molecular weight compounds whose hardness decreases from moderate to gel-like [186].

The influence of polar substituents, according to Toy and Cooper, is such that glass-like polymers are only formed when a substituent more electronegative than methyl is joined to the phosphorus atom of the diallyl ester: for example, the isobutenyl [186], aryl [184–186], benzyl [186] or phenoxyl [186] groups. If the electronegativity of the substituent is less or about the same as that of methyl, then the hardness of the polymer will be low; thus the polymer from diallyl isobutylphosphonate is resinous, whereas that from diallyl isobutenylphosphonate is an artificial glass.

Some atoms or groups in allyl esters of acids of phosphorus inhibit polymerization, permitting only oils or thick syrups to be obtained even in the most favourable cases, but not hard polymers. Such atoms or groups are: sulphur in diallyl phenylphosphonothionate, iso-octenyl- and dialkylamido-groups, nitrogen when it is found between phosphorus and the allylic group, and also trivalent phosphorus (in triallyl phosphite) [173]. Inhibition of polymerization by the action of sulphur is provoked by initiators of the peroxidic type and has been known for a long time; that the analogous influence of the amido-group in unsaturated esters of phosphorus acids is comparable has recently been demonstrated by Toy and Cooper [186] and confirmed by Kennedy et al. [173]. Controlled investigations (of the polymerization of diallyl phenylphosphonate and phthalate in the presence of a series of compounds containing phosphoramido-groups) have shown that the polymerizing capacity of diallyl esters of acids of phosphorus containing amido-groups is definitely decreased [186]. However, Kennedy and Ficken have obtained high molecular weight phosphorus-containing compounds with structures similar to those of the compounds discussed above, by the treatment of a previously prepared polymer of diallyl hydrogen phosphite with diethylamine and carbon tetrachloride [277]:

$$[HPO(OCH_2CH=CH_2)_2]_n + 2n(C_2H_5)_2NH + nCCl_4 \longrightarrow$$
$$[(C_2H_5)_2NPO(OCH_2CH = CH_2)_2]_n + nC_2H_5NH \cdot HCl + nCHCl_3$$

or with Schiff's bases [277]:

$$[HPO(OCH_2CH = CH_2)_2]_n + n(CH_3CH = NC_2H_5) \longrightarrow$$
$$\longrightarrow [C_2H_5NHCH(CH_3)PO(OCH_2CH = CH_2)_2]_n$$

Kamai and Kukhtin have found that the presence of two or three double bonds in a molecule does not always mean that such a substance can be polymerized. These authors concluded that the diallyl esters of methyl- and phenylphosphonic acids and of arylphosphonous acids — compounds with two double bonds — and also the vinyl and allyl esters of (dialloxyphosphinyl)acetic acid $[CH_2 = CHO_2CCH_2PO(OR)_2$ and $RO_2CCH_2PO(OR)_2$, where R = allyl] and diallyl allylphosphonate — compounds with three double bonds — are not capable of being polymerized (the first compound gives a dimer); and also that the saturated esters of diallyl carboxyalkylphosphonic $[RO_2C—$ $—CH_2PO(OCH_2CH = CH_2)_2]$ and carboxyphosphonic acids, and the diallyl esters of benzoyl-, trichloromethyl- and keto-phosphonic acids only form gel-like polymers of reticular structure [101, 105, 250]. However, other investigators have obtained hard, transparent polymers from the diallyl esters of arylphosphonous [183], allyl- [173, 187], methyl- [186], benzyl- [186] and trichloromethyl-phosphonic [173] acids.

Dimethallyl esters of acids of phosphorus polymerize significantly more quickly than the corresponding allyl esters, as can be seen from Table 80 [186].

TABLE 80. THE POLYMERIZATION OF THE ALLYL (R) AND METHALLYL (R′) ESTERS OF ISO-OCTENYLPHOSPHONIC ACID AT 87—88°

Percent of benzoyl peroxide	Viscosity (cP)			
	24 hr		48 hr	
	R	R′	R	R′
0	5	6	5	7
2	10	52	10	54
4	18	340	18	390
6	30	2,260	31	2,770
8	50	14,650	51	25,300
10	79	145,000	88	215,000

Allyl esters of acids of phosphorus can be copolymerized with styrene, methyl methacrylate, vinyl acetate, acrylonitrile, diallyl esters of dicarboxylic acids and other monomers [101, 105, 179, 184, 185, 189, 446–454].

One of the most important representatives of the class of compounds under discussion is diallyl phenylphosphonate, which is available in commercial quantities in the U.S.A. [455]. This substance was first synthesized by Toy [184] (see p. 99).

Investigations on the properties of polymers of diallyl phenylphonate have revealed the interesting result that the refractive index of its copolymers varies linearly with composition (Fig. 1).

It has been shown [185], that the copolymer of diallyl phenylphosphonate with methyl methacrylate (in the ratio 2 : 1) possesses a refractive index identical with that of certain types of silicate glass. Glass fibre prepared from such a glass, after being immersed in such a mixture of monomers, which are then co-polymerized, is practically invisible in the transparent copolymer. This discovery (which is one of the valuable properties of the polymers and copolymers of diallyl phenylphosphonate) shows that it is potentially possible to prepare transparent plastics with favourable mechanical properties by the strengthening of artificial glasses with silicates (glass fibre).

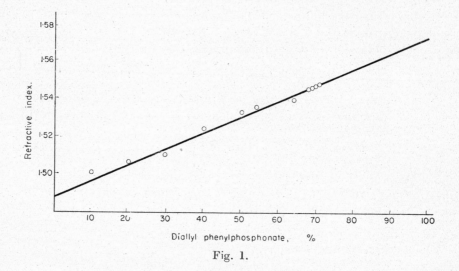

Fig. 1.

In a number of preparations of copolymers of diallyl phenylphosphonate, it has been recommended that the ester be heated alone for a certain time in an inert gas atmosphere in the presence of small quantities of peroxidic compounds (0.25%). After the removal of unreacted monomer in a good vacuum, there remains a viscous liquid which can be kept unchanged for a long time — the so-called "pre-polymer" of diallyl phenylphosphonate. If this substance is used, then the copolymer is formed much more readily than when monomeric diallyl phenylphosphonate is used [453].

Tables 81–83 record certain properties of polymers and co-polymers of this interesting compound.

The character of the unsaturated alcohol part of the ester molecule has a great influence on the polymerizing capacity of the monomer and on the properties of the polymer. Shokal and Whitehill [189], who investigated the polymerization of a number of unsaturated (allyl, methallyl, propenyl, butenyl, hexenyl, etc.) esters of arylphosphonic acids, showed that as the size of the alcohol part of the molecule increased, so the hardness of the formed polymer decreased. Evidently, increasing the molecular weight of the monomer (other factors, of course, remaining constant) impedes the polymerization.

TABLE 81. SOME PROPERTIES OF POLYMERIC DIALLYL
PHENYLPHOSPHONATE [185]

Colour	From water white to clear amber
n_D^{28}	1·573
d_4^{28}	1·273
Strength (kg/cm²)	
in tension	371
in compression	1470
in shear	420
Impact strength (notched Izod), cm-kg/m of notch	1·308
Rockwell hardness	M-95
Distortion point (°C)	102
Water absorption (24 hr) (%)	0·66
Deformation under static load (50°, 280 kg/cm², 24 hr) (%)	10·25
Dielectric strength (accurately), in kilo-volts required to puncture a test plate of thickness 4·3434 mm	54·5
Flammability	Extinguishes itself 30 sec after removing from the flame
Decomposition temperature (°C)	240–260°
Thermal stability	80°, 20 hr — colour unchanged 105–106°, 26 hr — slight yellowing, remains very hard 115–116° 11 days — becomes amber coloured, remains hard

It has been established that esters of phosphonic acids (particularly aryl-
and halogenoalkyl-phosphonic), but not of phosphoric acids, are capable of
forming glass-like polymers with good physicomechanical properties. This
might be due to the particular properties of the carbon-phosphorus bond, and
to the greater stability of the skeletons of esters of phosphonic acids as compared with esters of phosphoric acids.

$$-\overset{|}{\underset{\overset{|}{O}}{C}}-\overset{}{\underset{\|}{P}}\Big\langle\begin{smallmatrix}O-\\[4pt]O-\end{smallmatrix}\quad\text{and}\quad O=P-\overset{O-}{\underset{O-}{\Big\langle}} O-$$

In studies on the bulk polymerization of triallyl phosphate to make
artificial glass, it has been suggested that the great quantity of heat which is
produced causes the internal strain which often cracks the polymer. Cases are
known of the destruction of the ampoules or moulds, in which the polymerization was carried out, into small splinters and even glass dust.

By the polymerization of mixed esters of phosphoric acid under these
conditions, transesterification and symmetrization are often observed, whereas
in the case of phosphonic acids, these are almost unknown. It is well known

that in the synthesis of diallyl phenyl phosphate, small, difficultly separable mixtures of triallyl, allyl diphenyl and triphenyl phosphates are formed, and that often it is impossible to obtain reproducible results on polymerization. Besides this, if the polymerization is not carried out in an inert gas atmosphere, phenol is sometimes split out because of strong heating in the polymer mass; this also causes the formation of a dark, crumbled polymer [189].

TABLE 82. SOME PROPERTIES OF A COPOLYMER OF DIALLYL
PHENYLPHOSPHONATE (40%) AND VINYL ACETATE (60%) [185]

Visible light transmission (%)	95
n_D^{25}	1·5176
d_4^{25}	1·229
Strength (kg/cm²)	
in tension	735
in compression	1057
in shear	1043
Impact strength (notched Izod),	
cm-kg/cm, of notch	1·5805
Rockwell hardness	M-99·9
Distortion point (°C)	64·5
Water absorption (24 hr) (%)	0·71
Dielectric constant	
at 1 kc	3·88
at 1 Mc	3·69
Power factor	
at 1 kc	0·0136
at 1 Mc	0·013
Dielectric loss	
at 1 kc	0·053
at 1 Mc	0·048
Flammability	Self-extinguishing 1 min 46 sec, after removal from the flame
Abrasion wear (mg)	30·85 per 100 R

The high molecular weight compounds based on unsaturated esters of phosphoric and phosphoramidic acids find application in another important field, namely, as substances which render various articles fire-resistant (see the chapter entitled "Uses of High Molecular Weight Phosphorus-containing Compounds").

Investigations on the polymerization of allyl esters of phosphoric acids in bulk, in solution and in emulsion, have shown that the halogenated polymers are an interesting and valuable line of study. These substances can be obtained by several methods:

(1) By partial polymerization followed by halogenation of the remaining unreacted double bonds in the polymers.

(2) By the partial halogenation of allyl esters of phosphoric acid (it is also possible to prepare halogenoallyl esters, such as tri-(2-chloroallyl) phosphate [130]) followed by complete polymerization, or by the complete halogenation of these compounds followed by treatment with zinc dust in boiling

solvents; in this last case some of the halogen is split out and the resulting unsaturated compounds at once polymerize.

(3) By the copolymerization of allyl esters of phosphoric acid with halogen-containing compounds.

TABLE 83. THE ACTION OF SOLVENTS (AT ROOM TEMPERATURE) ON THE POLYMER AND COPOLYMERS OF DIALLYL PHENYLPHOSPHONATE [185]

Solvent	Polymeric diallyl phenylphosphonate	Copolymers of diallylphenylphosphonate (I) with methyl methacrylate (II) and vinyl acetate (III) (monomers taken in % by volume)		
	Over 6 days	I (1%) + II (99%) (over 66 hr)	I (50%) + III (50%) (over 66 hr)	I (50%) + III (50%) (over 15 days)
Chloroform	Insoluble, but attacked			Partial disintegration, becomes brittle
Dichloroethane	Insoluble, but attacked	Swells to a soft gel	No swelling, becomes brittle	Partial disintegration, becomes brittle
Benzene	No visible effect	Swells to a soft gel	Becomes soft and brittle	No visible effect
Carbon tetrachloride	No visible effect	Becomes resin-like	Remains hard and strong	No visible effect
Acetone	No visible effect	Swells to a soft gel	No swelling, becomes brittle	Becomes soft and brittle
Ethyl alcohol	No visible effect			Becomes soft and brittle
Gasoline	No visible effect	No change	No change	No visible effect
Ligroin	No visible effect			No visible effect
Butyl acetate	No visible effect	Swells to a soft gel	No swelling, becomes brittle	No visible effect
Ethyl ether	No visible effect			No visible effect
5% Caustic soda	No visible effect	No change	No change	No visible effect
5% Hydrochloric acid	No visible effect	No change	No change	No visible effect
30% Sulphuric acid	No visible effect (at 65° for more than 5 days)			No visible effect
Water	No visible effect (at 65° for more than 5 days)			No visible effect

The first two routes have been investigated by workers at the G. L. Martin Co. [135–137]. The mechanisms of these reactions were not elucidated, but the authors evolved methods of polymerizing triallyl and trimethallyl phosphates, diallyl phosphoramidate, diallyl N-hydroxymethylphosphoramidate, etc., into thick liquids (without forming gels) which contained a known percentage of free double bonds. The most simple of all these processes were carried out by refluxing a solution of the monomer in benzene, dichloroethane, isopropanol, etc., in the presence of peroxy-compounds, the quantity of which played a very important role. For example, by refluxing a solution of triallyl phosphate in dichloroethane in the presence of $1 \cdot 5\%$ or more of benzoyl peroxide for 1 hr gelatinization takes place, whereas with 1% of the initiator the system remains liquid for several hours. After this, the polymer, formed by this or any other method, is purified from unreacted monomer and low molecular weight fractions, and then halogenated in a suitable solvent.

Recently, Frick and his co-workers [456] have published the results of an investigation on the emulsion copolymerization of triallyl phosphate with halogen-containing derivatives of methane. This reaction, which quickly found practical application, is one of a large number of examples of the telomerization reaction, which has been widely studied all over the world [457–459]. By such a copolymerization a mixture of soluble and insoluble copolymers (in chlorinated hydrocarbons) is formed. The authors suggested that the polymerization lead first to the formation of products with the following structure:

$$CX_3-\left[\begin{array}{c}-CH_2-CH-\\ |\\ CH_2\\ |\\ OPO(OC_3H_5)_2\end{array}\right]_n-Y$$

where X = halogen; Y = halogen or hydrogen; $n = 1 \ldots \ldots 2 \cdot 5$.

At this stage the copolymer is a thick liquid with a linear structure and free double bonds. In the case of a molar ratio of $CX_3Y : PO(OC_3H_5)_3 \geq 2 : 1$ the addition product with $n = 1$ is obtained. The process continues further, depending on the size of the polymer chain, and the free double bonds enter into the reaction. Hence, as the overall yield of polymer increases, the percentage of soluble material at first increases and then falls, while the amount of insoluble cross-linked polymer increases continuously.

The general picture of the polymerization of allyl esters of acids of phosphorus is by no means clear. This is explained by the small amount of serious investigation which has taken place in this field, and also by the great difficulties which unavoidably arise in any study of the kinetics and mechanism of polymerization of these substances. This difficulty arises because allyl esters of acids of phosphorus are evidently incapable of forming linear high molecular weight compounds, since their polymerization leads either to low molecular weight products, or to polymers with reticulated structures which are infusible and insoluble in organic solvents (a similar state of affairs is observed in the polymerization of allyl esters of carboxylic acids [445, 460–463]).

In practice, this prevents the purification of such polymers by precipitation, the determination of their molecular weights, etc. All this prevents any final judgement being made about the polymerizing capacity of allyl esters of acids of phosphorus, and at this moment it is only possible to draw a few preliminary conclusions.

(1) The tendency of allyl esters of acids of phosphorus to polymerize, by initiation with peroxy compounds, is usually weaker than for the corresponding carboxylic esters.

(2) Esters with one allyl group in the molecule can either be converted into relatively low molecular weight polymers, or, more usually, they cannot be polymerized at all (see p. 147).

(3) Certain esters (in which the phosphorus atom is pentavalent) with two or three allyl groups are capable of giving high molecular weight compounds with reticulated structures which are infusible and insoluble in organic solvents.

(4) Allyl esters of acids of phosphorus with any number of unsaturated groups can take part in copolymerization.

(5) An increase in the molecular weight of the ester (all other things being equal) lowers its polymerization capacity.

The course of the polymerization of allyl esters of acids of phosphorus into artificial glasses can nowadays also be described only in the most general terms. This process goes in several stages. At first the viscosity of the system increases and the polymer, while it is still in small amount, remains soluble in the monomer. At this stage a viscous liquid, soluble in ethanol, acetone, chlorinated and aromatic hydrocarbons is produced. It is possible to precipitate from this liquid, by the addition of ether, a sticky, low molecular weight polymer, which is fusible and soluble in the above mentioned solvents.

Polymerization of the viscous system continues gradually until a specific point is reached, when gelatinization sets in and the reaction becomes faster and a considerable amount of heat is evolved. At this point, obviously, cross-linking has begun and the individual linear polymer chains are being joined to one another. This process is irreversible since it is impossible to reconvert the formed gel back into the fusible and soluble material. Further heating of the pliable gel converts it into a hard glass-like substance, which is entirely without thermoplasticity.

It may be supposed that linear polymers (the so called β-polymers) of the following type are formed at the beginning of the process:

$$
\cdots-CH-CH_2-CH-CH_2-CH-CH_2-\cdots
$$

$$
\begin{array}{ccc}
& CH_2 & & CH_2 \\
& | & & | \\
& O & & O \\
& | & & | \\
R-P=O & & R-P=O \\
& | & & | \\
& O & & O \\
& | & & | \\
& CH_2 & & CH_2 \\
& | & & | \\
& CH=CH_2 & & CH=CH_2
\end{array}
$$

As the process continues these polymers are converted into a cross-linked structure, the principal unit of which is:

$$
\begin{array}{c}
\vdots \\
| \\
CH_2 \\
| \\
\cdots-CH-CH_2-CH-CH_2-CH-CH_2-\cdots \\
| \qquad\qquad\qquad | \\
CH_2 \qquad\qquad\quad CH_2 \\
| \qquad\qquad\qquad | \\
O \qquad\qquad\qquad O \\
| \qquad\qquad\qquad | \\
R-P=O \qquad\quad R-P=O \\
| \qquad\qquad\qquad | \\
O \qquad\qquad\qquad O \\
| \qquad\qquad\qquad | \\
CH_2 \qquad\qquad\quad CH_2 \\
| \qquad\qquad\qquad | \\
\cdots-CH-CH_2-CH-CH_2-CH-CH_2-\cdots \\
| \\
CH_2 \\
| \\
\vdots
\end{array}
$$

The point of increase in viscosity of the system during the polymerization of diallyl phenylphosphonate at 87° depends on the quantity of benzoyl peroxide used, as shown in Fig 2 [185].

To obtain hard polymers the temperature of polymerization must be raised slowly; in particular at the time of gelatinization the temperature must not exceed 100° (Toy and Brown [185] recommend 84–85°). In the case of polymerization at 100°, gelatinization sets in after 1·5 hr when much heat is

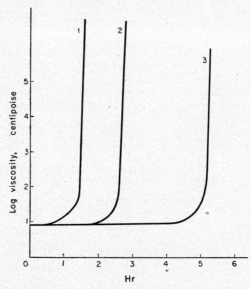

FIG. 2. (1) 2% benzoyl peroxide; (2) 1% benzoyl peroxide; (3) 0·5% benzoyl peroxide.

evolved (the temperature rises sharply to 168°) and the thick viscous liquid changes into a gel, but not into a glassy polymer.

It is necessary to point out that the polymerizing capacity of allyl esters of acids of phosphorus is sometimes invoked during their distillation, particularly if the compounds have previously been insufficiently washed and dried. Slow heating, even in the presence of inhibitors, may be accompanied by the partial decomposition of the substance with the formation of active initiating centres of polymerization, the number of which gradually increase. At a particular moment the velocities of decomposition and polymerization sharply increase: this is accompanied by the evolution of gas and much heat, and it may lead to explosion [122, 123, 128, 145].

In conclusion, it can be said that the polymerizing capacity of allyl esters of acids of phosphorus completely obeys the laws generalized in the well-known monographs of Korshak [464, 465].

POLYMERS AND COPOLYMERS OF OTHER UNSATURATED ESTERS OF ACIDS OF PHOSPHORUS

Studies on the capacity of other unsaturated esters of phosphorus acids to form high molecular weight compounds have only recently begun.

The polymerizing capacity of vinyl esters of acids of phosphorus has been elucidated by the investigations of Upson [156],* and Gefter and Kabachnik [120].

On being heated in the presence of benzoyl peroxide, such compounds with two or three double bonds form hard glass-like polymers which are infusible and insoluble in organic solvents [120]. Esters with only one double bond either do not polymerize at all, although they form copolymers [156]*, or they form thick liquids or jelly-like polymers [120].

Diethyl vinyl phosphate for example, does not polymerize in the presence of 2–5% of benzoyl peroxide or azodi-isobutyronitrile by heating at 125° for 42–70 hr; nor does it polymerize in the presence of sodium (2–4%) in liquid ammonia.

Hard polymers have only been successfully obtained from diethyl vinyl phosphate by copolymerization with styrene [156].*

Esters of acroylphosphonic acid polymerize extremely easily, however, and it is often very difficult to distill them *in vacuo*, even in the presence of inhibitors [99, 101]. This is, presumably, explained by two factors: by the presence of the $>C = C<$ and $>C = O$ groups contained in the acroyl residue, and by the comparatively high temperatures required for the distil-

* See footnote on p. 50

lation of these esters: all organophosphorus compounds, without exception, have higher boiling points than their carbon analogues.

The polymerizing capacity of esters of a,β-unsaturated phosphonic acids is not so great: they can all be distilled *in vacuo* without forming tars. Kabachnik [75] showed that diethyl and bis-2-dichloroethyl vinylphosphonate are unaffected by being heated to 100° for several hours in the absence of initiators. However, heating with 2–3% of benzoyl peroxide changes these esters into soft, transparent resins, although more recently Fields [85] has patented the preparation of hard transparent polymers from diethyl vinylphosphonate.

The polymerizing capacity of a number of esters of vinylphosphonic acid has been investigated in detail by Kabachnik and his co-workers [229, 230].

Esters of a,β-unsaturated phosphonic acids can be easily copolymerized with methyl methacrylate [466, 467], methyl acrylate, acrylonitrile [467], methyl vinyl ketone [468], styrene and other substances having one vinyl or vinylidene group, and also with divinylbenzene [469]; they form copolymers less readily, usually not at all, with dienes [466].

Arcus and Matthews [470] have studied the copolymerization of diethyl vinylphosphonate with styrene in the presence of *tert*-butyl hydroperoxide. The authors investigated the effect of various factors (molar ratio of monomers, amount of initiator, temperature) on the course of the copolymerization. It was also shown that styrene and diethyl vinylphosphonate form macromolecular chains which are terminated much more often by styrene than by organophosphorus radicals. If styrene is denoted by M_1, diethyl vinylphosphonate by M_2, and the growing polymers which are terminated respectively by styrene and diethyl vinylphosphonate radicals by $M_1^{\cdot}$ and $M_2^{\cdot}$, then the four possible reaction steps and their velocity constants will be:

$$M^{\cdot} + M_1 \longrightarrow M_1^{\cdot} \ (k_{1,1})$$

$$M_1^{\cdot} + M_2 \longrightarrow M_2^{\cdot} \ (k_{1,2})$$

$$M_2^{\cdot} + M_2 \longrightarrow M_2^{\cdot} \ (k_{2,2})$$

$$M_2^{\cdot} + M_1 \longrightarrow M_1^{\cdot} \ (k_{2,1})$$

and the relative reactivities of the monomers, or the copolymerization constants, will be:

$$r_1 = \frac{k_{1,1}}{k_{1,2}} \quad \text{and} \quad r_2 = \frac{k_{2,2}}{k_{2,1}}$$

The authors found that $r_1 = 3 \cdot 25$ and $r_2 = 0$. This indicates that the growing chain $M_1^{\cdot}$, which ends with a styrene radical, reacts $3 \cdot 25$ times faster with styrene than with diethyl vinylphosphonate, and that growing chain $M_2^{\cdot}$, which ends with the phosphonate radical, reacts only with styrene. It is to be noted that this result must be wrong since, according to it, diethyl vinylphosphonate is incapable of homopolymerizing, whereas it can, in fact, do this.

The authors also showed that the structure of the copolymer, judged by its phosphorus content, changes little with change in the temperature of copolymerization (at 80°, 100°, 116°, 133° and 154°). The amount of polymerization increases gradually with temperatures, reaches a maximum at 112°, and then quickly drops with a further increase in temperature.

The composition of the copolymer changes little with change in concentration of initiator from $0 \cdot 75$–$5 \cdot 1\%$, the further increase of its concentration only causes a small diminution in the quantity of the phosphorus-containing component in the copolymer. The degree of polymerization and the average molecular weight of the polymer gradually decrease with increasing concentration of peroxide.

Changing the molar ratio of styrene to diethyl vinylphosphonate from 1 : 1 to 9 : 1 increases the degree of polymerization and the molecular weight of the copolymer (from 14,300 to 55,600), lowers the phosphorus content from 4·5 to 1·5%, and at the same time increases the ratio of styrene to phosphorus-containing residues from 5 to 18·6.

The polymerization of other unsaturated organophosphorus compounds, that, is, not esters of phosphorus acids, has not as yet been studied. It is known only that triallylphosphine oxide polymerizes only slightly [173].

The conditions of polymerization (copolymerization) and the properties of the polymers (copolymers) of unsaturated esters of acids of phosphorus are recorded in Tables 84–98.

Tables of polymers and copolymers of unsaturated esters of acids of phosphorus

For uniformity and ease of reference the material in each table is listed under five headings with the following contents:

Monomer and comonomers	Conditions of polymerization (copolymerization)	Properties of the polymer (copolymer)	Notes	Reference
For phosphorus-containing monomers the formula is given For other monomers the name is given	(1) Atmosphere (nitrogen, air, etc.) (2) Percent of initiator, name of initiator (3) Temperature of polymerization (4) Time of polymerization (in hours or days) (6) Other information			

TABLE 84. COPOLYMERS OF DIETHYL VINYLPHOSPHONATE AND STYRENE [470]
(Soluble in benzene, insoluble in methanol)

Comonomers (%) $CH_2 = CHPO(OC_2H_5)_2$ + styrene		Copolymerization conditions	Notes	
			Yield of co-polymer (%)	% P in co-polymer
10·24	89·76	Nitrogen, 1 % $(CH_3)_3COOH$,, 116°, 11 hr	85	1·10
28	72	,, ,, ,, ,, ,,	66·4	2·86
50·5	59·5	,, ,, ,, ,, ,,	56·5	3·64
51·7	48·3	,, ,, ,, ,, ,,	51	4·88
34·5	65·5	Nitrogen, 1·65 %$(CH_3)_3COOH$, 80°, 11 hr	47	about 2
34·5	65·5	,, 100°, 11 hr	56	2·6
34·5	65·5	,, 116°, 11 hr	61	2·6
34·5	65·5	,, 133°, 11 hr	40	2·5
34·5	65·5	,, 154°, 11 hr	33	about 2
34·5	65·5	Nitrogen, 3 %$(CH_3)_3COOH$, 116°, 11 hr		2·5
34·5	65·5	Nitrogen, 4·1 %$(CH_3)_3COOH$, 116°, 11 hr		2·4
34·5	65·5	Nitrogen, 5·2 % $(CH_3)_3COOH$, 116°, 11 hr		2·3
61	39	Nitrogen, 1·65 %$(CH_3)_3COOH$, 165°, 11 hr	15	4·7
47	53	,, 165°, 11 hr	43	3·7
34·5	65·5	,, 165°, 11 hr	62	2·7
29·8	70·2	,, 165°, 11 hr	76	2·1
17·3	82·7	,, 165°, 11 hr	85	1·5

TABLE 84(a). POLYMERS AND COPOLYMERS OF ESTERS OF VINYL- AND α-ACETYLVINYL-PHOSPHONIC ACIDS

Monomer or comonomers	Polymerization (copolymerization) conditions	Properties of the polymer (copolymer)	Reference
$CH_2 = CHPO(OC_2H_5)_2$	2–3% Bz_2O_2, heat	transparent, viscous	[75]
$CH_2 = CHPO(OCH_2CH_2Cl)_2$	2–3% Bz_2O_2, heat	transparent, hard, fireproof	[85]
$CH_2 = CHPO(OCH_2CH_2Cl)_2$	2% Bz_2O_2, 60–110°	transparent, viscous	[75]
$CH_2 = CHPO(OCH_2CH_2Cl)_2$ (92–95%) + divinylbenzene (8–5%)	Several hours (in emulsion)	brittle	[469]
$CH_2 = C(OCOCH_3) PO(OC_2H_5)_2$*	Bz_2O_2, heat or stand for a long time	viscous syrup	[232]
$CH_2 = C(OCOCH_3) PO(OC_3H_7)_2$*	Bz_2O_2, heat or stand for a long time	viscous syrup	[232]
$CH_2 = C(OCOCH_3) PO(OC_3H_7—i)_2$*	Bz_2O_2, heat or stand for a long time	viscous syrup	[232]

* Presumed structure for the monomer.

TABLE 85. COPOLYMERS OF α-PHENYLVINYLPHOSPHONIC ACID AND ESTERS OF THE TYPE $CH_2=CRPO(OR')_2$, WHERE $R=CH_3$, C_6H_5, $COOCH_3$

Comonomers	Conditions of copolymerization	Properties of the copolymer	Notes		Reference
			Yield of co-polymer (%)	%P in co-polymer	
CH_2 = $C(CH_3)PO(OCH_3)_2$ (I) 15% + butadiene 85%	0.3% potassium persulphate, 50°, 18 hr (in emulsion)	resinous	45	0.27	[468]
I 25% + methyl acrylate 75%	Nitrogen, 1.5% ammonium persulphate, 50°, 40 hr (in emulsion)	Fire-resistant, soluble in chloroform	75	1.63	[468]
I 25% + methyl vinyl ketone 75%	Nitrogen, 0.5% Bz_2O_2, 70°, 44 hr	Soluble in benzene, non-flammable		2.16	[468]
I 25% + acrylonitrile 75%	1.92% ammonium persulphate, 30°, 6.5 hr (in emulsion)	Colourless	52.5	1.99	[468]
I 15% + methyl methacrylate 85%	Nitrogen, 1% Bz_2O_2, 45°, 48 hr; Nitrogen, 1% Bz_2O_2, 65°, 24 hr	Transparent, hard, forms hard transparent films	100	3.0	[466]
I 15% + methyl methacrylate 85%	Nitrogen, 1% ammonium persulphate, 40°, 47 hr (in emulsion)	Softens at 101°; easily forms completely transparent, yellowish articles	86.5	0.77	[466]
I 15% + styrene 85%	1% Bz_2O_2, 45°, 24 hr	Transparent, colourless, bright			[466]
I + ethylene (excess)	Absence of air; water, Bz_2O_2, 74–76°, 860–940 atm, 9.25 hr	Copolymer, m. w. about 2640		7.11	[466]
I + ethylene (excess)	Absence of air; water, Bz_2O_2, 73–78°, 760–950 atm, 9.5 hr	Copolymer, tensile strength 90.3 kg/cm/, elongation 215%, films can be cold drawn to 575% of original length		2.3	[466]
CH_2 = $C(CH_3)PO(OC_4H_9)$ + ethylene (excess)	Absence of air; water, Bz_2O_2, 74–76°, 860–940 atm, 9.25 hr	Copolymer formed		5.6	[466]

TABLE 85 — (contd.)

Comonomers	Conditions of copolymerization	Properties of the copolymer	Notes		Reference
			Yield of copolymer (%)	%P in copolymer (%)	
CH₂ = C(C₆H₅)PO(OH)₂ (I) + methyl methacrylate 23% 77% I (25%) + acrylonitrile (75%)	Nitrogen, 0·77% Bz₂O₂, 70°, 20 hr 1·92% ammonium persulphate, 30°, 6·5 hr (in emulsion)	glass-like, burns with difficulty white copolymer, soluble in dimethylformamide, burns with difficulty	12·5	2·56 0·52	[468] [468]
I + ethylene (excess)	Absence of air; water, Bz₂O₂, 73–78°, 760–950 atm, 9·5 hr	Copolymer formed			[466]
CH₂ = C(C₆H₅)PO(OC₆H₅)₂ + ethylene (excess)	„	„			[466]
CH₂ = C(CO₂CH₃)PO(OC₂H₅)₂ (I) + styrene	Bz₂O₂, heat	„			
I + acrylonitrile	„	„			
I + methyl vinyl ketone	„	„			
I + ethylene	„	„			[100]
I + vinyl chloride	„	„			
I + vinylidene chloride	„	„			
I + butadiene	„	„			
CH₂ = C(CO₂CH₃)PO(OC₄H₉)₂ (I) + styrene	Bz₂O₂, heat	„			
I + acrylonitrile	„	„			
I + methyl vinyl ketone	„	„			
I + ethylene	„	„			[100]
I + vinyl chloride	„	„			
I + vinylidene chloride	„	„			
I + butadiene	„	„			

11*

TABLE 86. COPOLYMERS OF ESTERS OF THE TYPE
$RO_2CCH=CHPO(OR')_2$, WHERE $R=CH_3$, C_2H_5 [100]
Copolymerization in the presence of Bz_2O_2 with heating

$$CH_3O_2CCH=CHP\begin{matrix} OCH_3 \\ \| \\ O \end{matrix}\!\!\!\!\begin{matrix} \\ \\ OC_2H_5 \end{matrix}+\text{styrene}$$

(I)

I + acrylonitrile

I + methyl vinyl ketone

I + ethylene

I + vinyl chloride

I + vinylidene chloride

I + butadiene

$CH_3O_2CCH = CHPO(OC_2H_5)_2 +$ styrene
(I)

I + acrylonitrile

I + methyl vinyl ketone

I + ethylene

I + vinyl chloride

I + vinylidene chloride

I + butadiene

$CH_3O_2CCH = CHPO(OC_3H_7)_2 +$ styrene
(I)

I + acrylonitrile

I + methyl vinyl ketone

I + ethylene

I + vinyl chloride

I + vinylidene chloride

I + butadiene

$CH_3O_2CCH = CHPO(OC_4H_9)_2 +$ styrene
(I)

I + acrylonitrile

I + methyl vinyl ketone

I + ethylene

I + vinyl chloride

I + vinylidene chloride

I + butadiene

$CH_3O_2CCH = CHPO(OC_4H_9\text{-iso})_2 +$
+styrene (I)

I + acrylonitrile

I + methyl vinyl ketone

I + ethylene

I + vinyl chloride

I + vinylidene chloride

I + butadiene

$C_2H_5O_2CCH = CHPO(OCH_3)_2$ (I) +
+styrene

I + acrylonitrile

I + methyl vinyl ketone

I + ethylene

I + vinyl chloride

I + vinylidene chloride

I + butadiene

$C_2H_5OCCH = CHPO(OC_4H_9)_2$ (I) +
+styrene

I + acrylonytrile

I + methyl vinyl ketone

I + ethylene

I + vinyl chloride

I + vinylidene chlor:d:

I + butadiene

TABLE 87. POLYMERS AND COPOLYMERS OF ESTERS OF THE TYPE $CH_2{=}CRCH_2PO(OR')_2$ WHERE $R{=}H$, CH_3, C_2H_5, CN

Monomer or comonomers	Conditions of polymerization (copolymerization)	Properties of the polymer (copolymer)	Reference
$CH_2 = CHCH_2PO(OR)_2$ (R=alkyl from C_1–C_4) (10–50 %) + acrylonitrile (90–50 %)	Not stated	Resinous, flame-resistant	[235]
$CH_2 = C(CH_3)—CH_2PO(OR)_2$ (R = alkyl from C_1–C_4) (10–50 %) + acrylonitrile (90–50 %)	,, ,,	,,	[235]
$CH_2 = C(C_2H_5)CH_2PO(OR)_2$ (R = alkyl from C_1–C_4) (10–50 %) + acrylonitrile (90–50 %)	,, ,,	,,	[235]
$CH_2 = C(CN)—CH_2PO(OCH_3)_2$ (I)	Nitrogen, 0·3 % $(CH_3CO_2)_2$, 100°	Transparent, hard, thermoplastic, flame-resistant, soluble in acetone, acetonitrile, dimethylformamide, Softens above 80°	[236]
I + acrylonitrile	Peroxide or persulphate, heat	Transparent, hard, thermoplastic, flame-resistant	[236]
I + vinyl chloride	,, ,, ,,	,,	
I + styrene	,, ,, ,,	,,	
I + methyl methacrylate	,, ,, ,,	,,	
I + vinyl acetate	,, ,, ,,	,,	

TABLE 87 — (contd.)

Monomers or comonomers	Conditions of polymerization (copolymerization)	Properties of the polymer (copolymer)	Reference
$CH_2 = C(CN)CH_2PO(OC_2H_5)_2$ (I)	Bz_2O_2 80–85°, 24 hr	Transparent, hard, thermoplastic, flame-resistant, soluble in acetone	[236]
I + acrylonitrile	,,	,,	
I + vinyl chloride	,,	,,	
I + styrene	,,	,,	
I + methyl methacrylate	,,	,,	
I + vinyl acetate	,,	,,	
$CH_2 = C(CN)CH_2PO(OC_3H_7)_2$ (I)	Peroxide, heat	Transparent hard, thermoplastic, flame-resistant	[236]
I + acrylonitrile	,,	,,	
I + vinyl chloride	,,	,,	
I + styrene	,,	,,	
I + methyl methacrylate	,,	,,	
I + vinyl acetate	,,	,,	
$CH_2 = C(CN)CH_2PO(OC_4H_9)_2$ (I)	Peroxide, heat	Transparent, hard, thermoplastic, flame-resistant	[236]
I + acrylonitrile	,,	,,	
I + vinyl chloride	,,	,,	
I + styrene	,,	,,	
I + methyl methacrylate	,,	,,	
I + vinyl acetate	,,	,,	

TABLE 88. POLYMERS AND COPOLYMERS OF ESTERS OF THE TYPE $CH_2=CRCOPO(OR')_2$, $CH_2=CRCH_2{\begin{matrix}Ar\\Ar\end{matrix}}P(O)OR'$, $RCH=CHCH_2{\begin{matrix}Ar\\ \end{matrix}}P(O)OR'$ WHERE R=H, CH₃, C₂H₅, AND POLYMERS OF ESTERS OF PHOSPHONIC ACIDS WITH TWO DOUBLE BONDS

Monomer and comonomers	Conditions of polymerization (copolymerization)	Properties of the polymer(copolymer)	Brinell hardness (kg/cm²)	Temperature stability (°C)	Reference
$CH_2=CHCOPO(OCH_3)_2$	Polymerizes during distillation in the presence of hydroquinone and in an atmosphere of nitrogen				[101]
$CH_2=CHCOPO(OCH_3)_2$ + methyl methacrylate					
10% 90%	Nitrogen, Bz₂O₂, heat, 12 hr	Transparent, hard, low flammability	12·7	115	[101]
40% * 60%	” , 4 hr	Transparent, hard, quickly extinguishes itself	2·6	85	
50% 50%	” , 3 hr	”		45	
$CH_2=CHCOPO(OC_2H_5)_2$	Polymerizes during distillation from hydroquinone				[101]
$CH_2=CHCOPO(OC_2H_5)_2$ + methyl methacrylate					
10% 90%	Nitrogen, Bz₂O₂, heat, 14 hr	Transparent, hard, low flammability	12·4	110	[101]
25% * 75%	” , 37 hr	” , quickly extinguishes itself	5	50	
50% 50%	” , 48 hr	” , non-flammable		50	
$CH_2=C(CH_3)COPO(OC_2H_5)_2$	Polymerizes during synthesis	After distillation of low-boiling products a viscous oil remained, which was soluble in water (59% yield). By heating with benzoyl peroxide it becomes more viscous; m. w. 510–532			[99]
${\begin{matrix}C_6H_5\\CH_2=CHCH_2\end{matrix}}P(O)OCH_3$	$[(CH_3)_3C—O—]_2$, 115°, 24 hr	Polymer formed			[239]

TABLE 88. — (contd.)

Monomer and comonomers	Conditions of polymerization (copolymerization)	Properties of the polymer (copolymer)	Notes — Brinell hardness (kg/cm²)	Notes — Temperature stability (°C)	Reference
$\begin{array}{c}C_6H_5\\CH_2=CHCH_2\end{array}\!\!>\!\!P(O)OCH_3$ + diallyl phthalate	$[(CH_3)_3C-O-]_2$, 115°, 24 hr	Copolymer formed			[239]
$\begin{array}{c}C_6H_5\\CH_2=CHCH_2\end{array}\!\!>\!\!P(O)OC_4H_9$	$[(CH_3)_3-C-O-]_2$, 115°, 24 hr	Polymer formed			[239]
$\begin{array}{c}4\text{-}CH_3C_6H_4\\CH_2=C(CH_3)CH_2\end{array}\!\!>\!\!P(O)OCH_3$	$[(CH_3)_3C-O-]_2$, 115_2, 24 hr	,,			[239]
$\begin{array}{c}(CH_3)_2C_6H_3\\CH_2=C(C_2H_5)CH_2\end{array}\!\!>\!\!P(O)OC_{10}H_{21}$	$[(CH_3)_3C-O-]_2$, 115°, 24 hr	,,			[239]
$\begin{array}{c}3{,}5\text{-}(C_4H_9)_2C_6H_3\\CH_3=CHCH_2\end{array}\!\!>\!\!P(O)OC_4H_9$	$[(CH_3)_3C-O-]_2$, 115°, 24 hr	,,			[239]
$CH_2=CH-CH=CH-PO(OC_2H_5)_2$	2% Bz_2O_2, 85°, 3 weeks	From viscous liquids to semi-solid substances			[73]
Mixture of $CH_2=CH-CH=CH-PO(OC_4H_9)_2$ and $CH_2=CH-C-PO(OC_4H_9)_2$ $\overset{\parallel}{CH_2}$	2% Bz_2O_2, 85°, 3 weeks	From viscous liquids to semi-solid substances			[73]
$CH_2=CH-CH=CH-PO(OC_4H_9)_2$	Bz_2O_2, 85°, 24 hr ,, 120°, 6 days	Gel Brown, rubber-like			[73] [73]

* The acroylphosphonic ester used was undistilled.

TABLE 89. POLYMERS AND COPOLYMERS OF UNSATURATED ESTERS OF ALKOXYCARBONYLALKYLPHOSPHONIC ACIDS OF THE TYPE $RO_2C—R'—PO(OR'')_2$, WHERE R = UNSATURATED RADICAL, AND R' AND R'' = SATURATED RADICALS

Monomer and comonomers	Conditions of polymerization (copolymerization)	Properties of the polymer (copolymer)	Notes				Reference
			Brinell hardness (kg/cm²)	Thermal stability (°C)	Impact strength (kg/mm²)	Transparency (%)	
$CH_2 = CHO_2CCH_2PO(OC_2H_5)_2$ (I)	Nitrogen, 1% Bz_2O_2, 60–70°, 200 hr.	Low molecular weight syrup, degree of polymerization 2–4					[250]
	Nitrogen, 1% Bz_2O_2, 65°, 10 hr. $AlCl_3$ and $(NH_4)_2S_2O_8$ also used as catalysts	Hard, wax-like polymer, soluble in hot ethanol, insoluble in water and benzene, m. w. 1300					[106]
I + styrene	,,	Copolymer formed					[106]
I + methyl methacrylate	,,	,,					[106]
I + vinyl acetate	,,	,,					[106]
I + vinyl chloride	,,	,,					[106]
I + ethylene	,,	,,					[106]
I + tetrafluoroethylene	,,	,,					[106]
$CH_2 = CHCH_2O_2CCH_2PO(OCH_3)_2$	Nitrogen, 1% Bz_2O_2, 60–70°, 200 hr	Transparent, thick syrup					[250]
$CH_2 = CHCH_2O_2CCH_2PO(OCH_3)_2$ 15% + methyl methacrylate 85%	Nitrogen, 0·3% Bz_2O_2, 50–70°, 16 hr	Hard, transparent, colourless or yellow	11·2	65	12·5	91·7	[250]
$CH_2 = CHCH_2O_2CCH_2PO(OC_2H_5)_2$	Nitrogen, 1% Bz_2O_2, 60–70°, 200 hr	Transparent, thick syrup					[250]

TABLE 89 — (contd.)

Monomer and comonomers	Conditions of polymerization (copolymerization)	Properties of the polymer (copolymer)	Brinell hardness (kg/cm²)	Thermal stability (°C)	Impact strength (kg/mm²)	Transparency (%)	Reference
CH₂ = CHCH₂O₂CCH₂PO(OC₂H₅)₂ + methyl methacrylate							
5%	Nitrogen, 0.3% Bz₂O₂, 50–70°, 7.5 hr	Hard, transparent, colourless or yellow	11·2	88			[250]
10%	" , 2 hr	Hard, transparent, colourless or yellow, self-extinguishing after 11 sec	6	115			[101]
10%	" , 9 hr	Hard, transparent, colourless or yellow	10·4	74	12	91·5	[250]
15%	" , 12 hr	,,	11·9	62		91·5	[250]
20%	" , 16 hr	,,	7·4	49	16	89·5	[250]
30%	" , 20 hr	,, almost immediately self-extinguishing	3	75			[101]
50%	" , 10 hr	Elastic, non-flammable					[101]
CH₂ = CHCH₂O₂CCH₂PO(OC₃H₇-iso)₂	Nitrogen, 1% Bz₂O₂, 60–70°, 200 hr	Thick, transparent syrup					[250]
CH₂ = CHCH₂O₂CCH₂PO(OC₃H₇-iso)₂ 15% + methyl methacrylate 85%	Nitrogen, 0.3% Bz₂O₂, 50–70°, 18 hr	Hard, transparent, colourless or yellow	12·3	72	11·4	91·5	[250]
CH₂ = CHCH₂O₂CCH₂PO(OC₄H₉)₂	Nitrogen, 1% Bz₂O₂, 60–70°, 200 hr	No polymer formed					[250]
CH₂ = CHCH₂O₂CCH₂PO(OC₄H₉)₂ 15% + methyl methacrylate 85%	Nitrogen, 0.3% Bz₂O₂, 50–70°, 17 hr	Hard, transparent, colourless or yellow	12·9	63	13·3	92·4	[250]
CH₂ = CHCH₂O₂CCH₂PO(OC₄H₉-iso)₂	Nitrogen, 1% Bz₂O₂, 60–70°, 200 hr	No polymer formed					[250]
CH₂ = CHCH₂O₂CCHPO(OC₄H₉-iso)₂ 15% + methyl methacrylate 85%	Nitrogen, 0.3% Bz₂O₂, 50–70°, 20 hr	Hard, transparent, colourless or yellow	14	67	13	91·5	[250]

TABLE 90. POLYMERS AND COPOLYMERS OF UNSATURATED ESTERS OF PHOSPHOROUS ACID, α,β-UNSATURATED ESTERS OF PHOSPHORIC ACID AND β,γ-UNSATURATED ESTERS (WITH ONE OR TWO DOUBLE BONDS) OF PHOSPHORIC ACID

Monomer or comonomers	Conditions of polymerization (copolymerization)	Properties of the polymer (copolymer)	Reference
CH_2—O $\rangle$ POCH=CH_2 CH_2—O	1·34% Bz_2O_2, 50–70°, 200 hr	Dark, soft. Swells in chloroform and slowly dissolves	[120]
POCH=CH_2	0·9% Bz_2O_2, 50–70°, 120 hr	Yellow, soft. Swells in chloroform	[120]
$HPO(OCH_2CH=CH_2)_2$	Nitrogen, 2% Bz_2O_2, 87–88°, 18 hr	Hard, glass-like, insoluble	[186]
$P(OCH_2CH=CH_2)_3$	Nitrogen, 1·5% Bz_2O_2, 98–100°, 6 hr	Similar to above	[173]
	Bz_2O_2 or α,α'-azodi-isobutyronitrile, heat	Does not polymerize	[173]
$(C_2H_5O)_2P(O)OCH=CH_2$ (I)	2–5% Bz_2O_2 or α,α'-azodi-isobutyro-nitrile, 80°, 42–70 hr	,,	[156]
	$[(CH_3)_3CO—]_2$, 125°	,,	[156]
	2–4% Na in liquid ammonia at −30°	,,	[156]
I* + styrene 63·4% 36·6%	Nitrogen, 4·93% Bz_2O_2, 80°, 42 hr	Colourless, viscous liquid, from which by treatment with methyl alcohol was obtained a hard, colourless copolymer softening at 68°	[156]
I* + methyl methacrylate 64% 36%	Nitrogen, 5% Bz_2O_2, 80°, 42 hr	Copolymer softening at 110°	[156]

TABLE 90 — (contd.)

Monomer or comonomers	Conditions of polymerization (copolymerization)	Properties of the polymer (copolymer)	Reference
I* + acrylonitrile $\quad$ 77% $\quad$ 23%	Nitrogen, 6% Bz_2O_2, 80°, 42 hr	Copolymer softening at 210–220°	[156]
I* + vinyl acetate	,,	No polymer formed	[156]
$PO(OCH = CH_2)_3$	1% Bz_2O_2, 50–70°, 5 hr ,, $\quad$ 100 hr	Hard, yellow, non-flammable, insoluble	[120]
$CCl_2 = CHOPO(OCH_2CH = CH_2)_2^+$	1.5% Bz_2O_2, 100° (in emulsion)	Hard, brittle, insoluble	[173]
$(C_2H_5O)_2P(O)OCH_2CH = CH_2$	Nitrogen, 3% Bz_2O_2, 87–88°, 18 hr	Liquid	[186]
$(C_6H_5O)_2POCH_2C(CH_3) = CH_2$ + styrene $\quad\quad\quad \overset{\|}{O} \quad$ 2% $\quad\quad$ 98%	140°, 48 hr	Resin-like, soluble in aromatic hydrocarbons, insoluble in acetone and ethanol	[471]
$[(CH_3)_2C_6H_3O_2PO[OCH_2C(CH_3) = CH_2]$ 10% + styrene 90%	100–110°, 4 days	Colourless. Tensile strength 3.5 kg/cm², softening point 93°, Shore hardness 83°	[471]
$CH_3OPO(OCH_2CH = CH_2)_2$	Nitrogen, 1.5% Bz_2O_2, 98–100°, 6 hr	Hard, brittle, insoluble	[173]
$C_6H_5OPO(OCH_2CH = CH_2)_2$	2% $[(CH_3)_3CO—]_2$, 115°, 43 hr	Soft, dark, crumbles	[189]
	2% Bz_2O_2, 65° for 27 hr then 90° for 6 hr and 115° for 18 hr	,, $\quad$,, $\quad$,,	[189]
	Nitrogen, 3% Bz_2O_2, 87–88°, 18 hr	Hard, glass-like	[189]

* See footnote on p. 50.

⁺ The bulk polymerization goes extremely rapidly and cannot be controlled.

TABLE 91. THE POLYMERS OF TRIALLYL PHOSPHATE* AND ITS COPOLYMERS WITH HALOGENOMETHANES PRODUCED BY EMULSION POLYMERIZATION [456]

Monomer or comonomers (moles)	Conditions of polymerization (copolymerization)		Properties of the polymer (copolymer)				
			Molecular weight	No. of units of I in a mole	Halide I ratio in copolymer	Residual unsaturation (ratio of double bonds to moles of I)	Yield of polymer as a % of the weight of the reagents
PO(OCH₂CH=CH₂)₃ (I)	2% potassium persulphate, 80–85°, 2 hr	a	276	1·3		0·40	6
		b					50
I + tetrabromomethane 1·0 + 0·6	"	a	810	2·0	0·55	1·39	18
		b			0·67	0·59	71
I + bromoform 1·0 + 0·3	"	a	500	1·7	0·30	1·84	14
		b			0·33	0·63	70
1·0 / 0·6	2% potassium persulphate, 70–75°, 2 hr	a	590	1·6	0·64	0·53	26
		b			0·65	1·54	72
1·0 / 0·6	1% potassium persulphate, 80–85°, 2 hr	a	840	2·3	0·60	0·53	59
		b			0·64	1·61	23
1·0 / 0·6	1·5% potassium persulphate, 80–85°, 2 hr	a	620	1·7	0·62	0·57	25
		b			0·60	1·55	71
1·0 / 0·6	2% potassium persulphate, 80–85°, 2 hr	a	600	1·5	0·72	0·47	12
		b			0·55	1·46	80
1·0 / 0·6	3% potassium persulphate, 80–85°, 2 hr	a	680	1·7	0·73	0·51	8
		b			0·63	0·93	82
1·0 / 1·0	2% potassium persulphate, 80–85°, 2 hr	a	700	1·5	1·16	0·40	13
		b			0·96		79
1·0 / 2·0	2% potassium persulphate, 80–85°, 2 hr	a	705	1·0	1·97	0·06	90
		b					0
1·0 / 3·0	"	a	883	0·9	2·29	0·02	7
		b					0
I + bromotrichloromethane 1·0 + 0·6	"	a	690	1·9			25
		b					47
I + carbon tetrachloride 1·0 + 0·6	2% potassium persulphate, 70–75°, 2 hr	a	260		0·18	0·64	22
		b					31

* See also Table 91(a).

(a) Viscous liquid soluble in CH₂Cl₂.

(b) Hard substance insoluble in CH₂Cl₂.

TABLE 91(a). POLYMERS AND COPOLYMERS OF β,γ-UNSATURATED ESTERS OF PHOSPHORIC ACID WITH THREE DOUBLE BONDS

Monomers or comonomers, wt. %	Conditions of polymerization (copolymerization)	Properties of the polymer (copolymer)	Reference
$PO(OCH_2CH=CH_2)_4$ (I)	Nitrogen, 1·5% Bz_2O_2, 98–100°, 6 hr	Hard, brittle, insoluble	[173]
	2% Bz_2O_2, 144 hr	,,	[189], [136]
	2% Bz_2O_2, 95°, in emulsion	33–34% of free double bonds left in the polymer	[136]
	1·25% Bz_2O_2, 90°, 45 min	Very viscous liquid, bromine number 150. After adding 1·25% hydroquinone and distilling off the unreacted monomer *in vacuo*, the residue had bromine number 90	[136]
	50% solution of I in CCl_4, 6·25% Bz_2O_2 by wt. of I, 110°, 25 min	,,	[136]
I + $PO(OC_2H_4OCOCH=CHCO_2CH_2CH=CH_2)_3$ I + vinyl acetate	Bz_2O_2, heat	Insoluble in organic solvents	[446]
2 98	0·5% Bz_2O_2, 40° for 2 days then 65° for 10 days	Copolymer formed	[472]
5 95	,,	Hard, transparent, can be worked by machine, non-flammable	[472]
10 90	,,		[472]
20 80	,,	,,	[472]
40 60	,,	,,	[472]
80 20	,,	Soft	[472]
10 10	,,	,,	[472]
95 5	,,	,,	[472]
9 + styrene 5 95	95°, 72 hr	Colourless, glass-like, can be moulded at 150°, cut, polished, etc. Insoluble in acetone and methanol; insoluble but swells in benzene. Tensile strength, 364 kg/cm²; softening temperature about 62°; Shore hardness about 75°	[471]

TABLE 91(a) — (contd.)

Monomers or comonomers, wt. %	Conditions of polymerization (copolymerization)	Properties of the polymer (copolymer)	Reference
I + styrene 5　　95	Boil the benzene solution of this mixture for 5 days	Stiff gel obtained, treatment of which with ethanol precipitated a powder of the copolymer. Properties of a moulded test specimen: Tensile strength 364 kg/cm², heat distortion point about 62°; Shore hardness about 75	[471]
I (10%) + partially polymerized (at 125° for several hr) styrene in the form of thick liquid (90%)	90°, 6 days, in emulsion	Colourless, translucent copolymer, insoluble in benzene. More brittle than polystyrene	[471]
$P[OCH_2C(CH_3)=CH_2]_3$ (II)	2% Bz_2O_2, 95°, in emulsion	33-34% of free double bonds left in the polymer	[137]
II + styrene 2　　98	100-110°, 4 days	The copolymer was precipitated from its dispersion in benzene by ethyl alcohol. A test specimen moulded at 150° had a power factor of 0·5% and a dielectric constant of 2·71	[471]
3·85　　96·15	100-110°, 89 hr	The product was obtained from a benzene dispersion by precipitation with ethanol. A test specimen which had been moulded at 150° was a clear, glass-like copolymer which swelled only slightly in benzene. It had tensile strength 770 kg/cm², dielectric constant 2·4 and power factor 0·04%. Heat distortion point 92°	[471]
4　　96	100-110°, 4 days	The product was dispersed in benzene and precipitated in finely divided form by addition of ethanol. A test sample which had been moulded at 150° was a clear, transparent resin, insoluble in acetone and ethanol and capable only of swelling when contacted with benzene. It had tensile strength 363 kg/cm³, heat distortion point about 62° and Shore hardness 75	[471]
II (5%) + partially polymerized (at 125° for several hr) styrene (95%)	125°, 48 hr	Colourless, resinous copolymer, insoluble in acetone and ethanol, swells but does not dissolve in benzene	[471]
$PO(OCH_2CHBrCH_2Br)_3$	50% benzene solution refluxed with zinc dust	Viscous oil, soluble in dichloroethane	[137]

TABLE 92. POLYMERS OF β,γ-UNSATURATED DERIVATIVES OF PHOSPHORAMIDIC ACID

Monomer	Conditions of polymerization	Properties of the polymer	Reference
$(C_2H_5O)_2PNHCH_2C(CH_3)=CH_2$, $\overset{\parallel}{O}$	Nitrogen, 3% Bz_2O_2, 87–88°, 18 hr	Liquid	[186]
$(C_2H_5O)_2PN(CH_2CH=CH_2)_2$, $\overset{\parallel}{O}$	Nitrogen, 3% Bz_2O_2, 87–88°, 18 hr	Liquid; initial viscosity, 2·8 cP; viscosity after polymerization 5·2 cP, 84% of the monomer distilled at 0·5 mm	[186]
$NH_2PO(OCH_2CH=CH_2)_2$	50% solution in benzene, 1·25% Bz_2O_2 by wt. of the monomer. The solution refluxed for 65 min	Polymer formed	[136]
$HOCH_2NHPO(OCH_2CH=CH_2)_2$	50% solution in isopropanol, 2% Bz_2O_2 by wt. of the monomer, and boiled for 2 hr	Soluble in methanol, insoluble in cyclohexane, ligroin, carbon tetrachloride	[137]
$(CH_3)_2NPO(OCH_2CH=CH_2)_2$	Nitrogen, 3% Bz_2O_2, 87–88°, 18 hr	Liquid, initial viscosity 2·3 cP; viscosity after polymerization 2·6 cP; 55·8% of the monomer distilled at 0·5 mm	[186]
$CH_2[-NHPO(OCH_2CH=CH_2)_2]_2$	50% solution in isopropanol, 2% Bz_2O_2 by wt. of the monomer, and refluxed for 2 hr	Soluble in methanol; insoluble in cyclohexane, ligroin, carbon tetrachloride	[137]
$[-CH_2NHPO(OCH_2CH=CH_2)_2]_2$	"	"	[137]

TABLE 93. POLYMERS AND COPOLYMERS OF ESTERS OF ALKYL- AND ARYL-PHOSPHONOUS AND PHOSPHONODITHIOUS ACID AND β,γ-UNSATURATED ALCOHOLS

Monomer and comonomers	Conditions of polymerization (copolymerization)	Properties of the polymer (copolymer)	Reference
$\underset{\text{H}}{\mid}$ $C_8H_{17}P(O)OCH_2CH=CH_2$ + diallyl phthalate	$[(CH_3)_3C\!-\!O\!-\!]_2$, 175°, 5 hr	Very viscous oil	[183a]
iso-$C_5H_{11}P(OCH_2CH=CH_2)_2$ (I)	Conditions not stated	Polymer formed	
I + diallyl phthalate	,,	Copolymer formed	[179]
I + acrylonitrile	,,	,,	
I + vinyl chloride	,,	,,	
I + isobutylene	,,	,,	
$C_6H_5P(OCH_2CH=CH_2)_2$ (I)	1% Bz_2O_2, 70°, 200 hr	No polymer formed	[431]
I + diallyl phthalate	Conditions not stated	Polymer formed	
I + acrylonitrile	,,	Copolymer formed	[179]
I + vinyl chloride	,,	,,	
I + isobutylene	,,	,,	
$C_6H_5P(SCH_2CH=CH_2)_2$ (I)	Conditions not stated	Polymer formed	
I + diallyl phthalate	,,	Copolymer formed	[179]
I + acrylonitrile	,,	,,	
I + vinyl chloride	,,	,,	
I + isobutylene	,,	,,	

TABLE 93 — (contd.)

Monomer and comonomers	Conditions of polymerization (copolymerization)	Properties of the polymer (copolymer)	Reference
4-ClC$_6$H$_4$P(OCH$_2$CH = CH$_2$)$_2$	1% Bz$_2$O$_2$, 70°, 200 hr	No polymer formed	[473]
4-ClC$_6$H$_4$P(OCH$_2$CH = CH$_2$)$_2$ (I)	Conditions not stated	Polymer formed	[179]
I + diallyl phthalate	,,	Copolymer formed	
I + acrylonitrile	,,	,,	
I + vinyl chloride	,,	,,	
I + isobutylene	,,	,,	
4-iso-C$_3$H$_7$C$_6$H$_4$P(OCH$_2$C=CH$_2$)$_2$ (I) CH$_3$	Conditions not stated	Polymer formed	[179]
I + diallyl phthalate	,,	Copolymer formed	
I + acrylonitrile	,,	,,	
I + vinyl chloride	,,	,,	
I + isobutylene	,,	,,	
2,4,6-(CH$_3$)$_3$C$_6$H$_2$P(OCH$_2$C=CH$_2$)$_2$ (I) CH$_3$	Conditions not stated	Polymer formed	[179]
I + diallyl phthalate	,,	Copolymer formed	
I + acrylonitrile	,,	,,	
I + vinyl chloride	,,	,,	
I + isobutylene	,,	,,	

TABLE 94. POLYMERS OF ESTERS OF α,β-UNSATURATED ALCOHOLS WITH ALKYL- AND ARYL-PHOSPHONIC AND ALKYLARYLPHOSPHINIC ACIDS [120]

Monomer	Conditions of polymerization	Properties of the polymer
CH₃P(=O)(OCH=CH₂)(OCH₂CH₂Cl)	1·5% Bz₂O₂, 50–70°, 150 hr	Yellow, soft, swells in chloroform and gradually dissolves
CH₃P(=O)(OCH=CH₂)(OC₄H₉)	1·45–1·84% Bz₂O₂, 50–70°, 200 hr	Pale yellow liquid
CH₃>P(O)(OCH=CH₂) C₆H₅	1·5% Bz₂O₂, 50–80°, 200 hr	Deep yellow, thick liquid
RPO(OCH=CH₂)₂ R		
CH₃—	1·4–1·9% Bz₂O₂, 50°, 50 hr	Pale yellow, hard, non-flammable, insoluble in organic solvents
ClCH₂—	0·67% Bz₂O₂, 50°, 30 hr	„
C₂H₅—	1·3% Bz₂O₂, 50–70°, 100 hr	„
C₆H₅—	1·2% Bz₂O₂, 50°, 150 hr	Dark, hard, non-flammable, insoluble in organic solvents
C₆H₅—*	1·3% Bz₂O₂, 80°	From viscous liquids to soft sticky polymers

* See reference (156). See footnote on p. 50.

TABLE 94a. POLYMERS AND COPOLYMERS OF ESTERS OF SATURATED DIALKYL- AND ALKYLARYLPHOSPHINIC ACIDS WITH β,γ-((AND OTHER) UNSATURATED ALCOHOLS CONTAINING ONE UNSATURATED BOND IN THE MOLECULE

$$\frac{R'}{R}\!\!>\!P(O)OCH_2CH=CH_2$$

Monomer or comonomers		Conditions of polymerization (copolymerization)	Properties of the polymer (copolymer)	Reference
R	R'			
CH_3-	CH_3-	1% Bz_2O_2, 80° for 25 hr, 115° for 25 hr, 140° for 65 hr	Viscous red-brown liquid	[273]
CH_3-	C_6H_5-	1% Bz_2O_2, 70°, 200 hr	Does not polymerize	[473]
C_2H_5-	C_6H_5-	1% Bz_2O_2, 70°, 200 hr	,,	[473]
C_4H_9-	C_6H_5-	$[(CH_3)_3CO-]_2$	Very viscous oil	[183a]
CH_3-	$4\text{-}ClC_6H_4-$	1% Bz_2O_2, 70°, 200 hr	Does not polymerize	[473]
C_4H_9-	C_4H_9-	$[(CH_3)_3CO-]_2$, 175°, 5 hr	Viscous oil, probably a decamer	[183a]
$C_8H_{17}-$	$C_8H_{17}-$	$[(CH_3)_3CO-]_2$, 175°, 5 hr	Viscous oil	[183a]
$\dfrac{C_4H_9}{\text{cyclo-}C_6H_{11}}\!\!>\!P(O)OCH_2CH=CH_2$ + allyl acetate		$[(CH_3)_3CO-]_2$, 175°, 5 hr	,,	[183a]
$(CH_3)_2P(O)OCH_2C(CH_3)=CH_2$		1% Bz_2O_2, 80° for 25 hr, 115° for 25 hr, 140° for 65 hr	Viscous red-brown liquid	[273]
$(CH_3)_2P(O)OCH_2CH=CHCH_3$		,,	,,	[273]
$(CH_3)_2P(O)OCH_2C\equiv CH$		,,	,,	[273]
$(CH_3)_2P(O)OCH_2CH_2C\equiv CH$		,,	,,	[273]

TABLE 95. POLYMERS AND COPOLYMERS OF ESTERS OF ALKYL-, ACETYL- AND BENZOYL-PHOSPHONIC ACIDS WITH β,γ-UNSATURATED ALCOHOLS CONTAINING TWO UNSATURATED LINKAGES IN THE MOLECULE

Monomer or comonomers	Conditions of polymerization (copolymerization)	Character of the polymer (copolymer)	Notes	Reference
$CH_3PO(OCH_2CH=CH_2)_2$	Nitrogen, 3% Bz_2O_2, 87–88°, 18 hr	From moderately hard polymers to soft and resin-like gels		[186]
$ClCH_2PO(OCH_2CH=CH_2)_2$ (I)	Nitrogen, 3% Bz_2O_2, 85°	Hard, transparent, insoluble, nonflammable		[274]
I + dichlorodiethyl ether (50%) (50%)	Nitrogen, 1% Bz_2O_2, 100°	Colourless powder, soluble in a mixture of methanol (30%) and dichloroethane (70%), insoluble in hexane	Yield of copolymer 43·6%	[474]
I + diallyl phthalate (10%) (90%)	Nitrogen, 3% Bz_2O_2, 85°	Hard, transparent, fire-resistant, insoluble		[274]
I + methyl methacrylate	„	„		[475]
I + vinyl acetate	„	„		[275]
$CCl_3PO(OCH_2CH=CH_2)_2$	1% Bz_2O_2, 60–70°, 80–90 hr	Gel, insoluble in organic solvents		[105]
	1·5% Bz_2O_2, 100° (in emulsion)*	Hard, brittle, insoluble		[173]
$C_2H_5PO(OCH_2CH=CH_2)_2$	Nitrogen, 3% Bz_2O_2, 87–88°, 18 hr	From moderately hard polymers to soft and resin-like gels		[186]
$CH_3COPO(OCH_2CH=CH_2)_2$ (I) I + methyl methacrylate	Bz_2O_2, heat	Gel		[101]
20% 80%	Bz_2O_2, heat, 40 hr	Hard, transparent, amber coloured, self-extinguishing in 3 sec	Brinell hardness, 5 kg/cm², thermal resistance 80°	[101]
30% 70%	Bz_2O_2, heat, 51 hr	Hard, transparent, amber coloured, self-extinguishing almost immediately	Brinell hardness 3·03 kg/cm², thermal resistance 70°	[101]

* Bulk polymerization proceeds extremely rapidly and cannot be controlled.

Table 95 — (contd.)

Monomer or comonomers	Conditions of polymerization (copolymerization)	Character of the polymer (copolymer)	Notes	Reference
$C_3H_7PO(OCH_2CH=CH_2)_2$	Nitrogen, 3% Bz_2O_2, 87–88°, 18 hr	From moderately hard polymers to soft and resin-like gels		[186]
iso-$C_3H_7PO(OCH_2CH=CH_2)_2$	,,	,,		[186]
$C_4H_9PO(OCH_2CH=CH_2)_2$ (I)	,,	,,		[186]
I + diallyl phthalate (90%)	1% $[(CH_3)_3CO—]_2$, 115°, 20 hr	Transparent		[183]
(10%)	2% Bz_2O_2, 45° for 24 hr, 90° for 6 hr, 115° for 18 hr	Hard		[183]
$RPO(OCH_2CH=CH_2)_2$ R= iso-C_4H_9—	Nitrogen, 3% Bz_2O_2, 87–88°, 18 hr	From moderately hard polymers to soft and resin-like gels		[186]
cyclo-C_6H_{11}—	From 70° to 115° for 7.5 hr	No polymerization		[188]
cyclo-C_6H_{11}—	1% Bz_2O_2, from 70° to 115° for 7.5 hr	Viscous liquid		[188]
cyclo-C_6H_{11}—	2% Bz_2O_2, from 70° to 115° for 7.5 hr	Transparent, thick gel		[188]
cyclo-C_6H_{11}—	5% Bz_2O_2, from 70° to 115° for 7.5 hr	Transparent, colourless, moderately hard polymer		[188]
cyclo-C_6H_{11}—	Nitrogen, 3% Bz_2O_2, 87–88°, 18 hr	From moderately hard polymers to soft and resin-like gels		[186]
$C_6H_5CH_2$—	Nitrogen, 3% Bz_2O_2, 87–88°, 18 hr	Hard, glass-like		[186]
$C_6H_5CH_2$—	1% $[(CH_3)_3CO—]_2$, 115°, 20 hr	Transparent		[183]
$C_6H_5COPO(OCH_2CH=CH_2)_2$ (I)	Bz_2O_2, heat	Gel		[101]

TABLE 95 — (contd.)

Monomer or comonomers	Conditions of polymerization (copolymerization)	Character of the polymer (copolymer)	Notes	Reference
I + methyl methacrylate 20% 80%	", 18 hr	Hard, transparent, brittle, self-extinguishing in 5 sec	Brinell hardness, 6·63 kg/cm², temperature resistance 100°	[101]
30% 70%	", 18 hr	", self-extinguishing almost immediately	Brinell hardness, 3 kg/cm², temperature resistance 60°	[101]
$(CH_3)_3CCH_2CH(CH_3)CH_2PO(OCH_2CH=CH_2)_2$	Nitrogen, 3% Bz_2O_2, 87–88°, 18 hr	From moderately hard polymers to soft and resin-like gels		[186]
$CH_3PO[OCH_2C(CH_3)=CH_2]$	Nitrogen, 3% Bz_2O_2, 87–88°, 18 hr	From moderately hard polymers to soft and resin-like gels		[186]
$ClCH_2PO[OCH_2C(CH_3)=CH_2]_2$ (50%) + dichlorodiethyl ether (50%)	Nitrogen, 1% Bz_2O_2, 100°	Colourless powder. Soluble in a mixture of methanol (30%) and dichloroethane (70%). Insoluble in hexane		[474]
$R—PO[OCH_2C(CH_3)=CH_2]_2$ R: $C_2H_5—$	Nitrogen, 3% Bz_2O_2, 87–88°, 18 hr	From moderately hard polymers to soft and resin-like gels		[186]
C_3H_7	"	"		
iso-$C_3H_7—$	"	"		
C_4H_9	"	"		
iso-$C_4H_9—$	"	"		
cyclo-C_6H_{11}	"	"		
$C_6H_5CH_2—$	"	Hard, glass-like		
2-C_8H_{17}	"	From moderately hard polymers to soft and resin-like gels		

TABLE 95(a). POLYMERS AND COPOLYMERS OF ESTERS OF ALKYLPHOSPHONIC
ACIDS AND β,γ-UNSATURATED ALCOHOLS CONTAINING FOUR
UNSATURATED LINKS IN THE MOLECULE [275]

Monomers or comonomers	Conditions of polymerization (copolymerization)	Properties of the polymer (copolymer)
$[(CH_2 = CHCH_2O)_2PCH—]_2O$ (I) $\overset{\|}{O}$	$[(CH_3)_3CO—]_2$, 110°, 20 hr	Polymer formed
I + diallyl phthalate	Bz$_2$O$_2$, 115°, 48 hr	Copolymer formed
I + butenyl stearate	Peroxide (or light), heat	Copolymer formed
I + cyclopentadiene	Peroxide (or light), heat	Copolymer formed
I + styrene	Peroxide (or light), heat	Copolymer formed
I + butadiene	Peroxide (or light), heat	Copolymer formed
I + methyl acrylate	Peroxide (or light), heat	Copolymer formed
I + vinyl acetate	Peroxide (or light), heat	Copolymer formed
I + allyl acetate	Peroxide (or light), heat	Copolymer formed
I + methyl vinyl ketone	Peroxide (or light), heat	Copolymer formed
I + acrylonitrile	Peroxide (or light), heat	Copolymer formed
I + acrolein	Peroxide (or light), heat	Copolymer formed
I + diallyl diglycollate	Peroxide (or light), heat	Copolymer formed
$[(CH_2 = CClCH_2O)_2PCH_2—]_2O$ (I) $\overset{\|}{O}$	Peroxide (or light), heat	Polymer formed
I + diallyl phthalate	Peroxide (or light), heat	Copolymer formed
I + butenyl stearate	Peroxide (or light), heat	Copolymer formed
I + cyclopentadiene	Peroxide (or light), heat	Copolymer formed
I + styrene	Peroxide (or light), heat	Copolymer formed
I + butadiene	Peroxide (or light), heat	Copolymer formed

TABLE 95(a) — *(contd.)*

Monomers or comonomers	Conditions of polymerization (copolymerization)	Properties of the polymer (copolymer)
I + methyl acrylate	Peroxide (or light), heat	Copolymer formed
I + vinyl acetate	Peroxide (or light), heat	Copolymer formed
I + allyl acetate	Peroxide (or light), heat	Copolymer formed
I + methyl vinyl ketone	Peroxide (or light) heat	Copolymer formed
I + acrylonitrile	Peroxide (or light), heat	Copolymer formed
I + acrolein	Peroxide (or light), heat	Copolymer formed
I + diallyl diglycollate	Peroxide (or light), heat	Copolymer formed
$[CH_2 = C(CH_3)CH_2O)_2PCH_2-]_2 O$ (I) $\overset{\|}{O}$	Peroxide (or light), heat	Polymer formed
I + diallyl phthalate	Peroxide (or light), heat	Copolymer formed
I + butenyl stearate	Peroxide (or light), heat	Copolymer formed
I + cyclopentadiene	Peroxide (or light), heat	Copolymer formed
I + styrene	Peroxide (or light), heat	Copolymer formed
I + butadiene	Peroxide (or light), heat	Copolymer formed
I + methyl acrylate	Peroxide (or light), heat	Copolymer formed
I + vinyl acetate	Peroxide (or light), heat	Copolymer formed
I + allyl acetate	Peroxide (or light), heat	Copolymer formed
I + methyl vinyl ketone	Peroxide (or light), heat	Copolymer formed
I + acrylonitrile	Peroxide (or light), heat	Copolymer formed
I + acrolein	Peroxide (or light), heat	Coplymer formed
I + diallyl diglycollate	Peroxide (or light), heat	Copolymer formed

TABLE 96. POLYMERS AND COPOLYMERS OF ESTERS OF ARYLPHOSPHONIC ACIDS AND β,γ-UNSATURATED ALCOHOLS

Monomers and comonomers	Conditions of polymerization (copolymerization)	Properties of the polymer (copolymer)	Reference
$C_6H_5PO(OCH_2CH=CH_2)_2$ (I)	Nitrogen, 0·25% Bz_2O_2, 100 hr, 2 hr	Unreacted monomer distilled *in vacuo*. The residual "pre-polymer" has n_D^{25} 1·5303 and d, 1·161; viscosity at 20°, 2000 cP	[453]
I + methyl methacrylate	Nitrogen, 0·5-5% Bz_2O_2, 77-100°, 9-24 hr	Hard, glass-like, non-flammable, insoluble	[184]
	From 0·1 to 3% Bz_2O_2 (while raising the amount of the phosphorus-containing component from 1 to 50%), 70°, 7-15 hr. Copolymerizes in any ratio of components	Hard, transparent, insoluble but swelling in certain organic solvents. 25% (or higher) of the phosphorus-containing component in the copolymer causes it to be self-extinguishing on removing from the flame	[185]
I + vinyl acetate (ratio — by volume — from 1:9 to 9:1)	From 0·1 Bz_2O_2, 70°, 33 hr (for 90% vinyl acetate) to 3% Bz_2O_2, 70°, 16 hr (for 40% vinyl acetate)	Moderately hard, transparent, colourless or pale yellow	[185]
I + diallyl oxalate I + diallyl succinate I + diallyl phthalate I + diallyl adipate I + diallyl sebacate I + diethylene glycol dicarbonate	2% Bz_2O_2, 70° for 24 hr, 90° for 24 hr. Copolymerization in all cases	Hard, transparent, yellowish: 10% (and above) of the phosphorus-containing component gives a pretty well fire-resistant resin	[451]
I + $(CH_3)_2C = CHPO(OCH_2CH = CH_2)_2$ 28% 26% + vinyl acetate — 46%	0·2% Bz_2O_2, 70°, 24 hr	Hard, transparent	[448]
4-$ClC_6H_4PO(OCH_2CH = CH_2)_2$ (I)	Nitrogen, 2% Bz_2O_2, 85-90°, 18-20 hr	Hard, glass-like, non-flammable, insoluble	[184]
I + methyl methacrylate	Bz_2O_2, heat	Hard, transparent	[184]
I + vinyl acetate	,,	,,	[184]

TABLE 96 — (contd.)

Monomers and comonomers	Conditions of polymerization (copolymerization)	Properties of the polymer (copolymer)	Reference
I + diallyl oxalate I + diallyl succinate I + diallyl phthalate I + diallyl adipate I + diallyl sebacate I + diethylene glycol dicarbonate	2% Bz$_2$O$_2$, 70° for 24 hr, then 90° for 24 hr. Copolymers formed in every case	Hard, transparent, yellowish; 10% (and above) of the phosphorus-containing component renders the resin fire-resistant	[451]
CH$_3$C$_6$H$_4$PO(OCH$_2$CH = CH$_2$)$_2$ (I) I + methyl methacrylate I + vinyl acetate	Nitrogen, 2% Bz$_2$O$_2$, 85–90°, 18–20 hr Bz$_2$O$_2$, heat ,,	Hard, glass-like, non-flammable, insoluble Hard, transparent ,,	[184]
I + diallyl oxalate I + diallyl succinate I + diallyl phthalate I + diallyl adipate I + diethylene glycol dicarbonate	2% Bz$_2$O$_2$, 70° for 24 hr, then 90° for 24 hr. Copolymers formed in every case	Hard, transparent, yellowish: 10% (and above) of the phosphorus containing component renders the resin fire-resistant	[451]
Cl(CH$_3$)C$_6$H$_3$PO(OCH$_2$CH = CH$_2$)$_2$	Organic peroxides, 70–90°, then 90–120°	Hard, glass-like	[449]
C$_6$H$_5$PO[OCH$_2$C(CH$_3$) = CH$_2$]$_2$ (I) I + methyl methacrylate I + vinyl acetate I + diallyl oxalate I + diallyl succinate	Nitrogen, 2% Bz$_2$O$_2$, 85–90°, 18–20 hr Bz$_2$O$_2$, heat ,,	Hard, glass-like,non-flammable,insoluble Hard, transparent ,,	[184] [184] [184]
I + diallyl phthalate I + diallyl adipate I + diallyl sebacate I + diethylene glycol dicarbonate	2% Bz$_2$O$_2$, 70° for 24 hr, then 90° for 24 hr. Copolymers formed in every case	Hard, transparent, yellowish; 10% (and above) of the phosphorus containing component renders the resin fire-resistant	[451]
4-ClC$_6$H$_4$PO[OCH$_2$C(CH$_3$) = CH$_2$]$_2$ (I)	Nitrogen, 2% Bz$_2$O$_2$, 85–90°, 18–20 hr	Hard,glass-like,non-flammable,insoluble	[184]

TABLE 96 — (contd.)

Monomers and comonomers	Conditions of polymerization (copolymerization)	Properties of the polymer (copolymer)	Reference
I + methyl methacrylate	Bz_2O_2, heat	Hard, transparent	[184]
I + vinyl acetate	"	"	[184]
I + diallyl oxalate			
I + diallyl succinate			
I + diallyl phthalate	2% Bz_2O_2, 70° for 24 hr, then 90° for 24 hr. Copolymers formed in every case	Hard, transparent, yellowish: 10% (and above) of the phosphorus-containing component renders the resin fire-resistant	[451]
I + diallyl adipate			
I + diallyl sebacate			
I + diethylene glycol dicarbonate			
$CH_3C_6H_4PO[OCH_2C(CH_3) = CH_2]_2$ (I)			
I + methyl methacrylate	Nitrogen, 2% Bz_2O_2, 85–90°, 18–20 hr	Hard, glass-like, non-flammable, insoluble	[184]
I + vinyl acetate	Bz_2O_2, heat	Hard, transparent	[184]
	"	"	[184]
I + diallyl oxalate			
I + diallyl succinate			
I + diallyl phthalate	2% Bz_2O_2, 70° for 24 hr, then 90° for 24 hr. Copolymers formed in every case	Hard, transparent, yellowish: 10% (and above) of the phosphorus-containing component renders the resin fire-resistant	[451]
I + diallyl adipate			
I + diallyl sebacate			
I + diethylene glycol dicarbonate			
$Cl(CH_3)C_6H_3PO[OCH_2C(CH_3) = CH_2]_2$			
$C_6H_5PO(OCH_2CH = CH—CH_3)_2(I) +$ diallyl oxalate	Organic peroxides 70–90°, then 90–120°	Hard, glass-like	[449]
I + diallyl succinate			
I + diallyl phthalate	2% Bz_2O_2, 70° for 24 hr, then 90° for 24 hr. Copolymers formed in every case	Hard, transparent, yellowish: 10% (and above) of the phosphorus-containing component renders the resin fire-resistant	[451]
I + diallyl adipate			
I + diallyl sebacate			
I + diethylene glycol dicarbonate			
$C_6H_5PO(NHCH_2CH = CH_2)_2$	Nitrogen, 3% Bz_2O_2, 87–88°, 18 hr	Liquid	[186]

TABLE 97. POLYMERS AND COPOLYMERS OF ESTERS OF ALKOXYCARBONYLALKYLALKYLPHOSPHONIC ACIDS OF THE TYPE RO_2C—R'—$PO(OCH_2CH=CH_2)_2$, WHERE R AND R' ARE SATURATED RADICALS OR R' IS ABSENT [250]

Monomers or comonomers	Condition of polymerization (copolymerization)	Properties of the polymer (copolymer)	Notes			
			Brinell hardness (kg/cm²)	Thermal stability (°C)	Impact strength (kg/cm²)	Transparency (%)
$C_2H_5O_2C$—$PO(OCH_2CH=CH_2)_2$ (I)	Nitrogen, 1% Bz_2O_2, 70°, 70–100 hr	Transparent gel, insoluble in acetone, methanol, benzene				
I + methyl methacrylate 80%	Nitrogen, 0·3% Bz_2O_2, 50–70°, 11 hr	Transparent, glass-like, low solubility in organic solvents	12·1	60		92
30% 70%	", 17 hr		4·5	36	10·9	90·5
CH_3O_2C—$CH_2PO(OCH_2CH=CH_2)_2$ (I)	Nitrogen, 0·3% Bz_2O_2, 70–100 hr	Transparent gel, insoluble in acetone, methanol, benzene	8	56		92
I (25%) + methyl methacrylate (75%)	Nitrogen, 0·3% Bz_2O_2, 50–70°, 26 hr	"				
$C_2H_5O_2C$—$CH_2PO(OCH_2CH=CH_2)_2$ (I)*	Nitrogen, 1·5% Bz_2O_2, 98–100°, 6 hr	Hard, brittle, insoluble				
I + methyl methacrylate	Nitrogen, 1% Bz_2O_2, 70–100 hr	Transparent gel, insoluble in acetone, methanol, benzene				
10% 90%	Nitrogen, 0·3% Bz_2O_2, 50–70°, 20 hr	Transparent, glass-like, low solubility in organic solvents	9	65	10·3	91·2
20% 80%	", 28 hr	"	8·9	74	7·8	92
30% 70%	", 37 hr	"	4·7	48	12	91·7
40% 60%	", 46 hr	"				
50% 50%	", 53 hr					
iso-$C_3H_7O_2C$—$CH_2PO(OCH_2CH=CH_2)_2$	Nitrogen, 1% Bz_2O_2, 70–100 hr	Transparent gel, insoluble in acetone, methanol, benzene				
$C_4H_9O_2C$—$CH_2PO(OCH_2CH=CH_2)_2$; iso-$C_4H_9O_2C$—$CH_2PO(OCH_2CH=CH_2)_2$ (I)	"	"				
I + methyl methacrylate 25% 75%	Nitrogen, 0·3% Bz_2O_2, 50–70°, 24 hr	Transparent, glass-like, low solubility in organic solvents	10·3	65	64	91·5

* See reference (173).

TABLE 98. POLYMERS AND COPOLYMERS OF ESTERS OF UNSATURATED PHOSPHONIC, PHOSPHINIC AND ALKOXYCARBONYL-ALKYLPHOSPHONIC ACIDS AND UNSATURATED ALCOHOLS

Monomers and comonomers, vol. %	Conditions of polymerization or copolymerization (the amount of benzoyl peroxide given is in g/10 ml of monomer)	Properties of the polymer (copolymer)	Reference
$CH_2 = CHPO(OCH = CH_2)_2$	0·7* Bz_2O_2, 70°, 30 hr	Yellow, hard, non-flammable, insoluble in organic solvents	[120]
$(CH_3)_2C = CHPO(OCH_2CH = CH_2)_2$ (I)	Nitrogen, 3 Bz_2O_2, 87–88°, 18 hr	Hard, glass-like	[186]
I + methyl methacrylate 1–70* 99–30*	Bz_2O_2, 70–80°	Thermosetting resins	[450]
I + vinyl acetate 10 90	0·01 Bz_2O_2, 70°, 20 hr	Transparent, colourless, hard, resin-like, fire-resistant, insoluble	[448]
10 90	0·01 Bz_2O_2, 70°, 20 days	Transparent, amber-coloured, hard, stable, fire-resistant, insoluble	[448]
30 70	0·1 Bz_2O_2, 70°, 16·5 hr	Transparent, colourless, elastic, fire-resistant	[448]
30 70	0·1 Bz_2O_2, 70°, 36·5 hr	Transparent colourless, hard, stable, fire-resistant, insoluble	[448]
50 50	0·2 Bz_2O_2, 70°, 16·5 hr	Transparent, colourless, elastic, fire-resistant	[448]
50 50	0·2 Bz_2O_2, 70°, 37·5 hr	Pale-yellow, hard, transparent, fire-resistant, insoluble	[448]
I + $C_8H_{15}PO[OCH_2C(CH_3) = CH_2]_2$ 70 30 15* 15*	0·5 Bz_2O_2, 70°, 20 hr	Pale-green, hard, stable, fire-resistant, insoluble	[448]
I + diethylene glycol maleate 70* 15*	Nitrogen, 2* Bz_2O_2, 85°, 16 hr	Hard, transparent, yellow, self-extinguishing	[452]
I + $C_6H_5PO(OCH_2CH = CH_2)_2$ 26* 28* + vinyl acetate 46*	0·2* Bz_2O_2, 70°, 24 hr	Hard, transparent	[448]
$C_6H_5CH = CHPO(OCH_2CH = CH_2)_2$ (I)	Nitrogen, 3* Bz_2O_2, 87–88°, 18 hr	From moderately hard polymers to soft and resin-like gels	[186]
I + methyl methacrylate	Conditions not stated	Copolymer formed	[450]

* wt. per cent.

TABLE 98 — (contd.)

Monomers and comonomers, vol. %	Conditions of polymerization or copolymerization (the amount of benzoyl peroxide given is in g/10 ml of monomer)	Properties of the polymer (copolymer)	Reference
I + vinyl acetate			
10 90	0·01 Bz$_2$O$_2$, 70°, 20 hr	Clear liquid	[448]
30 70	0·01 Bz$_2$O$_2$, 70°, 20 hr	„	[448]
50 50	0·01 Bz$_2$O$_2$, 70°, 20 days	Pale yellow, resin-like, flame-resistant	[448]
50 50	0·2 Bz$_2$O$_2$, 70°, 20 hr	Colourless, clear liquid	[448]
(CH$_3$)$_3$CCH$_2$C(CH$_3$) = CHPO(OCH$_2$CH = CH$_2$)$_2$	Nitrogen, 3* Bz$_2$O$_2$, 87–88°, 18 hr	Liquid	[186]
(CH$_3$)$_3$C = CHPO[OCH$_2$C(CH$_3$) = CH$_2$]$_2$ (I)	Nitrogen, 3* Bz$_2$O$_2$, 87–88°, 18 hr	Hard, glass-like	[186]
I + methyl methacrylate	Conditions not stated	Copolymer formed	[450]
I + iso-C$_8$H$_{15}$PO[OCH$_2$C(CH$_3$) = CH$_2$]$_2$ + methyl methacrylate	„	„	[450]
I + vinyl acetate			
10 90	0·01 Bz$_2$O$_2$, 70°, 20 hr	Transparent, resin-like, flame-resistant	[448]
30 70	0·01 Bz$_2$O$_2$, 70°, 20 days	Transparent, colourless, very hard, stable, flame-resistant, insoluble	[448]
30 70	0·1 Bz$_2$O$_2$, 70°, 16·5 hr	Transparent, insoluble, elastic, non-flammable	[448]
30 70	0·1 Bz$_2$O$_2$, 70°, 37·5 hr	Transparent, colourless, hard, stable, non-flammable, insoluble	[448]
50 50	0·2 Bz$_2$O$_2$, 70°, 16·5 hr	Transparent, pale yellow, hard, stable, non-flammable, insoluble	[448]
70 30	0·5 Bz$_2$O$_2$, 70°, 20 hr	Pale green, hard, stable, non-flammable, insoluble	[448]
C$_6$H$_5$CH = CHPO[OCH$_2$C(CH$_3$) = CH$_2$]$_2$ (I)	Nitrogen, 3* Bz$_2$O$_2$, 87–88°, 18 hr	From moderately hard polymers to soft and resin-like gels	[186]
I + methyl methacrylate	Conditions not stated	Copolymer formed	[450]
(CH$_3$)$_3$CCH$_2$C(CH$_3$) = CHPO[OCH$_2$C(CH$_3$) = CH$_2$]$_2$ (I)	Nitrogen, 3* Bz$_2$O$_2$, 87–88°, 18 hr	Liquid	[186]
I + iso-C$_8$H$_{15}$PO[OCH$_2$C(CH$_3$) = CH$_2$]$_2$ + methyl methacrylate	Conditions not stated	Copolymer formed	[450]

* wt. per cent.

TABLE 98 — (contd.)

Monomers and comonomers, vol. %	Conditions of polymerization or copolymerization (the amount of benzoyl peroxide given is in g/10 ml of monomer)	Properties of the polymer (copolymer)	Reference
I + vinyl acetate			
10 90	0·01 Bz_2O_2, 70°, 20 hr	Very viscous liquid	[448]
30 70	0·01 Bz_2O_2, 70°, 20 days	Pale yellow, resin-like, flame-resistant	[448]
30 70	0·1 Bz_2O_2, 70°, 16·5 hr	Viscous liquid	[448]
30 70	0·1 Bz_2O_2, 80°, 36 hr	Soft, resin-like, flame-resistant	[448]
30 70	0·5 Bz_2O_2, 70°, 20 hr	Viscous clear liquid	[448]
30 70	0·5 Bz_2O_2, 70°, 20 days	Transparent, greenish, resin-like, flame-resistant	[448]
50 50	0·2 Bz_2O_2, 70°, 16·5 days	Viscous liquid	[448]
50 50	0·2 Bz_2O_2, 80°, 35 hr	Very soft, rubber-like	[448]
$CH_2 = CHCH_2{\rangle}P(O)OCH_2CH = CH_2$ with C_6H_5	1* Bz_2O_2, 70°, 60 hr	Transparent, colourless, sticky, low molecular weight resin, soluble in acetone, methanol benzene, dichloroethane	[473]
$CH_2 = CHCH_2{\rangle}P(O)OCH_2CH = CH_2$ with 4-ClC_6H_4	1* Bz_2O_2, 70°, 100 hr	,,	[473]
$CH_2 = CHCH_2{\rangle}P(O)OCH_2C(CH_3) = CH_2$ with C_6H_5	$[(CH_3)_3C{-}O]_2$, 115°, 24 hr	Polymer formed	[250]
$CH_2 = CHCH_2PO(OCH_2CH = CH_2)_2$	Nitrogen 1·5* Bz_2O_2, 98–100°, 6 hr	Hard, brittle, insoluble	[173]
$CH_2 = CHCH[N(C_2H_5)_2]PO(OCH_2CH = CH_2)_2$	,,	Does not polymerize	[173]
$CH_2 = CHCOPO(OCH_2CH = CH_2)_2$ (I)	Polymerizes during distillation from hydroquinone		[101]
I (undistilled) + methyl methacrylate			
10* 90*	Bz_2O_2, heat, 34 hr	Transparent, hard, amber-coloured, non-flammable	[101]
30* 70*	,, , 45 hr	Translucent, hard, brown, non-flammable	[101]
$CH_2 = CHO_2C{-}CH_2PO(OCH_2CH = CH_2)_2$	Nitrogen, 1* Bz_2O_2, 70°, 70–100 hr	Does not polymerize	[250]
$CH_2 = CHCH_2O_2C{-}CH_2PO(OCH_2CH = CH_2)_2$ (I)	,,	Does not polymerize	[250]
I + methyl methacrylate			
5* 95*	Nitrogen, 1* Bz_2O_2, 70°, 6 hr	Transparent, hard, yellow, low flammability	[101]
10* 90*	Nitrogen, 1* Bz_2O_2, 70°, 2 hr	,,	[101]

* wt. per cent.

POLYMERS AND COPOLYMERS OF AMIDES, AMIDO-ESTERS, AND ETHYLENIMIDES OF ACIDS OF PHOSPHORUS

Depending on their structure, the amides of acids of phosphorus are capable of forming carbochain and heterochain high molecular weight phosphorus-containing compounds. Amides having double bonds or ethylenimine groups in the molecules are converted, by the action of peroxidic or acidic reagents, into macromolecular compounds which do not have phosphorus atoms in the main chain [59, 416, 417, 422, 424, 430]:

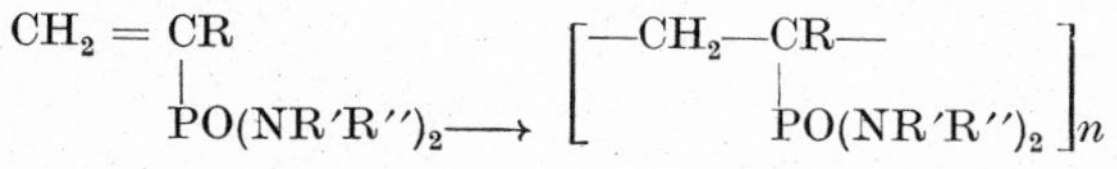

$$CH_2 = CR \quad\quad \left[\begin{array}{c} -CH_2-CR- \\ | \\ PO(NR'R'')_2 \end{array} \right]_n$$
$$| \\ PO(NR'R'')_2 \longrightarrow$$

or

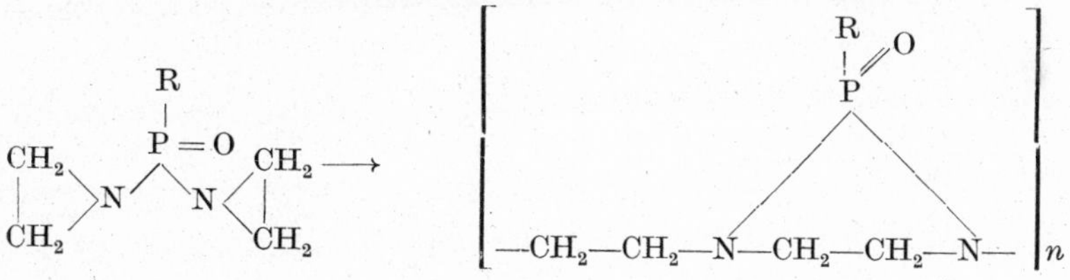

or

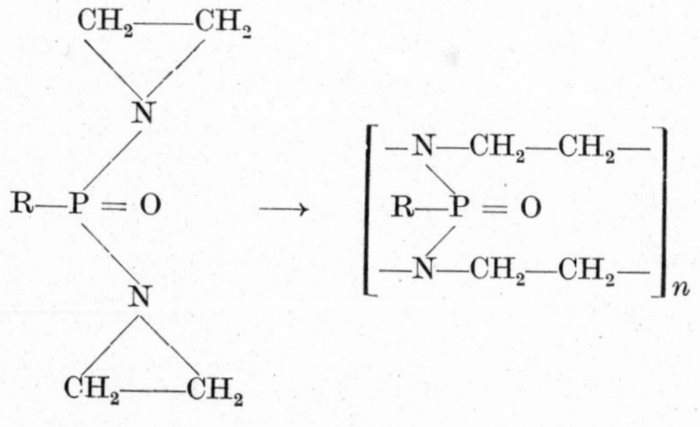

Copolymerizations of amides of unsaturated phosphonic acids with several monomers having one double bond in the molecule have been carried out. Such polymers and copolymers have a linear structure, can be moulded and have a low flammability. The structures of the polymers of ethylenimides of phosphorus acids have not as yet been elucidated.

The properties of the polymers and copolymers of amides, amido-esters and ethylenimides of phosphorus acids are recorded in Tables 99 and 100.

TABLE 99. POLYMERS AND COPOLYMERS OF AMIDES AND AMIDO-ESTERS OF UNSATURATED ACIDS OF PHOSPHORUS

Monomer or comonomers	Conditions of polymerization (copolymerization)	Properties of the polymer (copolymer)	Reference
$CH_2 = C(CH_3)PO[N(CH_3)_2]_2$ (I) (15%) + methylmethacrylate (85%)	Nitrogen, 1% ammonium persulphate, 45°, 47 hr	88·4% of copolymer formed, containing 0·57% phosphorus. Softening point 111°. Can be moulded into transparent blocks	[466]
I + ethylene (excess)	In the absence of air; Bz_2O_2, water, 74–76°, 860–940 atm, 9·24 hr	Copolymer contains 2·23% phosphorus	
$CH_2 = C(CN)CH_2P[N(C_2H_5)_2]_2$ (I) =O	Bz_2O_2, heat	Hard, mouldable resin	[60]
I + acrylonitrile	,,		
I + methyl acrylate	,,	Copolymer formed	
I + methyl methacrylate	,,	,,	
I + styrene	,,	,,	
$CH_2 = C(CN)CH_2P[(C_3H_7)_2]_2$ (I) =O	Bz_2O_2, heat	Hard, mouldable resin	[60]
I + acrylonitrile	,,		
I + methyl acrylate	,,	Copolymer formed	
I + methyl methacrylate	,,	,,	
I + styrene	,,	,,	
$CH_2 = C(CN)CH_2P(NHCH_3)_2$ (I) =O	Bz_2O_2, heat	Hard, mouldable resin	[60]
I + acrylonitrile	,,		
I + methyl acrylate	,,	Copolymer formed	
I + methyl methacrylate	,,	,,	
I + styrene	,,	,,	
$CH_2 = C(CN)CH_2P\genfrac{}{}{0pt}{}{R}{OR'}$ =O	Bz_2O_2, heat	Polymer formed	[60]
	,,	,,	

R	R'
—NHCH₃	—C₂H₅
—N(C₂H₅)₂	—C₄H₉
—N(C₂H₅)₂	—C₆H₅

TABLE 100. POLYMERS OF DI- AND TRI-ETHYLENIMIDES OF PHOS-
PHORUS ACIDS

Monomer	Reference	Monomer	Reference
$R-PO\left[N\begin{smallmatrix}CH_2\\ \\CH_2\end{smallmatrix}\right]_2$		R	
R		$(C_4H_9)_2N-$	[422]
C_2H_5O-	[416]	$(C_8H_{17})_2N-$	[422]
$ClCH_2CH_2O-$	[416]	$\dfrac{C_6H_5}{CH_3}N-$	[416]
C_4H_9O-	[417]		
$C_8H_{17}O-$	[417]	$\dfrac{C_6H_5}{C_2H_5}N-$	[416]
C_6H_5O-	[416]		
$(CH_3)_2C_6H_3O-$	[416]		
$2\text{-}C_{10}H_7O-$	[416]	$(C_2H_5)_2NPS\left[N\begin{smallmatrix}CH_2\\| \\CH_2\end{smallmatrix}\right]_2$	[430]
$\dfrac{CH_2}{CH_2}N-$	[420]	$PS\left[N\begin{smallmatrix}CH_2\\ \\CH-CH_3\end{smallmatrix}\right]_3$	[430]
$(C_2H_5)_2N-$	[420]	$R-\overset{\|}{\underset{O}{P}}\left[N\begin{smallmatrix}CH_2\\| \\CH_2\end{smallmatrix}\right]_2$	
$(CH_2)_5 \ N-$	[416]	R	
$PO\left[N\begin{smallmatrix}CH_2\\ \\CH-CH_3\end{smallmatrix}\right]_3$	[424]	C_2H_5-	
		$(CH_3)_2C=CH-$	
$RPO\left[N\begin{smallmatrix}CH_2\\| \\CH_2\end{smallmatrix}\right]$		cyclo-$C_6H_{11}-$	[59]
		C_6H_5-	
		$4\text{-}ClC_6H_4-$	
		$4\text{-}CH_3C_6H_4-$	
		$2\text{-}C_{10}H_7-$	

Besides the earlier-known, classical methods of polymerization and copolymerization, in recent years new methods have appeared for obtaining various high molecular weight compounds possessing valuable properties. Since these methods will probably become useful in the synthesis of macromolecular phosphorus-containing compounds, we will briefly consider them here. We will discuss the methods of obtaining the so-called block copolymers, graft copolymers and stereoregular polymers. In recent years a great deal of work has been carried out on the experimental details of these processes and on the theories which can be applied to them [476–481].

It is known that by various mechanical processes (extrusion, rolling or cutting of polymers) polymers undergo destruction with the formation of shorter chains. These processes, which are referred to as "mechano-chemical", take place via free radicals which are formed by cleavage of the main chain bonds in the macromolecules.

The action of light, heat, ultra-violet irradiation, ultrasonics, etc., on the polymers can also lead to the formation of macromolecular free radicals (but without rupture of the main polymer chain) as a result, for example, of the splitting out of an atom of hydrogen, halogen, etc. Such high molecular weight free radicals can initiate the polymerization of monomers, if these are present in the system: they can also give rise to new macromolecules by recombination and disproportionation reactions. These effects are the basis of the preparation of some new types of polymers.

If a given polymer is swollen in a monomer of another type, and the system is subjected to a powerful mechanical action, then the macromolecular free radicals initiate the polymerization of the monomer. A copolymer formed in this way consists of alternating sections — blocks — of both polymers (for example, rubber-styrene): it can be represented schematically in the following way:

$$\ldots-\text{AAAABBBBAAAABBBB}-,\ldots$$

Such block copolymers often possess the good qualities of both component parts; for example, the elasticity of rubber and the hardness of polystyrene.

Graft copolymers are obtained by producing on the main chain of a polymer by some method (the action of heat, light, oxygen, ultrasonics, ionizing radiation, etc.), free radicals, that is reactive centres, on which a more or less linear side chain of another polymer can begin to grow. Thus, for example, graft copolymers may be obtained from unsaturated polyesters and styrene, poly(methyl vinyl ketone) and acrylonitrile, polystyrene or sodium rubber and methyl methacrylate, sodium rubber and acrylonitrile, etc., as illustrated in the following diagram:

High molecular weight substances obtained in such a way possess very valuable properties which are often absent from the starting polymers. Thus, for example, improved types of rubber [477, 481], polyamide fibres [481], etc., have been obtained. This field of the chemistry of high molecular weight compounds opens up great possibilities for the construction of polymeric materials with complex, new and important properties.

Great interest has been aroused by the work of Natta and his co-workers [480] in the field of synthesis and study of the so-called stereoregular polymers, which possess a regular macromolecular structure. It is well known that the spatial arrangement of the macromolecular chains has a great influence on the properties of high molecular weight compounds.

If the carbon skeleton of an unsymmetric polyolefin (polypropylene, polystyrene, etc.) is projected onto a plane, then a zig-zag line is obtained on the plane (see below). The substituent groups joined to the tertiary carbon atoms are found on one or the other sides of this plane. In this way a new type of stereoisomerism arises which depends on the relative arrangements of the substituents on the tertiary carbon atoms. In the usual type of polymer ("atactic" according to Natta's terminology) the substituents are arranged in a disorderly fashion on both sides of the plane: amorphous structures, very low softening temperatures and poor mechanical properties (relative to the stereoregular polymers) are characteristic of such polymers.

Natta and his co-workers have studied in detail the polymerization of a range of unsaturated compounds under the influence of the heterogeneous catalysts of crystalline structure which are obtained by the reaction of the lower chlorides of titanium ($TiCl_2$ or $TiCl_3$) with halogen-containing aluminium alkyls. Natta's results, which are a continuation and extension of the investigations of Zeigler in the field of polymerization under the influence of organo-metallic compounds (preparation of polyethylene without pressure, etc.), show that in the presence of such catalysts (called "stereospecific" by Natta) a single type — from the point of view of spatial isomerism — of chain arises. In this way the polymers formed have the substituent groups on the tertiary carbon atoms either all on one side of the plane of the chain — the so-called "isotactic" polymers — or on both sides regularly alternating with hydrogen – the so-called "syndiotactic" polymers.

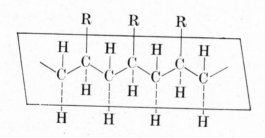

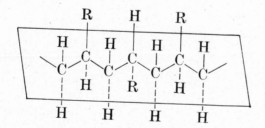

Such polymers usually have crystalline structures and better mechanical properties in comparison with the usual (atactic) polymers.

The Italian chemists have also discovered methods of obtaining block copolymers containing a definite percentage of crystalline structure. In such polymers sections with isotactic and atactic structures are alternated. This makes it possible to prepare high molecular weight compounds with a wide variety of chosen properties.

In the phosphorus field there have been no detailed investigations along these lines. We only wished to point out these attainments of macromolecular chemistry because there is no doubt that these features, to a greater or lesser degree, will be incorporated into the fields of element-organic and in particular, phosphorus-containing high molecular weight compounds (already isotactic silicon-containing vinyl polymers are known [482]).

CARBOCHAIN PRODUCTS FROM THE POLYCONDENSATION OF ORGANOPHOSPHORUS COMPOUNDS

Several cases of the polycondensation of phosphorus-containing aromatic compounds to give high molecular weight cross-linked substances have been described. Examples are the reaction of resorcinol monophosphates [483, 484] or aryloxymethylphosphonic acids [485] with an excess of formaldehyde. By heating such mixtures in acidic or alkaline media, phenol-formaldehyde polycondensates of the usual type are produced.

In cases where the *ortho*- or *para*-positions of the aromatic nuclei are blocked, linear products of polycondensation, and not cross-linked, are obtained [485]. The properties of carbochain products from the polycondensation of organophosphorus compounds are recorded in Table 101.

TABLE 101. PRODUCTS OF THE POLYCONDENSATION
OF ARYLOXYMETHYLPHOSPHONIC ACIDS WITH FORMALDEHYDE [485]

Components	Reaction conditions	Properties of the reaction product
$C_6H_5OCH_2PO(OH)_2$ + 37% formaldehyde (excess)	Heat the mixture for 3 hr while gradually raising the temperature (and removing water) from 110° to 140°	Fusible, water-soluble soluble
$C_6H_5OCH_2PO(OH)$ + 37% formaldehyde (excess)	,, but over 4 hr	Hard, brittle, infusible, insoluble
$C_6H_5OCH_2PO(ONa)_2$ + 37% formaldehyde (excess)	,, but over 4 hr (with acidification)	..
$C_6H_5OCH_2PO(OH)_2$ + phenol + + 10·6% formaldehyde	,,	Hard, amber-coloured substance
$C_6H_5OCH_2PO(OH)_2$ + para-formaldehyde + melamine	The mixture of the first two components was heated for 2 hr, neutralized with ammonia, then the melamine was added and the mixture was heated for 1 hr more	Resin containing the —$PO(OH)_2$ group
4-$ClC_6H_4OCH_2PO(OH)_2$ + 37% formaldehyde	110° for 4 hr, then 140° for 16 hr	Fusible, soluble in cold water
3-$CH_3C_6H_4OCH_2PO(OH)_2$ + + 37% formaldehyde (excess)	,,	Hard, brittle

HIGH MOLECULAR WEIGHT ORGANOPHOSPHORUS COMPOUNDS SYNTHESIZED BY THE REACTION OF ORGANIC POLYMERS WITH PHOSPHORUS-CONTAINING COMPOUNDS

Poly(vinyl phosphonates) and poly(vinyl phosphates) have been prepared by treating poly(vinyl alcohol) with phosphoryl chloride, with acid chlorides of phosphoric or phosphonic acids — usually under the influence of an organic base [486–491] — with orthophosphoric acid (sometimes in the presence of phosphorus pentoxide) [488, 490, 492, 493], and also with urea phosphate or phosphoric acid and urea [490, 494], for example:

$$\left[\begin{array}{c} -CH_2-CH-CH_2-CH- \\ | \quad\quad\quad | \\ OH \quad\quad OH \end{array} \right] + nC_6H_5POCl_2 + 2nC_5H_5N \longrightarrow$$

$$\longrightarrow \left[\begin{array}{c} -CH_2-CH-CH_2-CH- \\ | \quad\quad\quad | \\ O \quad\quad\quad O \\ \backslash\quad\quad / \\ C_6H_5-P=O \end{array} \right]_n + 2nC_5H_5N \cdot HCl$$

In compounds of the described type which have been obtained, the phosphorus atoms are joined through oxygen with one, two or three carbon chains:

$$\left[\begin{array}{c} -CH_2-CH- \\ | \\ O \\ | \\ P=O \\ \wedge \end{array} \right]_n \qquad\qquad \begin{array}{c} [-CH_2-CH-]n \\ | \\ O \\ | \\ O=P- \\ | \\ O \\ | \\ [-CH_2-CH-]n \end{array}$$

or

$$\begin{array}{c} [-CH_2-CH-]_n \\ | \\ O \\ | \\ O=P-O-\left[\begin{array}{c} CH \\ | \\ CH_2 \\ | \end{array} \right]_n \\ | \\ O \\ | \\ [-CH_2-CH-]_n \end{array}$$

In an analogous way it is possible to introduce phosphorus into other high molecular weight hydroxy-containing compounds, such as, for example, into poly(allyl alcohol) [487], starch and other polysaccharides [495–502].

By introducing the phosphinyl group into starch, various types of compounds are obtained, depending on the kind of starch, the method of drying it and the method of carrying out the process. By phosphorylating various types of starch, previously dried in air or by azeotropic distillation of the water with benzene, in aqueous media a reaction product is formed which is water soluble and obviously therefore has a linear structure. If, however, the starch is dried by azeotropic distillation of the water with pyridine, which is also an activating agent for the subsequent phosphorylation, then an insoluble product with a cross-linked structure is obtained. The swelling of an insoluble starch phosphate depends on the source of the starch. For example, the starches from potatoes, wheat, tapioca and certain other substances give phosphates which swell to a certain extent in hot water, whereas the phosphate of corn starch is virtually hot swollen by it [495]. A review has appeared of the chemistry of hydrocarbon phosphates by Foster and Overend [503].

Many investigations have been directed to the obtaining of phosphorus-containing products from cellulose and its derivatives [504]. Usually, in order to do this, the cellulose or the articles made from it are swollen in suitable solvents and the resulting mass is treated with phosphorus acids or their acid chlorides, mono- and di-ammonium phosphates, urea phosphate, guanidine pyrophosphate or other phosphorus-containing compounds. In this way the cellulose units are joined with phosphorus through oxygen thus:

In as much as this type of compound has been discussed in some detail in Little's monograph [504], we shall only discuss results reported after the publication of this monograph [505–513].

For a long time the only phosphorus-containing groups which were introduced into cellulose were inorganic. A few years ago Marvel and Bluestein [514] treated an acetyl cellulose ($2 \cdot 09$ acetyl groups per glucose unit) with diethyl phosphorochloridate in pyridine and obtained the diethyl phosphate of the acetyl cellulose. A similar reaction in the presence of an inorganic base has been recently carried out by Schwenker and Pascu [515]. Other organic phosphorus-containing groups have been introduced into cellulose by treating it with the pentaerythritol phosphoric acids [516].

Besides the above described compounds, in which the initial macromolecules are joined with phosphorus through oxygen, many polymers are known in which the joining is effected via a phosphorus-carbon bond. Marvel and Bluestein chloroacetylated partially esterified celluloses and treated the products with triethyl phosphite [514]. It was shown that the halogen-containing celluloses underwent the Arbusov rearrangement in just the same way as many alkyl halides, and as a result phosphorus-containing derivatives of cellulose were obtained which contained the phosphorus-carbon bond:

$$ROCOCH_2Cl + P(OC_2H_5)_3 \longrightarrow ROCOCH_2{-}PO(OC_2H_5)_2 + C_2H_5Cl$$

where R = acetylcellulose.

Other cases of the Arbusov rearrangement with trialkyl phosphates and polymers containing halogenated methyl groups have been described [517–519].

It is known [520] that the reaction of phosphorus trichloride with carbonyl-containing compounds leads to a-hydroxyalkylphosphonic acids. Upson [521] and also Marvel and Wright [522] have investigated the application of this reaction to high molecular weight compounds having carbonyl groups in the macromolecules. The authors treated the requisite copolymers (for example, from methyl vinyl ketone, methacrolein, benzalacetone, etc.) with acid chlorides of trivalent phosphorus [PCl_3, $C_6H_5PCl_2$, $ROPCl_2$, $(RO)_2PCl$]. The products obtained were treated with glacial acetic acid and then water. As a result, the carbonyl groups in the copolymers were replaced by a-hydroxyphosphonic acid groups, thus:

$$\left[\begin{array}{c} -CH-CH_2- \\ | \\ C=O \\ | \end{array}\right]_n \xrightarrow[CH_3CO_2H \; ; \; H_2O]{PCl_3} \left[\begin{array}{c} -CH-CH_2- \\ | \\ HO-C-PO(OH)_2 \\ | \end{array}\right]_n$$

In this reaction it is possible to regulate the phosphorus content of the high molecular weight compounds by using the requisite amount of carbonyl-containing component for the preparation of the copolymer.

Polymers containing phosphinic acid groups have been obtained by treating polyethylene with arylphosphonous dichlorides and oxygen [523]:

$$A + ArPCl_2 + \frac{1}{2}O_2 \longrightarrow \begin{array}{c} Ar \\ \diagdown \\ A \diagup P \diagup {}^{O} _{Cl} \end{array} \xrightarrow{hydrolysis} \begin{array}{c} Ar \\ \diagdown \\ A \diagup P(O)OH \end{array}$$

where A is a unit of polyethylene. (A similar method for the synthesis of acid chlorides of alkylphosphonic acids is described on p. 19.)

It is important to note that the solubility in various solvents of many high molecular weight compounds with free phosphonic acid groups is usually reduced, sometimes to zero, by heating or reprecipitating, presumably on account of the cross-linking of the linear macromolecular chains [490, 491, 522]:

$$\left[\begin{array}{c} -CH_2-CH- \\ | \\ OPO(OH)_2 \end{array}\right]_n + \left[\begin{array}{c} OH \\ | \\ -CH_2-CH- \end{array}\right]_n \longrightarrow \left[\begin{array}{c} -CH_2-CH- \\ | \\ O \\ | \\ PO(OH) \\ | \\ O \\ | \\ -CH_2-CH- \end{array}\right]_n + nH_2O$$

$$2\left[\begin{array}{c} -CH-CH_2- \\ | \\ HOC-CH_3 \\ | \\ OP(OH)_2 \end{array}\right]_n \longrightarrow \left[\begin{array}{c} -CH-CH_2- \\ | \\ HOC-CH_3 \\ | \\ OPOH \end{array}\right]_n \quad \left[\begin{array}{c} -CH-CH_2- \\ | \\ HOC-CH_3 \\ | \\ OPOH \end{array}\right]_n + nH_2O$$

O

A recent development in the introduction of phosphorus into high molecular weight compounds is the use of aluminium chloride. If the cross-linked copolymer of styrene or vinylnaphthalene with divinylbenzene is treated with phosphorus trichloride in the presence of aluminium chloride, hydrogen chloride is evolved and the $-PCl_2$ group is introduced into the aromatic rings of the chain: by the usual transformations it is possible to convert the $-PCl_2$ group into ester or acid groups [524–527]:

$$R-\langle\bigcirc\rangle + PCl_3 \xrightarrow{AlCl_3} R-\langle\bigcirc\rangle-PCl_2 + HCl$$

where R is the cross-linked copolymer.

If chloromethylated copolymers of styrene and divinylbenzene are subjected to such a reaction, then each copolymer unit can add on two phosphoric acid groups: one to the aromatic nucleus and the other to the methylene group joined to the ring [528]. In an analogous way the $-PCl_2$ group has been introduced into poly(vinyl chloride) [173].

The treatment of various high molecular weight compounds containing α-hydroxy-groups with phosphonic and phosphoric acids has been described: for example, the treatment of copolymers of allyl alcohol and styrene. In this way are formed linear polyphosphates, which are soluble in organic solvents, and which change into cross-linked, infusible and insoluble resins on being heated [529–531].

In patents, there is described the production of high molecular weight phosphorus-containing compounds, which obviously have carbochain structures, by the treatment of various rubbers or polyolefins with phosphonous halides [532–534] or phosphorus pentasulphide [535–537], and also by the reaction of phenol- formaldehyde resins with tetra-ethyl pyrophosphate [173]. In a number of cases phosphorus has been introduced into organic polymers by utilizing the reactive hydrogen atoms in dialkyl hydrogen phosphites. These last compounds easily condense with the products from the reaction of poly[(aminomethyl) styrene] and acetaldehyde [277]:

$$\begin{bmatrix} -CH_2-CH- \\ | \\ C_6H_4 \\ | \\ CH_2N=CHCH_3 \end{bmatrix}_n + HPO(OC_2H_5)_2 \longrightarrow$$

$$\longrightarrow \begin{bmatrix} -CH_2-CH- \\ | \\ C_6H_4CH_2NHCH(CH_3)PO(OC_2H_5)_2 \end{bmatrix}_n ;$$

and with the products from poly(aminostyrene) and pyridine-2-aldehyde [277]:

$$\begin{bmatrix} -CH_2-CH- \\ | \\ C_6H_4-N=CH-Py \end{bmatrix}_n + HPO(OC_2H_5)_2 \longrightarrow$$

$$\longrightarrow \begin{bmatrix} -CH_2-CH- \\ | \\ C_6H_4NHCH(Py)PO(OC_2H_5)_2 \end{bmatrix}_n$$

where Py = pyridyl-2 and with certain other polymers [277].

Reactions of saturated and unsaturated organic polymers with various esters of phosphorus acids are known. The saturated [538] react by a chain transfer mechanism, and the unsaturated by a variation of copolymerization [453, 454, 475, 539–541].

$$
\begin{array}{c}
\ldots—R—CH = CH—R—\ldots \\[4pt]
\hspace{4em} + CH_2 = CHPO(OCH_2CH_2Cl)_2 \longrightarrow \\[4pt]
\ldots—R—CH = CH—R—\ldots
\end{array}
$$

$$
\begin{array}{c}
\vdots \\
| \\
\ldots—R—CH—CH—R—\ldots \\
| \\
\longrightarrow \hspace{2em} CH_2 \\
| \\
CHPO(OCH_2CH_2Cl)_2 \\
| \\
\ldots—R—CH—CH—R—\ldots \; ,
\end{array}
$$

where R = rest of macromolecular chain.

As a result of such reactions cross-linked organophosphorus polymers are formed, in which the phosphorus is joined to the macromolecular chains neither directly nor through oxygen, as was described earlier, but through carbon, carbon–oxygen or carbon–nitrogen links: for example:

$$
\begin{array}{c}
\vdots \hspace{10em} \vdots \\
| \hspace{10em} | \\
\ldots—R—CH—CH—R—\ldots \hspace{4em} \\
| \hspace{5em} | \\
CH_2 \hspace{4em} O \hspace{4em} CH_2 \\
| \hspace{4em} \| \hspace{4em} | \\
CH—CH_2O—P—OCH_2—CH \\
| \hspace{8em} | \\
\ldots—R—CH—CH—\ldots \hspace{1em} R\ldots—CH—CH—R—\ldots
\end{array}
$$

Recently there has been described the strengthening of certain hydroxy-methylpolyamides by means of hydroxymethylphosphonic acid. In this way cross-linked phosphorus-containing polymers are formed [542]. The way in which the phosphorus is linked to the macromolecular chains in these polymers is not as yet known. The properties of high molecular weight phosphorus-containing compounds, synthesized by the reaction of organic polymers with phosphorus-containing substances, are recorded in Tables 102–104.

TABLE 102. POLYMERS IN WHICH THE PHOSPHORUS IS JOINED TO THE MACROMOLECULE BY A P–O–C BOND

Organic high molecular weight substance	Phosphorus-containing component	Reaction conditions	Properties of the reaction product	Notes Content of P (%)	Reference
Poly(vinyl alcohol) (low viscosity)	$POCl_3$	Carried out in dioxan: HCl evolved removed in vacuo	Grey powder containing chlorine; insoluble in organic solvents		[490]
"	$POCl_3$	Hydrolysis of the product obtained above	Yellow-orange product, not containing chlorine. Swells but does not dissolve in organic solvents. By analysis, it contains one phosphate group for every three vinyl groups	14·72	[490]
Poly(vinyl alcohol) (high viscosity)	$POCl_3$	Carried out in chloroform, followed by hydrolysis	Yellow granular product insoluble in water		[490]
Poly(vinyl alcohol) (low viscosity)	85% H_3PO_4	The mixture was heated	Black, water insoluble product	traces	[490]
"	85% H_3PO_4	H_3PO_4 (300 g), urea (175 g) and poly(vinyl alcohol) (100 g) were allowed to react at 110–150°. The product was dissolved in water, precipitated with alcohol and dried in vacuo	Hard, colourless product, soluble in water, insoluble in organic solvents. The structure may be: $$\left[-CH_2-CH\genfrac{}{}{0pt}{}{}{}\underset{O-P\genfrac{}{}{0pt}{}{O\ \ ONH_4}{OH}}{|}\right]_n$$	19·6	[490, 494]
Poly(vinyl alcohol)	H_3PO_4	Conditions not stated	Gel- or rubber-like product, insoluble in water		[488]
Poly(vinyl alcohol) (fibre) containing 10–15% water	$H_3PO_4 + P_2O_5$	Room temperature, 24 hr	Fibres of poly(vinyl phosphate)	12	[492]
Poly(vinyl alcohol)	$H_3PO_4 + P_2O_5$ $H_3PO_4 + P_2O_5$	", 96 hr Poly(vinyl alcohol): H_3PO_4 = 1 : 100. The mixture kept at room temperature for 3 days	Insoluble in water	18·9 20·0	[492] [496]

TABLE 102— (contd.)

Organic high molecular weight substance	Phosphorus-containing component	Reaction conditions	Properties of the reaction product	Notes — Content of P (%)	Reference
Poly(vinyl alcohol) (low viscosity)	$H_3PO_4 + P_2O_5$	Poly(vinyl alcohol): H_3PO_4 = 1 : 2. Conditions as above	Partially soluble in water	8·0	[490]
,,	85% H_3PO_4	Poly(vinyl alcohol): H_3PO_4 = 1 : 3·5; the mixture kept for 3 days in a vacuum desiccator over P_2O_5	Solubie in water	2·4	[240]
,,	$(C_6H_5)_2POCl$	Carried out in excess of pyridine: the $C_5H_5N \cdot HCl$ was filtered off and the residue of poly(vinyl phosphonate) was washed with aqueous alkali and dried	Colourless resin, insoluble in water	10·98	[486]
		The reaction product was treated with propionaldehyde to give the corresponding acetal	,, but the product is very hard		[486]
Poly(vinyl alcohol)	$C_6H_5POCl_2$	Carried out in excess of pyridine: the $C_5H_5N \cdot HCl$ was filtered off and the residue of poly(vinyl phosphonate) was washed with aqueous alkali and dried	Colourless, non-flammable, insoluble in water		[486]
Poly(vinyl butyral) (containing 20% of unreacted hydroxyl groups)	$C_6H_5POCl_2$	,,	Colourless powder	5·23	[486]
,,	$(C_6H_5)_2POCl$	,,	Transparent colourless granules, softening at 100°, melting at 160°		[486]
Cellulose	The product of the reaction of $(C_2H_5O)_2 \cdot P(O)OCH_2CH_2OH$ with 2-methoxy-1,4-phenylenediisocyanate	The cellulose was impregnated with the second component and heated	Phosphorus- and nitrogen-containing derivative of cellulose		[543]

TABLE 102—(*contd.*)

Organic high molecular weight substance	Phosphorus-containing component	Reaction conditions	Properties of the reaction product	Notes: Content of P (%)	Reference
Cellulose	The product of the reaction of $(C_2H_5O)_2 \cdot P(O)CH_2NHCH_3$ with the dimer of tolylene-2,4-di-isocyanate	The cellulose was impregnated with the second component and heated	Phosphorus- and nitrogen-containing derivative of cellulose		[543]
Cellulose	The product of the reaction of $(CH_3)_2PC_6H_4OH$ with the $=O$ dimer of tolylene-2,4-di-isocyanate	„	„		[543]
Partially aminized cellulose	$(HOCH_2)_4PCl$ (see p. 2457)				
Partially acetylated cellulose	$ClPO(OC_2H_5)_2$	Carried out in pyridine at room temperature; the product was filtered off, washed and dried	The product was insoluble in acetone, methylene chloride and methylene chloride/ethanol. Non-flammable, decomposes in the flame. Average structure of a polymer unit: $C_6H_7O_2(OH)_{0.21}$ $(OCOCH_3)_{2.05}$ $\cdot[OPO(OC_2H_5)_2]_{0.70}$	6·27	[514]
Cotton	H_3PO_4	The cotton article was dissolved in the following mixture (in %): urea—49·6; H_3PO_4—18·4; water—32; the excess of solvent was removed and the article was dried at 150° and washed	Fibres of phosphorylated cotton		[507]
Cotton	$ClCH_2CH_2OPO(OH)_2$	Not described	Not described		[507]
Cotton	Pentaerythritol phosphoric acid or its ammonium salt	Carried out at 130–160° for 15 min	Penta-erythritol phosphoric acid ester of cellulose		[512]

Notes : For phosphorus-containing derivatives of cellulose, see also reference (504).

TABLE 102(a) STARCH PHOSPHATES

(Insoluble and unswollen in water) [495]

The mixture of reagents in pyridine — dried maize starch (activated in pyridine) and $POCl_3$ — was heated at 70°, cooled and filtered; the residue was treated with water, 5% NaOH and, finally, HCl.

Reaction conditions		Properties of the reaction product			
Ratio of POCl₃ to units of dry glucose (moles)	Time (hr)	Content of P (%)	Method of linking the phosphorus to the macromolecules (%)		
			to one chain	to two chains	to three chains
0·75	3	7·0	52	37	11
1·50	3	12·2	59	28	13
3	0·5	6·9	54	40	7
3	1 (at 40°)	2·8	61	26	13
3	1	10·8	57	31	12

Reaction conditions		Properties of the reaction product			
Ratio of POCl₃ to units of dry glucose (moles)	Time (hr)	Content P (%)	Method of linking the phosphorus to the macromolecules (%)		
			to one chain	to two chains	to three chains
3	1 (at 115°)	12·1	62	23	15
3	2	11·8	61	30	10
3	4	12·4	62	26	12
3	6	12·5	62	27	11
3	10	12·3	64	26	10

TABLE 103. POLYMERS IN WHICH THE PHOSPHORUS IS JOINED TO THE MACROMOLECULE BY A P—C BOND

Organic high molecular weight substance	Phosphorus-containing component	Reaction conditions	Properties of the reaction-product	Notes		Reference
				Extent of reaction (%)	Content of P (%)	
Polymeric methyl vinyl ketone (I)	PCl_3	A solution of the polymer was kept at room temperature for 10–24 hr with an excess of PCl_3, and then treated with glacial acetic acid for 24–48 hr and finally with water. The product deposited was purified by reprecipitation	Brown colour; insoluble in benzene, chloroform and dimethylformamide; swollen but not dissolved by 15% aqueous ammonia; does not soften below 320°; very flame resistant	89	18·1	
Copolymers of I + styrene 13% 87%	PCl_3	,,	Soluble in dioxan, chloroform and dimethylformamide; slightly soluble in benzene; softens at 257–262°; flammable	40	0·96	
24%	PCl_3	,,	Soluble in chloroform; slightly soluble in dimethylformamide and benzene; after reprecipitation it softens (with decomposition) at 240°; flammable	37	1·8	[522]
29%	$C_6H_5POCl_2$	,,	Slightly soluble in benzene; melts at 135–240°; burns with difficulty	10	0·39	
I + butadiene 36% 64%	PCl_3	,,	Soluble in dioxan; insoluble in benzene; flammable	4	0·28	
I + methyl acrylate 19% 81%	PCl_3	,,	Insoluble in dioxan, chloroform and benzene; softens at 310°; decomposes in a flame but does not burn	69	2·67	

TABLE 103 — (contd.)

Organic high molecular weight substance	Phosphorus-containing component	Reaction conditions	Properties of the reaction-product	Notes		Reference
				Extent of reaction (%)	Content of P (%)	
Copolymers of: I + methyl methacrylate 32% 68%	PCl₃	A solution of the copolymer in dioxan was kept at room temperature for 10–24 hr with an excess of PCl₃, then treated with glacial acetic acid for 24–48 hr and finally with water. The product deposited was purified by reprecipitation	Partially soluble in dioxan, insoluble in benzene; does not soften below 310°; fire-resistant	62	4·09	[522]
Methacrolein + styrene 29% 71%	PCl₃	"	Soluble in dimethylformamide, partially soluble in chloroform and benzene; softens and decomposes at 210°; burns only in the flame	10	7·33	
cinnamaldehyde + styrene 12% 88%	PCl₃	"	Soluble in benzene, chloroform and dioxan; softens and chars at 225–235°; flammable	100	2·24	
methyl isopropenyl + styrene ketone 28% 72%	PCl₃	"	Soluble in dioxan and chloroform; 28% soluble in benzene; softens at 234–237°; less flammable than the starting copolymer			
Benzalacetone + styrene 11% 89%	PCl₃	"	Virtually no reaction			
Benzalacetophenone + styrene 29% 71%	PCl₃	"	"			
Poly(vinyl chloride)	PCl₃	The mixture was refluxed the presence of AlCl₃; the residue was filtered off and decomposed with water	The product contained phosphoric acid groups and was insoluble in organic solvents			[173]

TABLE 103 — (contd.)

Organic high molecular weight substance	Phosphorus-containing component	Reaction conditions	Properties of the reaction product	Notes		Reference
				Extent of reaction (%)	Extent of P (%)	
Copolymer of styrene and divinylbenzene containing chloromethyl groups	$P(OC_2H_5)_3$	The copolymer was treated with triethyl phosphite at 150°; the product obtained was hydrolysed	Insoluble copolymer containing the functional group $-PO(OH)_2$			[518]
Copolymer of styrene and divinylbenzene	PCl_3	The mixture was refluxed in the presence of $AlCl_3$; the product was hydrolysed and acidified	,,			[525, 526]
Copolymer of styrene and divinylbenzene containing chloromethyl groups	PCl_3	,,	,,			[528]
Copolymer of vinylnaphthalene and divinylbenzene	PCl_3	,,	,,			[527]
Copolymer of: styrene 15 % + isobutylene 85 %	P_2S_5	150–180°, 30 min	Copolymer containing phosphorus formed			[533]
Rubber (crepe)	Various arylphosphonous dichlorides	The mixture was stirred and heated, the solvent removed and the residue treated with water	Rubber-like products, resistant to solvents and oils			[532]

TABLE 104. POLYMERS IN WHICH THE PHOSPHORUS IS JOINED TO THE MACROMOLECULE WITH BRIDGES OF ATOMS OF CARBON, CARBON AND OXYGEN, OR CARBON AND NITROGEN

Organic high molecular weight substances	Phosphorus-containing component	Reaction conditions	Properties of the reaction product	Reference
Unsaturated polyesters obtained by the reaction of maleic anhydride, phthalic anhydride and polyglycols	$CH_2 = CHPO(OCH_2CH_2Cl)_2$	Heat the mixture of components and styrene in the presence of peroxides	Fire-resistant polyesters with a cross-linked structure	[539]
Poly(vinyl acetate) (80%)	$PO(OCH_2CH = CH_2)_3$ (20%)	2% Bz_2O_2, 120°, 15 min, 280 atm	Non-flammable; insoluble in organic solvents; good mechanical properties	[538]
Unsaturated polyesters	$ClCH_2PO(OCH_2CH = CH_2)_2$	Bz_2O_2, heat	Hard, transparent, fire-resistant, insoluble	[475]
Alkyd resins. Constituents: ethylene glycol, propylene glycols, maleic anhydride, dichlorophthalic or tetrachlorophthalic anhydrides, dialkyl phthalates, hydroquinone, fillers	$C_6H_5PO(OCH_2CH = CH_2)_2$	Solution, Bz_2O_2 in $C_6H_5PO(OCH_2CH = CH_2)_2$	,,	[454]
Unsaturated alkyd resins from: diethylene glycol maleate	$C_6H_5PO(OCH_2CH = CH_2)_2$ (pre-polymer)	Nitrogen, acetyl or benzoyl peroxide, 85–100°	Transparent resin: fire-resistance increases rapidly with increasing amount of phosphorus-containing component	[453]
triethylene glycol maleate	$C_6H_5PO(OCH_2CH = CH_2)_2$ (pre-polymer)	,,	,,	
diethylene glycol fumarate-sebacate	$C_6H_5PO(OCH_2CH = CH_2)_2$ (pre-polymer)	,,	,,	
Unsaturated alkyd resins	$4\text{-}ClC_6H_5PO(OCH_2CH = CH_2)_2$ $CH_3C_6H_4PO(OCH_2CH = CH_2)_2$	Peroxide, heat	Fire-resistant product	
Unsaturated alkyd resin from diethylene glycol maleate	$C_6H_5PO[OCH_2C(CH_3) = CH_2]_2$	Nitrogen, acetyl or benzoyl peroxide, 85–100°	Transparent resin: fire-resistance increases rapidly with increasing amount of phosphorus-containing component	

TABLE 104 — (contd.)

Organic high molecular weight substances	Phosphorus-containing component	Reaction conditions	Properties of the reaction product	Reference
Unsaturated alkyd resin from: triethylene glycol maleate	$C_6H_5PO[OCH_2C(CH_3) = CH_2]_2$	Nitrogen, acetyl or benzoyl peroxide, 85–100°	Transparent resin: fire-resistance increases rapidly with increasing amount of phosphorus-containing component	[453]
diethylene glycol fumarate	$C_6H_5PO[OCH_2C(CH_3) = CH_2]_2$	,,	,,	
diethylene glycol maleate	$4\text{-}ClC_6H_4PO[OCH_2C(CH_3) = CH_2]_2$	,,	,,	
triethylene glycol maleate	$4\text{-}ClC_6H_4PO[OCH_2C(CH_3) = CH_2]_2$	,,	,,	
diethylene glycol fumarate-sebacate	$4\text{-}ClC_6H_4PO[OCH_2C(CH_3) = CH_2]_2$	,,	,,	
diethylene glycol maleate	$CH_3C_6H_4PO[OCH_2C(CH_3) = CH_2]_2$	,,	,,	
triethylene glycol maleate	$CH_3C_6H_4PO[OCH_2C(CH_3) = CH_2]_2$	,,	,,	
diethylene glycol fumarate-sebacate	$CH_3C_6H_4PO[OCH_2C(CH_3) = CH_2]_2$	,,	,,	
Phenol-formaldehyde resin	$[(C_2H_5O)_2P{-}]_2O$	The mixture was treated with aqueous alkali, washed with water and dried in vacuo	Insoluble polymer formed containing phosphoric acid groups	[173]
Poly(N-ethylideneamino-methylstyrene) $[-CH_2{-}CHC_6H_4CH_2N = CH_2]_n$	$HPO(OC_2H_5)_2$	The mixture was heated at 100° for 17 hr, extracted with ethanol and dried	Polymer formed containing 5·7 % N, 9·0 % P	[277]
The product of the reaction of a resin (from acetophenone and formaldehyde) with ethylamine	$HPO(OC_2H_5)_2$	Similar to above	Polymer formed containing 4·0 % N, 8·4 % P	
The product of the reaction of poly(aminostyrene) and pyridine-2-aldehyde	$HPO(OC_2H_5)_2$ HNC_2H_5	,,	Polymer formed containing 7·5 % N; 8·5 % P	
Diazotized poly(amino-styrene)	$HOC_6H_4CHPO(OC_2H_5)_2$ (in solution)	The mixture was treated with alkali and water: the polymer was washed, filtered and dried	Polymer formed containing 3·2 % P	

HETEROCHAIN HIGH MOLECULAR WEIGHT COMPOUNDS CONTAINING PHOSPHORUS IN THE MAIN CHAIN

In the previous chapter, the methods of synthesis which lead to the formation of carbochain and heterochain high molecular weight compounds of the following type were examined:

(the wavy line represents the macromolecular chain).

The other principal type of heterochain high molecular weight phosphorus compound has the phosphorus in the main chain:

(the wavy lines represent units of the macromolecular chain).

HIGH MOLECULAR WEIGHT COMPOUNDS CONTAINING PHOSPHORUS AND CARBON IN THE MAIN CHAIN

The high molecular weight compounds of this type have been little investigated. McCormack [544, 545] has patented a process for the copolymerization of alkyl- and aryl-phosphonous dichlorides with olefins, dienes, unsaturated esters, etc. These reactions proceed under the influence of free radical initiators. By treating the products obtained with methanol, methyl chloride is evolved and polymers containing phosphinyl groups are formed. The author did not propose a mechanism for these processes, but it is plausible to suppose that they proceeded by the following route:

$$nCH = CH_2 + nPCl_2 \longrightarrow \left[-CH-CH_2-\underset{\underset{R}{|}}{\overset{Cl\ \ Cl}{\overset{\diagdown\diagup}{P}}}- \right]_n \xrightarrow{2nCH_3OH}$$

$$\longrightarrow 2nCH_3Cl + nH_2O + \left[-CH-CH_2-\underset{\underset{R'}{|}}{\overset{O}{\overset{\|}{P}}}- \right]_n$$

When the diene reaction is carried out in the presence of polymerization inhibitors, then an alternative reaction occurs to give, finally, monomeric unsaturated cyclic phosphine oxides [283, 284] (see p. 87), although some polymeric products are always produced. This is explained first, by the presence of inhibitors which hinder the course of polymerization processes, and secondly, by the greater stability of the five-membered rings (formed in the case of dienes) as compared with the three-membered which would have to be formed with olefins.

Heterochain polymers having carbon and phosphorus in the main chain have also been obtained by the reaction of pentamethylenedimagnesium bromide with dibutyl hydrogen phosphite or with diethylphosphoramidic dichloride; [546] for example:

$$nBrMg(CH_2)_5MgBr + nHPO(OC_4H_9)_2 \longrightarrow \left[-\underset{\underset{O}{\|}}{\overset{H}{\overset{|}{P}}}(CH_2)_5- \right]_n$$

and by the polycondensation of phosphonium salts with aldehydes [547].

Kolesnikov, Korshak and Zhubanov [367, 368, 548] have shown that arylphosphonous dichlorides will condense with 1,2-diphenylethane in the presence of aluminium chloride:

$$nCl-\underset{\underset{Ar}{|}}{P}-Cl + n\langle \bigcirc \rangle-CH_2-CH_2-\langle \bigcirc \rangle \xrightarrow{AlCl_3}$$

$$\longrightarrow H\left[-\langle \bigcirc \rangle-CH_2-CH_2-\langle \bigcirc \rangle-\underset{\underset{Ar}{|}}{P}- \right]_n \langle \bigcirc \rangle-CH_2-CH_2-\langle \bigcirc \rangle$$

Other polycondensations are known in which the arylation of 1,2-diphenylethane takes place.

The properties of high molecular weight compounds containing phosphorus and carbon in the main chain are recorded in Table 105.

TABLE 105. THE PRODUCTS OF THE REACTIONS OF ALKYL- AND ARYL-PHOSPHONOUS DICHLORIDES WITH UNSATURATED COMPOUNDS OR WITH 1,2-DIPHENYLETHANE, AND ALSO OF CERTAIN ORGANOPHOSPHORUS COMPOUNDS WITH PENTAMETHYLENEDIMAGNESIUM BROMIDE

Components	Reaction conditions	Properties of the copolymer	Notes % Phosphorus	Reference
$C_2H_5PCl_2$ + 2-bromo-1,3-butadiene	The mixture of components was treated in cyclohexane (at 40–60°) with α,α'-bis(α-methylisocapronitrile). Then the copolymer was treated with water or methanol, extracted with a suitable solvent and dried	Yellow, hard	12·3	[545]
$C_2H_5PCl_2$ + isoprene	,,	Brown, glass-like	18·0	[545]
$C_6H_5PCl_2$ + acrylonitrile 77% 23%	,,	Cream-coloured, hard	2·5	[544]
$C_6H_5PCl_2$ + allyl methyl ether 77% 23%	,,	Reddish liquid	15·1	[544]
$C_6H_5PCl_2$ + methyl methacrylate	,,	Glass	2·9	[544]
$C_6H_5PCl_2$ + butadiene	,,	Yellow, hard		[545]
$C_6H_5PCl_2$ + 2-chloro-1,3-butadiene	,,	Reddish, hard	13·3	[545]
$C_6H_5PCl_2$ + 2,3-dichloro-1,3-butadiene	,,	Cream-coloured, hard	1·7	[545]
$C_6H_5PCl_2$ + isoprene (equi-molecular amounts)	,,	Reddish, glass-like copolymer and an addition product b. p. 160–165°/2 mm	15·5	[544]

TABLE 105 — (contd.)

Components	Reaction conditions	Properties of the copolymer	Notes % Phosphorus	Reference
$C_6H_5PCl_2$ + isoprene (equi-molecular amounts)	,, , but after the hydrolysis and before the extraction the product was treated with NaCl solution	Polymer and addition product		[545]
,,	The components were caused to react without an initiator, and the product was hydrolysed and then extracted and dried	,,		[545]
,,	The reaction was conducted under the influence of benzoyl per-oxide and the product obtained was filtered off and then treated as above	Polymer formed	14·9—15·9	[545]
$C_6H_5PCl_2$ + cyclopentadiene	The components were caused to react in the presence of a,a'azobis-(a-methylisocapronitrile), and then the product was treated as above	Hard	11·8	[545]
$C_6H_5PCl_2$ + styrene	The components were caused to react in the presence of a,a'-azobis(a-methylisocapronitrile), then as above	Hard	7·3	[544]
$C_6H_5PCl_2$ + acrylonitrile + isoprene	,,	Brown, glass-like	15·0	[545]
$4\text{-}BrC_6H_4PCl_2$ + isoprene	,,	Colourless, hard	11·0	[545]

TABLE 105 — (contd.)

Components	Reaction conditions	Properties of the copolymer	Notes (%) Phosporus	Reference
$C_6H_5PCl_2$ + 1,2-diphenylethane	The mixture of components was heated (150–225°, 1–5 hr) in the presence of $AlCl_3$	Pale yellow film-forming polymer. Burns only in the flame; extinguishes itself on removing from the flame; softens at 35°. The polymer unit is: $$\left[-C_6H_4-CH_2-CH_2-\underset{C_6H_5}{P}-\right]_n$$		[367, 368]
$4\text{-}ClC_6H_4PCl_2$ + 1,2-diphenyl-ethane	,,	,, , softens at 60° Polymer unit: $$\left[-CH_2-CH_2-C_6H_4-\underset{4\,ClC_6H_4}{P}-\right]_n$$		[367, 368, 548]
$(C_2H_5)_2NPOCl_2$ + pentamethyl-enedimagnesium bromide	The reaction was carried out in refluxing ether followed by hydrolysis. The monomer was separated from the polymer and the latter was treated with PCl_5 and then with sodium butyl	Dark, viscous, undistillable substance. Decomposed by strong heating *in vacuo*. Supposed structure: $$\left[-\overset{C_4H_9}{\underset{O}{PO(CH_2)_5}}-\right]_n$$		[546]
$HPO(OC_4H_9)_2$ + pentamethyle-nedimagnesium bromide	The reaction was carried out in refluxing ether followed by hydrolysis. The product was oxidised with bromine water	Waxy, semi-solid substance, partially soluble in alkali. Supposed structure: $$\left[-\overset{H}{\underset{O}{P}}(CH_2)_5-\right]_n$$		[546]

HIGH MOLECULAR WEIGHT COMPOUNDS CONTAINING PHOSPHORUS, OXYGEN AND CARBON IN THE MAIN CHAIN (PHOSPHORUS-CONTAINING POLYESTERS)

One of the commonest methods of obtaining phosphorus-containing poly-esters is the polycondensation reaction between equimolecular quantities of di-acid chlorides of acids of phosphorus with glycols or difunctional phenols having the hydroxyls in *meta* or *para* relation. This reaction proceeds at ele-vated temperatures, with good stirring of the reaction mixture, often in the presence of heavy metal halide catalysts. During the course of the polyconden-sation the reaction mass thickens, so that the evolution of hydrogen chloride becomes difficult and the process ceases. Hence, during the reaction an inert gas is usually passed into the system: also, when the reaction is almost over, the temperature of the reaction mixture is raised (sometimes to 250–300°), so that it does not become too thick, and the remaining hydrogen chloride is removed *in vacuo*. The scheme of this reaction is thus:

$$n\text{Cl}\underset{\underset{\text{R}}{|}}{\overset{\overset{\text{O}}{\|}}{\text{P}}}\text{Cl} + n\text{HO}\text{—R}'\text{—OH} \longrightarrow \left[\underset{\underset{\text{R}}{|}}{\overset{\overset{\text{O}}{\|}}{\text{P}}}\text{—O—R}'\text{—O—}\right]_n + 2n\text{HCl}$$

where R = alkyl, aryl, alkoxy, or dialkyl- or diaryl-amido, and R' = alkylene or arylene.

The character of the hydroxyl-containing component exerts a profound influence on the course of the reaction and on the properties of the product. A. Ye. Arbusov and his co-workers, [383, 394, 395] and also other investi-gators [396, 398–401, 409], showed that the reaction of glycols with di- or tri-acid chlorides of acids of tri- and sometimes penta-valent phosphorus yields mainly single products — cyclic esters or acid chlorides of phosphorus acids. For example:

$$\text{RPOCl}_2 + \text{HOR'OH} \longrightarrow \text{RP}\underset{\underset{\text{O}}{\|}}{\overset{\text{O}}{\diagdown}}\diagup\text{R}'$$

or

$$\text{PCl}_3 + \text{HOCH}_2\text{CH}_2\text{OH} \longrightarrow \underset{\text{CH}_2\text{O}}{\overset{\text{CH}_2\text{O}}{|}}\diagup\text{PCl}$$

As well as these substances, there are always formed various quantities of more or less high molecular weight compounds which are thick liquids with, presumably, polyester structures [396, 401, 405].

If this particular reaction is carried out at high temperatures and with not completely pure or even undistilled starting materials, then the formation of polyester products [396] predominates. Korshak and his co-workers [401] found that the heating of the individual cyclic compounds mentioned above caused the rings to split and change into comparatively low molecular weight polyester chains: in this way an equilibrium can be established between the cyclic and linear forms.

Certain of the individual compounds of cyclic structure, however, are so unstable that they are changed spontaneously and gradually at room temperature into gellike substances [383, 394, 395], this process is sometimes accompanied by the separating out of white phosphorus.

Individual reaction products are not produced by the polycondensation of di-acid chlorides of phosphorus acids with aromatic dihydroxy compounds. Instead, the reaction mixtures gradually thicken and finally change into hard resins of linear structure, coloured from light yellow to black, and with various softening temperatures [302, 549–559]. It must be emphasized that in order to obtain polyesters with high molecular weights, it is necessary to use precisely equimolecular ratios of both components.

Polyesters based on phosphonic acids

$$\left[-\overset{\overset{\displaystyle O}{\|}}{\underset{\underset{\displaystyle R}{|}}{P}} - O - \left\langle \bigcirc \right\rangle - O - \right]_n \qquad (302)$$

$$n\mathrm{RPOCl_2} + n\mathrm{HO} - \left\langle \bigcirc \right\rangle - \mathrm{OH} \longrightarrow \left[-\overset{\overset{\displaystyle O}{\|}}{\underset{\underset{\displaystyle R}{|}}{P}} - O - \left\langle \bigcirc \right\rangle - O - \right]_n + 2n\mathrm{HCl}$$

Polyesters of phosphonic acids have been obtained by the condensation of the acid chlorides of the corresponding acids with hydroquinone in the presence of metallic tin (1%). The reactions were carried out in a test tube, fitted with a device for passing nitrogen. The starting components were taken in equimolecular amounts. The condensation conditions were as follows: heat in a stream of nitrogen for 4 hr at 140°; then 7 hr at 170°; then 1 hr at 180°; then 1 hr at 190°; and finally for 3 hr at 200°. The metallic tin catalyst was added to the reaction mixture at 170°.

Polyesters are sometimes synthesized by the reaction of glycols or dihydroxy aromatic compounds with tri-acid halides of phosphorus acids [560–562], or with mixtures of di- and tri-halides of these acids [563, 564]. More special methods for obtaining phosphorus-containing polyesters are the reactions of glycols with dialkyl hydrogen phosphites [565], phosphorus pentoxide [566], or trialkyl [567] or triaryl [142] phosphites (in the last case monomeric cyclic esters are formed as well as polyesters — see p. 117):

$$n\mathrm{P(OAr)_3} + n\mathrm{HOROH} \Bigg\langle \begin{array}{l} \left[\underset{\underset{\displaystyle O}{|}}{\overset{\overset{\displaystyle Ar}{|}}{\underset{\underset{\displaystyle |}{|}}{}}} - P - O - R - O - \right]_n + 2n\mathrm{ArOH} \\[2em] n\mathrm{ArOP} \underset{O}{\overset{O}{\diagdown}} R + 2n\mathrm{ArOH} \end{array}$$

Phosphorus-containing polyesters have been prepared by the transesterification of phosphonic diesters with dihydroxy aromatic compounds [568]:

$$nRPO(OAr)_2 + nHOAr'OH \longrightarrow \left[\begin{array}{c} O \\ \parallel \\ -P-O-Ar'-O- \\ \mid \\ R \end{array}\right] + 2nArOH$$

or with partially esterified glycerol [569]; and also by the thermal polycondensation of the 2-chloroethyl esters of phosphorus acids, a reaction which is accompanied by the evolution of dichloroethane [570–572]:

$$2nRPO(OCH_2CH_2Cl)_2 \longrightarrow (2n-1)ClCH_2CH_2Cl +$$

$$+ ClCH_2CH_2-\left[\begin{array}{c} O \\ \parallel \\ -P\,O-CH_2CH_2- \\ \mid \\ R \end{array}\right]_{2n}-Cl$$

Recently the reactions of di-acid chlorides of substituted phosphoric acids with quinones have been studied; polyesters were formed which contained phosphorus and chlorine, presumably by the following route [573]:

$$Cl-\overset{\overset{\displaystyle O}{\parallel}}{\underset{\underset{\displaystyle OR}{\mid}}{P}}-Cl + O=\!\!\!\!\left\langle\!\!\!\bigcirc\!\!\!\right\rangle\!\!\!=O \longrightarrow \left[\begin{array}{c} O \quad Cl \qquad Cl \\ \parallel \\ -P-O\!\!-\!\!\left\langle\!\!\bigcirc\!\!\right\rangle\!\!-\!\!O- \\ \mid \\ OR \end{array}\right]_n$$

The formation of phosphorus-containing polyesters as side products from the thermal isomerization of tri-(2-chloroethyl) phosphite [574] or by the Arbusov rearrangement of this ester by the action of halogen-containing compounds [575] has been described.

It is interesting to note that the widely applied synthesis of carboxylic polyesters, involving the reaction of dicarboxylic acids with glycols, cannot be applied to organophosphorus compounds. The presence of an atom of phosphorus in the molecules so reduces the reactivity of the hydroxyl-groups contained in them that only one of the hydroxyl-groups can be esterified. It is obviously impossible, therefore, to produce a polyester chain by this route.

Recently a detailed study of polyesters of the following general structure — the so-called "Phoryl" resins — has been made [549–551]:

$$\left[\begin{array}{c} O \\ \parallel \\ -P-O-Ar'-O- \\ \mid \\ O \\ \mid \\ Ar \end{array}\right]_n$$

They are transparent, slightly coloured or almost colourless, glass-like and sometimes brittle substances with molecular weights of about 15,000. They are thick syrups above their melting-points. According to X-ray investigations on drawn out fibres, Phoryl resins do not form orientated crystals. These resins are soluble in a range of halogenated aliphatic hydrocarbons, aromatic hydrocarbons and their mixtures with alcohols, and insoluble in water, alcohols, aliphatic hydrocarbons and (except Phoryl 3) esters. The following mixture (in volume %) is a solvent for them all: ethanol or methanol-8; toluene-65; xylene-23; butanol-4.

Phoryl resins are stable to water-soluble inorganic salts and to dilute alkaline or acidic solutions at room temperature. They adhere well to many metals, glass, wood, fibres, asbestos and a range of polymers. They adhere poorly to polyethylene and polytetrafluoroethylene.

The properties of the Phoryl resins are presented below (Tables 106–108). Phoryl 3 forms thixotropic gels containing 60–65% of resin with certain solvents. The electrical power factors at 10^6 cycles for Phoryls 1 and 2 are similar to those quoted for silicone on glass and talc on ebonite.

TABLE 106. PHYSICOMECHANICAL PROPERTIES OF PHORYL RESINS [550]

Resin	Side-chain*	n_D^{20}	d^{20}	Acid no.	Intrinsic viscosity η	Softening temp. (°C)		Hardness (diamond indentation method)
						Ball and ring method	Vicat	
Phoryl 1	4-phenylphenyl	1·621	1·35	10	0·21	120	58	16·5+
Phoryl 2	2-phenylphenyl	1·619	1·34	10	0·30	115	51·5	19·3+
Phoryl 3	4-octylphenyl	1·550	1·34	9	0·28	100	43·5	10·3
Phoryl 23	Phenyl + 4-phenyl-phenyl	1·607						
Phoryl 70	Phenyl	1·580	1·36		0·21	60	32	
Phoryl 100	2,4-dichlorophenyl	1·602						
Phoryl 100B	2,4-dibromophenyl	1·625						

* The difunctional phenol used to prepare the Phoryl resins is hydroquinone in all cases.

+ Similar to the hardness of unplasticised poly(methyl methacrylate) and polystyrene

TABLE 107. TENSILE STRENGTHS (KG/CM^2) OF BONDS BETWEEN PHORYL RESINS AND OTHER MATERIALS [550]

Resin	Steel	Copper	Brass	Duralumin	Glass
Phoryl 1	105	91	87·5	70	45·5
Phoryl 2	108·5	112	77	66·5	105
Phoryl 3	28	52·5	17·5	49	—
Phoryl 23	—	—	—	—	108·5
Phoryl 70	119	133	126	129·5	98
Phoryl 80	182	136·5	224	15·4	168

TABLE 108. STABILITY OF PHORYL RESINS 1 AND 2 TOWARDS CERTAIN CHEMICAL REAGENTS* [550]

Reagents which do not have any effect even after 2 yr immersion	Reagents which attack rapidly or after less than one month's immersion	Reagents which do not have any effect even after 2 yr immersion	Reagents which attack rapidly or after less than one month's immersion
H_2O H_2SO_4 (10–50%) HCl (3–32%) HNO_3 (10%)	H_2SO_4 (97%) HNO_3 (70%) CH_3COOH (98%) HCOOH (98%)	CH_3COOH (10%) HCOOH (10%) NaCl, Na_2CO_3 $NaHCO_3$ (saturated solutions)	NaOH (35%) HF (50%) $ClCH_2COOH$ (10%) Chlorine water; water saturated with SO_2; sodium hypochlorite

* The water vapour permeability of the Phoryl resins at 25° and 75% relative humidity s 2·2 - 2·3 g/m² per 24 hr. [poly(vinyl chloride) has a value of 5·5].

Of considerable interest, but as yet little studied, are the polyesters which are similar to the Phoryl resins but which have the side chains joined directly to the phosphorus. The chain unit of such polyesters is:

$$-\overset{\displaystyle \overset{O}{\|}}{\underset{\displaystyle R}{P}}-OAr-O-, \quad \text{where } R = \text{alkyl or aryl}$$

The interest in these compounds and their advantage lies in the fact that the side chains in these compounds are joined more strongly to the macro-molecular chains than the side chains in the Phoryl resins are: this is because the C—P bond is more stable than the C—O—P link. These polyesters can be synthesized in a similar way to the Phoryl resins by using the di-acid hali-des of alkyl- and aryl-phosphonic acids [302, 555–559], or alternatively by other methods which have been listed previously [568, 570].

Phosphorus-containing polyesters, although they have many valuable properties (non-flammability; adhesion to glass, metals; etc.), also have cer-tain disadvantages: they have comparatively low softening temperatures in the majority of cases (below 120°) and are incapable of being hardened; one patent claims, however, although not very clearly, that phosphorus-contain-ing polyesters can be vulcanized by treatment with paraformaldehyde [553]. Recently another method has been described which enables these deficiences to be overcome. The essential feature of this method involves including side chain halogeno-alkyl groups in the polyesters: hydrogen halide can then be eliminated to give unsaturated side chains which, at elevated temperatures and in the presence of initiators, cross-link the linear polyesters chains and thus strengthen them [576]:

$$n\text{ClCH}_2\text{CH}_2\overset{\displaystyle \underset{\displaystyle O}{\|}}{P}\text{Cl}_2 + n\text{HO}-\text{R}-\text{OH} \longrightarrow \left[\begin{array}{c} O \\ | \\ -P-O-R-O- \\ | \\ CH_2 \\ | \\ CH_2 \\ | \\ Cl \end{array} \right]_n \xrightarrow{-HCl}$$

$$\longrightarrow \left[\begin{array}{c} \overset{O}{\|} \\ -P-O-R-O- \\ | \\ CH \\ \| \\ CH_2 \end{array} \right]_n \longrightarrow \left[\begin{array}{l} \text{Three-dimensional} \\ \text{phosphorus-con-} \\ \text{taining polyester} \end{array} \right]$$

The first phosphoric acid polyesters were obtained by heating in the pre-sence of ferric chloride, mixtures of chlorinated tricresyl phosphates — which contain mobile chlorine atoms in the side chains — with aromatic hydrocarbons or triaryl phosphates having mobile hydrogen atoms [577]. The course of this reaction may be represented in the following way:

$$n\text{ClCH}_2\!-\!\!\langle\bigcirc\rangle\!-\!\text{O}\!-\!\overset{\overset{\displaystyle O}{\|}}{\underset{\displaystyle \text{OAr}}{\text{P}}}\!-\!\text{O}\!-\!\langle\bigcirc\rangle\!-\!\text{CH}_2\text{Cl} +$$

$$+\ n\text{H}\!-\!\text{Ar}'\!-\!\text{H}\ \xrightarrow[\text{FeCl}_3]{150-200°}$$

$$\longrightarrow \left[-\text{CH}_2\!-\!\!\langle\bigcirc\rangle\!-\!\text{O}\!-\!\overset{\overset{\displaystyle O}{\|}}{\underset{\displaystyle \text{OAr}}{\text{P}}}\!-\!\text{O}\!-\!\langle\bigcirc\rangle\!-\!\text{CH}_2\!-\!\text{Ar}'\!-\right]_n + 2n\text{HCl}$$

where $\text{Ar}' = $ arylene. In the products obtained the P—O—C units are not formed as a result of polycondensation, as in all the previously described cases, but are present in one or both of the starting materials.

Another type of phosphorus-containing polyester is known which is a carboxylic polyester and which also contains phosphorus in the main chain. This type of substance has been prepared by the reaction of tertiary phosphine oxides, containing not less than two carboxylic ester groups in the molecules, with glycols [578] in the presence of zinc borate — in one case with pentaerythritol [579] — or lithium hydroxide [367]. The synthesis of such polyesters is based on the transesterification reaction:

$$n\text{RPO}\!\left(-\!\langle\bigcirc\rangle\!-\!\text{COOCH}_3\right)_2 + n\text{HO}\!-\!\text{R}'\!-\!\text{OH} \longrightarrow$$

$$\longrightarrow \left[-\text{OOC}\!-\!\langle\bigcirc\rangle\!-\!\overset{\overset{\displaystyle O}{\|}}{\underset{\displaystyle \text{R}}{\text{P}}}\!-\!\langle\bigcirc\rangle\!-\!\text{COOR}'\!-\right] + 2n\text{CH}_3\text{OH}.$$

Another route to the preparation of similar carboxylic polyesters is the reaction of bis-(hydroxymethyl)-phosphinic acid with dicarboxylic acids or their anhydrides [580].

Besides the polyesters synthesized as described previously, another phosphorus-containing resin has been described: it was obtained by the polymerization of p-anisylthionophosphine sulphide. According to the authors of this communication this resin might have had a polyester structure (one of the two possible variants) [581]. It seems that the macromolecule also possesses a similar structure to the products of polycondensation of aldehydes with acid esters of phosphoric acid [582].

The properties of phosphorus-containing polyesters are recorded in Tables 109–115.

TABLE 109. POLYESTERS OBTAINED BY THE REACTION OF PHOSPHORYL OR THIOPHOSPHORYL CHLORIDE WITH DIFUNCTIONAL ALCOHOLS OR PHENOLS

Components	Reaction conditions	Properties of the polymer	Reference
POCl₃ + polyglycol (m. w. 700) 18% 82%	The mixture was refluxed in benzene for 80 min followed by treatment with water and removal of solvent	Waxy product	[561]
25·5% 74·5%	PCl₃(0·2%) catalyst. The mixture was refluxed in benzene and esterified with alcohols of average m. w. 186, and then treated with water	Opalescent foaming liquid	[561]
POCl₃ + polyglycol + xylenol (m. w. 300) 26% 52% 22%	The mixture was refluxed in trichloroethylene and then treated with steam	Waxy product	[561]
POCl₃ + hydroquinone	The mixture was heated in an atmosphere of an inert gas. The product was extracted with boiling chlorobenzene and the solvent was evaporated	Elastic polyester soluble in organic solvents	[562]
POCl₃ + 2,2-bis (4-hydroxyphenyl)-propane	The mixture was refluxed in xylene	,,	[561]
POCl₃ + 2,2-bis (4-hydroxyphenyl)-propane + phenol	The mixture was refluxed in xylene for 18·5 hr. The solvent and unreacted phenol were removed in steam and the product was dried in vacuo	Pale-coloured resin, reminiscent of balsam; soluble in esters	[560]
POCl₃ + 2,2-bis (4-hydroxyphenyl)-propane 31% 69%	Similar to above	Pale-brown, rather brittle resin	[560]
POCl₃ + 1,5-dihydroxynaphthalene	The mixture was heated in an atmosphere of an inert gas. The product was extracted with boiling chlorobenzene and the solvent was evaporated	Elastic polyester, soluble in organic solvents	[562]
POCl₃ + 4,4'-dihydroxydinaphthyl	,,	,,	[562]
PSCl₃ + 2,2-bis-(4-hydroxyphenyl)-propane 32% 68%	PCl₃ catalyst. The mixture was refluxed in xylene for 2·25 hr. The solvent was removed in steam and the product dried in vacuo	Pale-brown, rather brittle resin	[560]

TABLE 110. POLYESTERS OBTAINED FROM THE REACTION OF ARYL PHOSPHORODICHLORIDATES WITH DIFUNCTIONAL PHENOLS

Polyesters obtained from the reaction of mixtures of di-acid chlorides of phosphonic and phosphoric acids with difunctional phenols are listed in Table 114.

Components (in equimolecular amounts)	Reaction conditions	Properties of the polyester	Reference
$C_6H_5OPOCl_2$ + resorcinol	290°	Brown resin of probable linear structure	[553]
$C_6H_5OPOCl_2$ + hydroquinone	Nitrogen; 140°–4 hr, 170°–7 hr, 180°–1 hr, 190°–1, hr, 200°–3 hr; tin catalyst added at 170°	Rubber-like, $t \approx 50°$	[302]
$C_6H_5OPOCl_2$ + hydroquinone	120–215° 20–26 hr	, $t = 60°$ (by the ring and ball method)	[554]
$C_6H_5OPOCl_2$ + hydroquinone	Nitrogen, 120–215°, 20–26 hr	Very hard, durable, self/extinguishing, $t = 80°$ (by the ring and ball method)	[554]
$C_6H_5OPOCl_2$ + hydroquinone	168–197°, 14 hr; then in a vacuum system	Brown resin of probable linear structure	[553]
$C_6H_5OPOCl_2$ + hydroquinone	Polyester obtained on previous experiment heated to 300°	Resin-like	[553]
$C_6H_5OPOCl_2$ + 4,4′-dihydroxydiphenyl	165–245°	Resin, $t = 300°$	[553]
$C_6H_5OPOCl_2$ + 4,4′-dihydroxydiphenyl	Nitrogen, 170–220°, 20–26 hr	Brown, transparent, hard, $t = 110°$ (by the ring and ball method)	[554]
$C_6H_5OPOCl_2$ + 4·4′-dihydroxydiphenyl	Nitrogen, BF_3-diacetate catalyst, 170–220°, 20–26 hr	Brown, transparent, hard, $t \approx 125°$	[554]
4-$ClC_6H_4OPOCl_2$ + resorcinol	165–195°, 20 hr	Transparent, clear resin, $t = 55°$ (by the ring and ball method)	[554]
2,4-$Cl_2C_6H_3OPOCl_2$ + hydroquinone	Nitrogen, 130–220°, 20–26 hr	Very hard, durable, non-flammable, $t = 105°$ (by the ring and ball method)	[554]
2·4-$Cl_2C_6H_3OPOCl_2$ + 4,4′-dihydroxydiphenyl	Tin catalyst; 130–160° for 6 hr, 180–195° for 8 hr, then at 170–180°/ 1 mm	Hard, durable, $t = 160°$	[554]
2,4,6-$Cl_3C_6H_2OPOCl_2$ + hydroquinone	160–200°, 20–26 hr	Hard, durable, non-flammable, $t \approx 115°$	[554]

TABLE 110 — (contd.)

Components (in equimolecular amounts)	Reaction conditions	Properties of the polyester	Reference
2,4-Br$_2$C$_6$H$_3$OPOCl$_2$ + hydroquinone	Nitrogen, 95–200°, 13 hr	Clear, transparent resin, $t = 105°$ (by the ring and ball method)	[554]
4-CH$_3$OC$_6$H$_4$OPOCl$_2$ + hydroquinone	Nitrogen, tin catalyst, 140–200°, 16 hr	Brittle, transparent, $t \approx 35–38°$	[302]
4-NO$_2$C$_6$H$_4$OPOCl$_2$ + hydroquinone	„	Brittle, pale brown, $t \approx 36–38°$	[302]
2-CH$_3$C$_6$H$_4$OPOCl$_2$ + hydroquinone	Nitrogen, 120–215°, 20–26 hr	Brittle, pale brown, $t \approx 75°$	[554]
2-C$_6$H$_5$C$_6$H$_4$OPOCl$_2$ + hydroquinone	150° for 3 hr, then 0·1% tin added and heated at 190° for 27 hr	Whitish, hard, $t = 110°$ (by the ring and ball method)	[552]
4-C$_6$H$_5$C$_6$H$_4$OPOCl$_2$ + hydroquinone	150° for 7 hr, then 180–185° fo 25 hr	Slightlycoloured, transparent, hard, $t = 115°$	[552]
4-C$_6$H$_5$C$_6$H$_4$OPOCl$_2$ + 4,4'-dihydroxy-diphenyl ether	180°–4 hr, then 0·1% tin added and heated at 180–210° for 16 hr and 210°/25 mm for 2 hr	Transparent, colourless, hard $t \approx 190°$	[552]

Note: t = sottening temperature

TABLE 111. POLYESTERS OBTAINED FROM THE REACTION OF PHOSPHORAMIDIC DICHLORIDES WITH DIFUNCTIONAL PHENOLS (563)

Polyesters obtained by the reaction of mixtures of di-acid chlorides of phosphonic and phosphoramidic acids with difunctional phenols are listed in Table 114.

Components (in equimolecular amounts)	Reaction conditions	Properties of the polyester
(CH$_3$)$_2$NPOCl$_2$ + hydroquinone	Nitrogen, MgCl$_2$ catalyst; 205°–4 hr, 230°/5 mm—2 hr	Pale yellow, durable, fire-resistant resin. Soluble in dimethylformamide. Softens at 100–130°
(C$_2$H$_5$)$_2$NPOCl$_2$ + hydroquinone + 4,4'-dihydroxydiphenyl sulphone	Similar to above	Similar to above
(cyclo-C$_6$H$_{11}$)NPOCl$_2$ + resorcinol	„	„
(C$_6$H$_5$)$_2$NPOCl$_2$ + hydroquinone	„	„

TABLE 112. POLYESTERS OBTAINED BY THE POLYMERIZATION OF CYCLIC ESTERS OF PHOSPHONIC ACIDS OR BY THE THERMAL POLYCONDENSATION OF DI-(2-CHLOROETHYL) ESTERS OF PHOSPHONIC ACIDS

Components	Reaction conditions	Properties of the polyester	Yield of polymer (%)	Reference
$CH_3P{=}O$, $O{-}(CH_2)_2$	Room temperature, 16 months. The polyester was washed with benzene and dried to constant weight	Viscous liquid, $\eta = 0.10$	99.1	[401]
$CH_3P{=}O$, $O{-}(CH_2)_2$	Water (0.5%) as catalyst; 110°—5 hr, 130°—6 hr. Polyester treated as above	,,	88	[401]
$CH_3P{=}O$, $O{-}(CH_2)_2$	Nitrogen, Na (3%) catalyst, 140°, 10 hr. Polyester treated as above	Viscous liquid, $\eta = 0.08$ (the molecular weight corresponds to a tetramer)	96.4	[401]
$CH_3P{=}O$, $O(CH_2)_2{-}O(CH_2)_2{-}O$	,,	Viscous liquid, $\eta = 0.157$	59.7	[401]
$CH_3P{=}O$, $O{-}(CH_2)_3$	,, , 20 hr	,, , $\eta = 0.06$ (the molecular weight corresponds to a tetramer)	52.7	[401]

15*

TABLE 112 — (contd.)

Components	Reaction conditions	Properties of the polyester	Yield of polymer %	Reference
CH_3P(=O) ring with $(CH_2)_4$	Nitrogen, Na (3%) catalyst, 10 hr. Polyester treated as above	Viscous liquid, $\eta = 0.11$	56	[401]
CH_3P(=O) ring with $(CH_2)_5$	,,	,, $\eta = 0.12$	65	[401]
$ClCH_2P$(=O) ring with $(CH_2)_4$	,, (5% Na)	,, $\eta = 0.07$	62·8	[401]
C_6H_5P(=O) ring with $(CH_2)_2$	,,	,, $\eta = 0.34$	92·1	[401]
$CH_3PO(OCH_2CH_2Cl)_2$	230°, 10 hr. The polymer was washed from the product with benzene	,, $\eta = 0.08$	50–55	[571]
$ClCH_2PO(OCH_2CH_2Cl)_2$	,,	,, $\eta = 0.09$	52·8	[571]
$C_6H_5PO(OCH_2CH_2Cl)_2$	250°, 10 hr. Isolated as above	,, $\eta = 0.08$ (m. w. = 5000)	62·4	[571]

Note : η = Specific viscosity of a 1·5% solution in cresol.

TABLE 113. POLYESTERS OBTAINED BY THE REACTION OF DIESTERS OR DIACID CHLORIDES OF PHOSPHONOUS, PHOSPHONIC OR PHOSPHONOTHIONIC ACIDS WITH DIFUNCTIONAL PHENOLS

Components (in equimolecular amounts)	Reaction conditions	Properties of the polyester	Reference
$C_6H_5PCl_2$ + hydroquinone	Carbon dioxide gas; 100–280° for 4 hr; 260°/6–7 mm for 40 hr	Pale yellow, infusible, smells of phosphine	[555]
CH_3POCl_2 + hydroquinone	Nitrogen, tin catalyst, 140–200°, 16 hr	Brittle, transparent, softens at 63–65°	[302]
$ClCH_2PO(OC_6H_5)_2$ + hydroquinone	$MgCl_2$ catalyst, 200° for 1–2 hr, 250°/1–2 mm for 4–5 hr	Hard, durable, non-flammable, softens at about 110°	[568]
$ClCH_2POCl_2$ + hydroquinone	Nitrogen, $MgCl_2$ catalyst, 90° for 1 hr, 90–150°/1–2 mm for 2·5 hr, 150–250° for 3 hr	,, ; soluble in dimethylformamide and dichloroethane	[583]
$ClCH_2POCl_2$ + hydroquinone	,, , but the acid chloride was added in two equal portions (the second at 120°) and not all at once	,,	[583]
cyclo-$C_6H_{11}POCl_2$ + hydroquinone	145° for 11 hr, then 1% tin added and heated at 150–160° for 3 hr, 180–200° for 8 hr, 200–220° for 15 hr	Slightly coloured, durable: softening point (by the ring and ball method) 135°; soluble in a range of halogen-containing solvents and in their mixtures with aromatic hydrocarbons	[557]
cyclo-$C_6H_{11}POCl_2$ + 4,4'-dihydroxydiphenyl	190°–10 hr, then to 280° as in the previous case	,, ; softens at about 200°	[557]
$C_6H_5PO(OC_6H_5)_2$ + resorcinol	$MgCl_2$ catalyst, 150° for 1 hr, 150–250° for 2–3 hr, 250°/1–2 mm for 3 hr	Hard, durable, non-flammable; softening point 120° (by the ring and ball method)	[568]
$C_6H_5POCl_2$ + resorcinol (excess)	70–120°/1–2 mm for 21 hr, 100–125° for 67 hr, then heated from 125–360°	Hard, brittle, m. p. 85–90°	[555]

TABLE 113 — (contd.)

Components (in equimolecular amounts)	Reaction conditions	Properties of the polyester	Reference
$C_6H_5POCl_2$ + hydroquinone	Carbon dioxide gas, 125–220° for 20·5 hr, 135–300°/1–4 mm for 115 hr	Hard, durable, horny; softens at 130°	[555]
$C_6H_5POCl_2$ + hydroquinone	70–80°/13 mm for several hr, 110–115° for 40 hr, then from 115° to 360° at 1–2 mm	Reddish, hard, brittle, glass-like; softens at 95°, m. p. 105°	[555]
$C_6H_5POCl_2$ + hydroquinone	Nitrogen, tin catalyst, 140–200°, 16 hr	Brittle, transparent; softens at 83–85°	[302]
$C_6H_5POCl_2$ (0·33 M) + hydroquinone (0·15 M) + tetrachlorohydroquinone (0·15 M)	Carbon dioxide gas, 170–220° for about 100 hr, 190–270°/1–2 mm for about 70 hr	Hard, bright, black; m. p. 190–210°	[556]
$C_6H_5POCl_2$ + dichlorohydroquinone	Similar to above	Hard, durable, resin-like; m. p. 180–186°	[556]
$C_6H_5POCl_2$ (0·2 M) + dichlorohydroquinone (0·1 M) + tetrachlorohydroquinone (0·1 M)	,,	Hard, softens at 195°; m. p. 197–210°	[556]
$C_6H_5POCl_2$ + tetrachlorohydroquinone	,,	Black, hard, brittle; m. p. 241°	[556]
$C_6H_5POCl_2$ + 1,5-dihydroxynapthalene	Carbon dioxide gas, temp. raised from 80° to 140° and then at 230° for 2·5 hr, 210–230°/4mm for17 hr, 250°/4 mm for 2 hr	Black, brittle; m. p. 196–198°	[555]
$C_6H_5PCl_2$ + hydroquinone (5 % excess)	$C_6H_5PCl_2$ catalyst, 180–205° for 6 hr, 150–245°/5 mm for 102 hr	Dark, transparent glass; m. p. 165–172°; soluble in chlorinated hydrocarbons and benzene	[555]
,, , in trichlorobenzene	Refluxed (220°) for 47 hr, then the solvent removed and the residue heated at 230–280°/2 mm for 40 hr	Black, hard, durable; softens at 125°; m. p. 250°; soluble in chlorinated hydrocarbons	[555]

TABLE 114. POLYESTERS OBTAINED BY THE REACTION OF MIXTURES OF DI- (AND TRI-) ACID CHLORIDES OF ACIDS OF PHOSPHORUS (PHOSPHONIC, PHOSPHONOTHIONIC, PHOSPHORIC, PHOSPHORAMIDIC) WITH DIFUNCTIONAL PHENOLS

Components (in molar proportions)	Reaction conditions	Properties of the polyester	Reference

CH_3POCl_2 + $C_6H_5OPOCl_2$ + hydroquinone
0·75 ... 0·25 ... 1
0·5 ... 0·5 ... 1
0·25 ... 0·75 ... 1
0·2 ... 0·8 ... 1
0·15 ... 0·85 ... 1
	Nitrogen, tin catalyst, 140–200°, 16 hr
	  ,,
	  ,,
	  ,,
	  ,,
		Softening-point, 50–52°
		  ,, , 41–43°
		  ,, , 32–34°
		  ,, , 29–30°
		  ,, , 26–27°
			[302]

$ClCH_2POCl_2$ + $C_7H_{15}POCl_2$ + hydroquinone 0·076 ... 0·05 ... 0·1	Nitrogen, $MgCl_2$ catalyst; 90° for 1 hr, 150°/1–2 mm for 2·5 hr, 150–250° for 3 hr. [At the beginning of the reaction a mixture of the acid chlorides (0·025 moles of each) with all the hydroquinone was used, and at 120° the remaining $ClCH_2POCl_2$ and $C_7H_{15}POCl_2$ were added.]	Very hard, durable, flame resistant	[583]
$ClCH_2POCl_2$ + $C_6H_5OPOCl_2$ + hydroquinone 0·102 ... 0·5 ... 0·1	Similar to above. At the beginning of the reaction $ClCH_2POCl_2$ (0·055 mole) and all the hydroquinone were used, and the $C_6H_5OPOCl_2$ and the remaining $ClCH_2POCl_2$ were added at 120°	,,	[564]
$C_7H_{15}POCl_2$ + $POCl_3$ + resorcinol 0·5 ... 0·0025 ... 0·5	Similar to above. The reaction was conducted on a mixture of the total amounts of all the components	,,	[564]
$C_7H_{15}POCl_2$ + C_6H_5POCl + 4,4'-dihydroxy-diphenyl 0·05 ... 0·05 ... 0·1	Similar to above	,, , softening-point, 105°	[568]

$C_6H_5POCl_2$ + $C_6H_5OPOCl_2$ + hydroquinone
0·1 ... 0·9 ... 1·0
0·2 ... 0·8 ... 1·0
	Nitrogen, tin catalyst, 140–220°, 16 hr
	  ,,
		Softening-point, 28–30°
		  ,, , 36–39°
			[302]

TABLE 115. POLYESTERS OBTAINED BY THE REACTION OF TERTIARY PHOSPHINE OXIDES CONTAINING ESTER GROUPS WITH GLYCOLS

Components (in molar proportions)	Reaction conditions	Properties of the polyester	Reference
$CH_3PO(—C_6H_4—CO_2CH_3)_2$ (I) + ethylene glycol 0.03 : 0.18	Zinc borate catalyst 197° for 15–20 hr, 259° for 1–8 hr, glycol derivative obtained 259°/0.2–0.5 mm, for 7–25 hr: polycondensation occurred	Hard, durable, does not support combustion, $\eta = 0.46$	[579]
0.07 : 0.7	Zinc borate and pentaerythritol catalyst, 259°/0.2–0.5 mm for 7–25 hr	", $\eta = 0.40$	[579]
I + diethylene glycol 0.07 : 1.0	Similar to above	", $\eta = 0.35$	[579]
I + dimethyl terephthalate + ethylene glycol 0.63 : 1.1 : 9.0	Zinc borate, 259°/0.2–0.5 mm, 7–25 hr	", $\eta = 0.48$	[579]
$C_2H_5PO(—C_6H_4—CO_2CH_3)_2$ + ethylene glycol 0.35 : 9.0	Similar to above	", $\eta = 0.38$	[579]
$C_2H_5PO(—C_6H_4—CO_2CH_3)_2$ + dimethyl terephthalate + ethylene glycol 0.147 : 0.26 : 2.63		", $\eta = 0.62$	[579]
0.65 : 1.16 : 4.26	"	", $\eta = 0.60$	[579]
$C_6H_5PO(—C_6H_4—CO_2CH_3)_2$ (I) + ethylene glycol	Nitrogen, LiOH catalyst, 150–230° for 6 hr, 200–250°/1 mm for 6 hr	Hard, burns, but is extinguished on removing from the flame, $\eta = 0.075$, m. p. 137°	[367]
I + butan-1,4-diol	"	", $\eta = 0.091$, m. p. 124°	[367]
I + pentan-1,5-diol	"	", $\eta = 0.102$, m. p. 125°	[367]
I + hexan-1,6-diol	"	", $\eta = 0.16$, m. p. 100°	[367]
I + p-di-(2-hydroxyethyl)benzene	"	Insoluble and infusible	[367]

Note: η = specific viscosity in m-cresol.

TABLE 115 — (contd.)

Components (in molar proportions)	Reaction conditions	Properties of the polyester	Reference
I + dimethyl terephthalate + ethylene glycol 0·14 0·24 3·58	Zinc borate catalyst, 197° for 18 hr, 259°/0·3 mm for 21 hr	Durable, clear, does not support combustion, $\eta = 0.35$	[579]
$C_6H_5POCl_2$ + $C_6H_5OPOCl_2$ + hydroquinone 0·25 0·75 1 0·3 0·7 1 0·4 0·6 1 0·5 0·5 1 0·6 0·4 1 0·7 0·3 1 0·75 0·25 1 0·8 0·2 1 0·9 0·1 1 0·95 0·05 1	Nitrogen, tin catalyst, 140–200°, 16 hr	Softening-point, 36–38° ,, 40–43° ,, 46–49° ,, 50–55° ,, 58–60° ,, 63–65° ,, 65–70° ,, 69–72° ,, 76–77°	[302]
$C_6H_5POCl_2$ + 4-$CH_3OC_6H_4OPOCl_2$ + hydroquinone 0·5 0·5 1	Nitrogen, $MgCl_2$ catalyst, 90–250°, 6·5 hr	Very hard, durable, flame-resistant, softening-point 105°	[564]
	Nitrogen, tin catalyst, 140–200°, 16 hr	Softening-point, 63–65°	[302]
$C_6H_5POCl_2$ + $NO_2C_6H_4OPOCl_2$ + hydroquinone 0·5 0·5 1	,,	Softening-point, 67–69°	[302]
$C_6H_5POCl_2$ + $C_6H_5PSCl_2$ + hydroquinone 0·5 0·5 1	Carbon dioxide gas; 125–220° for 20 hr, 135–300°/1–4 mm for 135 hr	Dark, hard, durable	[555]
$C_6H_5POCl_2$ + $(CH_3)_2NPOCl_2$ + hydroquinone 0·05 0·05 0·06 0·1	A mixture of the di-acid chlorides (0·025 moles) and all the hydroquinone was heated at 90° for 1 hr. Then the remaining di-acid chlorides were added and the mixture was heated at 250°/1–2 mm (in nitrogen) for 5–8 hr	Amber-coloured, durable, fire-resistant resin; softening-point 100–103°	[563]
$C_6H_5POCl_2$ + $\begin{array}{c}CH_3\\C_2H_5\end{array}\!\!>NPOCl_2$ + 4,4'-dihydroxydiphenyl 0·26 0·25 0·5	225° for 3 hr, 225–240°/5 mm for 4 hr	,,	[563]

HIGH MOLECULAR WEIGHT COMPOUNDS CONTAINING PHOSPHORUS, NITROGEN AND OTHER ELEMENTS IN THE MAIN CHAIN POLYAMIDES AND POLYURETHANES CONTAINING PHOSPHORUS

Heterochain high molecular weight compounds which have phosphorus and nitrogen atoms, and sometimes carbon and oxygen as well, alternating in the main chains, have, save for the phosphonitrilic chlorides, been little investigated as yet.

The following methods are known for the synthesis of compounds of this type:

(1) The thermal polycondensation of diamides or substituted diamides of phosphonic acids [57]. This reaction is usually carried out in an atmosphere of an inert gas at 200–300°, sometimes *in vacuo*. During the reaction ammonia or the corresponding amine is evolved and hard, high molecular weight compounds are formed, the main chains of which are made up of phosphorus and nitrogen only:

$$n\text{R}'\text{PO(NHR)}_2 \xrightarrow{200-300°} \left[\begin{array}{c} \text{O} \quad \text{R} \\ \| \quad | \\ -\text{P}-\text{N}- \\ | \\ \text{R}' \end{array} \right] + n\text{RNH}_2$$

where R = H or alkyl and R' = alkyl or aryl.

(2) The reaction of diamides of phosphonic acids with urea, thiourea or their derivatives [56]. This reaction is carried out under conditions similar to (1) above, and either equimolecular amounts of the components are used, or an excess of the phosphonic diamide (but not of urea). During the course of the reaction, two processes can occur; first, the reaction of the phosphonic diamide with the urea derivative:

$$n\text{RPO(NH}_2)_2 + n\text{CO(NH}_2)_2 \xrightarrow{200-300°} \left[\begin{array}{c} \text{O} \\ \| \\ -\text{P}-\text{NHCONH}- \\ | \\ \text{R} \end{array} \right]_n + n\text{NH}_3$$

This predominates when equimolecular amounts of the components are used. Secondly, homopolymerization of the phosphonic diamide (as described above) can occur, particularly when an excess of the diamide is used. In this case the basic unit of the chain of the high molecular weight product of the reaction consists of two pieces:

$$\left[\begin{array}{c} \text{O} \quad \text{R}' \quad \text{O} \quad \text{R}' \\ \| \quad | \quad \| \quad | \\ -\text{R}-\text{N}-\text{P}-\text{N}- \\ | \qquad | \\ \text{R} \qquad \text{R} \end{array} \right] \text{ and } \left[\begin{array}{c} \text{O} \\ \| \\ -\text{P}-\text{NHCONH}- \\ | \\ \text{R} \end{array} \right]$$

(3) The reaction of phosphonic dichlorides with urea [584]:

$$n\text{RPOCl}_2 + n\text{CO(NH}_2)_2 \longrightarrow \text{Cl}-\left[\begin{array}{c} \text{O} \\ \| \\ -\text{P}-\text{NHCONH}- \\ | \\ \text{R} \end{array} \right]_n -\text{H} + n\text{HCl}$$

This reaction takes place at 100–160° with the powerful evolution of hydrogen chloride: to complete the reaction the mixture is heated *in vacuo* at 250–300°. In order to carry the polymerization to completion, it is recommended that equimolecular amounts of the components be used or else a very slight excess of urea. An excess of the phosphonic dichloride must not be used since in this case the polymer contains easily hydrolysable chlorine.

(4) The reaction of dicarboxylic acids containing phosphinyl groups with diamines [367, 578, 579, 585]. First a salt of the corresponding acid and diamine (taken in equimolecular amounts) is obtained, and this is then heated, *in vacuo*, to 200–250°. Polycondensation occurs, water is evolved and a polyamide is formed:

$$\text{RPO}\left(-\langle\!=\!\rangle-\text{COOH}\right)_2 + \text{NH}_2-\text{R}'-\text{NH}_2 \longrightarrow$$

$$\longrightarrow \text{RPO}\left(-\langle\!=\!\rangle-\text{COOH}\right)_2 \cdot \text{NH}_2-\text{R}'-\text{NH}_2 \longrightarrow \overrightarrow{\text{heat}}$$

$$\longrightarrow \left[-\overset{\overset{\displaystyle}{\|}}{\underset{\displaystyle O}{C}}-\langle\!=\!\rangle-\overset{\overset{\displaystyle O}{\|}}{\underset{\displaystyle R}{P}}-\langle\!=\!\rangle-\text{CONHR}'\text{NH}- \right]_n$$

(5) The reaction of phosphonic di-isocyanates with difunctional alcohols and phenols [372]. This reaction usually takes place very easily even at room temperature, and a considerable amount of heat is evolved. To complete the process the mixture is then heated to 100–250°. In this way a polyurethane containing phosphorus in the main chain is obtained:

$$n\text{RPO(NCO)}_2 + n\text{HOR}'\text{OH} \longrightarrow \left[-\text{OOC}-\text{NH}-\overset{\overset{\displaystyle O}{\|}}{\underset{\displaystyle R}{P}}-\text{NHCOOR}'- \right]_n$$

All the high molecular weight compounds of these types which have been investigated undoubtedly have linear structures. This conclusion can be drawn from the fact that they are soluble in various solvents, melt and can be moulded.

These substances usually soften at moderately high temperatures — in most cases in the range 175–300°. Such polymers resist the action of water, and of weak acids and alkalis at moderate temperatures: under more drastic conditions hydrolysis occurs.

The possibility of preparing cross-linked polymers must be pointed out. If, for example, the high molecular weight compounds, obtained by the homopolycondensation of phosphonic diamides having unsaturated radicals on the phosphorus, are heated above their melting-points, then the elastomeric materials gradually change into resin-like substances [57]. Obviously, the key reaction is the joining together of the linear chains; this arises because of the double bonds in the unsaturated radicals. All the compounds described are either non-flammable or extinguish themselves on removal from the flame. The properties of phosphorus-containing polyamides and polyurethanes are recorded in Table 116.

TABLE 116. PHOSPHORUS CONTAINING POLYAMIDES AND POLYURETHANES

Components (in molar proportions)	Reaction conditions	Properties of the product	Reference
$CH_3PO(NH_2)_2 + C_2H_5PO(NH_2)_2$	Nitrogen, about 250°, several hr	Hard, transparent, $t \approx 220°$, soluble in acetone	[57]
$C_2H_5PO(NH_2)_2$	,,	$t \approx 200°$, soluble in acetonitrile	[57]
$C_2H_5PO(NHCH_3)_2$	,,	$t \approx 150,,$ soluble in acetone and acetonitrile	[57]
$C_4H_9PO(NH_2)_2$	,,	$t \approx 200°$, soluble in dimethyl-acetamide	[57]
$C_6H_5PO(NH_2)_2$	then heated above 250°, in vacuo	$t \approx 225°$, soluble in ethanol	[57]
$C_6H_5PO(NHCH_3)_2$	but heated without vacuum	$t \approx 175°$, soluble in acetone and dimethylformamide	[57]
$CH_2 = C(CH_3)PO(NH_2)_2$	heated in vacuo (2 mm)	$t \approx 200°$, soluble in dimethyl-acetamide	[57]
$CH_2 = C(CH_3)PO(NHCH_3)_2$	heated without vacuum	soluble in acetone	[57]
$CH_3CH = C(C_2H_5)PO(NH_2)_2$		Resin-like	[57]
$CH_3CH = C(C_2H_5)PO(NHCH_3)_2$		,,	[57]
$C_2H_5CH = C(C_3H_7)PO(NH_2)_2$		,,	[57]
$C_2H_5CH = C(C_3H_7)PO(NHCH_3)_2$			[57]
$CH_3PO(NH_2)_2 + C_6H_5PO(NH_2)_2 +$ thiourea 0·021 0·032 0·026	210° for 2 hr, 250° for 4 hr	Hard, transparent, $t \approx 200°$, does not support combustion, soluble in dimethylacetamide	[56]
$C_4H_9PO(NH_2)_2 + $ N,N'-dimethylurea 0·1 0·011	250°, 10 hr	,, soluble in acetone	[56]
$C_6H_5PO(NH_2)_2 + $ urea 0·1 0·1	250°, 5 hr	,, soluble in dimethylforma-mide	[56]
$C_6H_5PO((NHCH_3)_2 + $ urea 0·05 0·017	250° for 2 hr, 300° for 3 hr	$t \approx 150°$, soluble in aceto-nitrile	[56]
$ClCH_2POCl_2 + $ urea 0·12 0·12	100°–120°, then 300°/40 mm for 0·5 hr	White powder, $t \approx 300°$, soluble in water and ethanol, insoluble in boiling dimethylformamide	[584]
$Cl_2CHPOCl_2 + $ urea 0·12 0·12	100°–120°, then 300°/40 mm, for 0·5 hr	,, soluble in water, ethyl alcohol, and dimethyl-formamide	[584]

TABLE 116— (contd.)

Components (in molar proportions)	Reaction conditions	Properties of the product	Reference
CCl_3POCl_2 + urea 0·085 0·085	150–160°, then 250–275°	soluble in dimethylformamide, slightly soluble in water and ethanol	[584]
Salt of $CH_3PO(\!-\!\bigcirc\!-\!CO_2H)_2$ and di-(3-aminopropyl) ether	Nitrogen, 245° for 1 hr, 259° for 1 hr, 259°/0·7 mm for 2 hr	Pale-yellow, $\eta = 0.72$	[579]
Salt of $C_6H_5PO(\!-\!\bigcirc\!-\!CO_2H)_2$ and tetramethylenediamine	Nitrogen, from 170–200° to 250–260°	Slightly coloured, transparent, non-flammable, soluble in cresol, formic and acetic acids: $t_1 = 180°$, $t_2 = 204°$, $\eta = 0.18$	[585]
Salt of $C_6H_5PO(\!-\!\bigcirc\!-\!CO_2H)_2$ and hexamethylenediamine	,,	$t_1 = 180°$, $t_2 = 190°$, $\eta = 0.42$	[585]
Salt of $C_6H_5PO(\!-\!\bigcirc\!-\!CO_2H)_2$ and decamethylenediamine	,,	$t_1 = 150°$, $t_2 = 179°$, $\eta = 0.38$	[585]
$C_6H_5PO(\!-\!\bigcirc\!-\!CO_2H)_2$ + 1,2-phenylenediamine (molar ratio 1:1,15% excess of diamine)	,,	$t_1 = 168°$, $t_2 = 184°$, $\eta = 0.08$	[585]
$C_6H_5PO(\!-\!\bigcirc\!-\!CO_2H)_2$ + 1,3-phenylenediamine	,,	$t_1 = 249°$, $t_3 = 340°$, $\eta = 0.20$	[585]

TABLE 116 — (contd.)

Components (in molar proportions)	Reaction conditions	Properties of the product	Reference
$C_6H_5PO(—\bigcirc—CO_2H)$ + 1,4-phenylenedia-mine	Nitrogen, from 170–200° to 250–260°	Slightly coloured, transparent, non-flammable; soluble in cresol, formic and acetic acids; $t_1 = 260°$, $t_3 = 340°$, $\eta = 0·24$	[585]
$C_6H_5PO(—\bigcirc—CO_2H)_2$ + 2,4-tolylenediamine*	,,	$t_1 = 239°$, $t_2 = 252°$, $\eta = 0·18$	[585]
$C_2H_5PO(NCO)_2$ + hexan-1,6-diol*	Violent reaction at room temperature, then the mixture was heated at 250° for 2 hr	Colourless, viscous, partially soluble in refluxing ethanol, insoluble in water	[372]
$C_2H_5PO(NCO)_2$ + resorcinol*	The di-isocyanate was added dropwise to a toluene solution of the resorcinol, the mixture was refluxed for 1 hr, then the solvent was removed *in vacuo*	m.p. 75°, soluble in acetone, insoluble in toluene end chloroform	[372]
$C_2H_5PO(NCO)_2$ + hydroquinone*	Violent reaction at room temperature, then the mixture was heated at 225°	Brittle, glass-like, m. p. 200°, non-flammable	[372]
$C_2H_5PO(NCO)_2$ + phenylenediamine*	,, then the mixture was heated at 90° for 1·5 hr	Powders, m.p. 300°, insoluble in water, ethanol, pyridine, 6 N hydrochloric acid	[372]

Notes : (1) t = softening temperature; t_1 = temperature at which softening begins; t_2 = flow point; t_3 = decomposition temperature.

(2) η = intrinsic viscosity

* Equimolecular ratio of components.

PHOSPHONITRILIC HALIDES AND THEIR DERIVATIVES

Phosphonitrilic chloride was first made, together with other substances, by Liebig and Wöhler [586] by the action of ammonia on phosphorus penta-chloride. Later on, the methods of synthesis of phosphonitrilic chloride, and also the structure and properties of this compound, were carefully studied by many investigators [587–597], and it was found that the substance with empirical formula $PNCl_2$ was actually a mixture of low molecular weight polymers, $(PNCl_2)_n$ where n lies between 3 and 11. These substances, and also the corresponding fluorides and bromides which will be described below, have the properties listed in Tables 117 and 118.

The usual starting materials for the preparation of the polyphosphonitrilic chlorides are the cyclic trimer and tetramer. As yet the monomeric and dimeric forms of $PNCl_2$ have not been made, presumably because of their instability.

These substances are nowadays obtained from phosphorus pentachloride and ammonium chloride:

$$PCl_5 + NH_4Cl \longrightarrow (PNCl_2)_n + 4\ HCl$$

TABLE 117. LOW MOLECULAR WEIGHT POLYPHOSPHONITRILIC HALIDES

Formula	b. p., °C (mm)	m. p., °C	d	Reference
$(PNF_2)_3$	51·8			[598]
$(PNF_2)_3 \cdot 2HF \cdot 2H_2O$		32·5		[599]
$(PNF_2)_4$	89·7			[598]
$P_4N_4F_6Cl_2$	106	—12·4		[600]
$(PNFCl)_4$	130·5	—25		[599]
$(PNCl_2)_3$	256; 127 (13)	114	1·98	[587]
Mixtures of $(PNCl_2)_3$ and $(PNCl_2)_4$ (60–70 mole % of trimer)		88·5–89		[601]
$(PNCl_2)_4$	328·5; 188 (13)	123·5	2·18	[587]
$(PNCl_2)_5$	223–224 (13)	40·5–41		[587]
$(PNCl_2)_6$	261–263 (13)*	90–91		[587]
$(PNCl_2)_7$	289–294 (13)*	—18		[587]
$(PNCl_2)_{11}$	Oil			[587]
$(PNBr_2)_3$		190		[597]
$(PNBr_2)_4$		202		[597]

* Tars are formed when attempts are made to distill at atmospheric pressure.

TABLE 118. SOLUBILITY OF $(PNCl_2)_n$ (WHERE $n = 3$ AND 4)
IN GRAMS PER 100 G OF SOLVENT [601]

Solvent	$n = 3$	$n = 4$
Ether	46·37	12·4
Dioxan	29·55	8·23
Benzene	55·0	21·42
Toluene	47·3	17·8
Xylene	38·85	13·85
Saturated petroleum hydrocarbons	27·9	8·39
Carbon tetrachloride	38·88	16·55
Carbon disulphide	52·05	22·00
Phosphoryl chloride	soluble	
Terpentine	,,	
Sulphur dioxide (liquid)	,,	
Sulphuric acid (concentrated)	,,	

This method, as described by Stokes [587], was at first dangerous and somewhat expensive, but more recently, simple and more suitable variations have been evolved for obtaining mixtures of tri- and tetra-meric phosphonitrilic chlorides: in one method solvents were used (Schenk and Römer [588]) and in the other they were not (Steinman, Schirmer and Audrieth [602]).

The preparation of the mixture of trimeric and tetrameric phosphonitrilic chloride (588)

Ammonium chloride (120–130 g) was added to a solution of phosphorus pentachloride (400 g) in tetrachloroethane (1 l.) and the mixture was heated in a round-bottomed flask at 135° for 20 hr. The flask was fitted with a reflux condenser to which was attached a calcium chloride drying tube and an absorption train for the hydrogen chloride evolved during the process. The flask was immersed in an oil bath in such a way that the ammonium chloride was above the oil level. The reaction was over in 7 hr, but the heating was continued until no more hydrogen chloride was evolved. The flask was then cooled, the unchanged ammonium chloride was filtered off and the solvent was distilled at reduced pressure: as a result of this about 100 g of product were obtained, consisting of 75% of the trimer and 25% of the tetramer. Treatment with benzene purified the trimer and tetramer mixture from the higher molecular weight homologues. The trimer and tetramer themselves can be separated by fractional distillation; the trimer is more volatile. It is also possible to distil the trimer in steam: the tetramer hydrolyses under these conditions.

The chemical properties of the low molecular weight phosphonitrilic chlorides will not be considered in this book since they have been discussed in some detail in the papers of Audrieth, Steinman and Toy [599], Remond [603] and Dishon [604]. Here, some results of investigations into the polymerization of phosphonitrilic chloride, and the properties of the high molecular weight compounds obtained, will be briefly discussed.

The heating of the trimeric and tetrameric phosphonitrilic chlorides (or their mixtures) to 250–350° leads to the conversion of these low molecular compounds into a rubber-like substance, the so-called "inorganic rubber" whose elasticity approaches that of natural rubber.

X-ray investigations by Meyer and his co-workers [605] have shown that these polymers have a fibrous structure and consist of linear chains containing not less than 200 $PNCl_2$ units, that is, the molecular weights lie in the range 20,000–25,000. However, according to Kuhn's calculations the macromolecular chain of polyphosphonitrilic chloride contains not less than 700 units which corresponds to a molecular weight of 80,000: and according to the views of Patat, Kollinsky and Frombling [605, 606] the molecular weight is even greater. A crystalline polymer is produced by drawing out.

Since there are no unsaturated links in molecules of phosphonitrilic chlorides, and since no side products are formed when the high molecular weight substances are made, then the polycondensation process must proceed by the ring-opening of the trimeric and tetrameric phosphonitrilic chlorides with the formation of linear chains (according to Patat and Derst [608] polyphosphonitrilic chloride is made up of rings of various sizes bonded to one another):

$$
\begin{array}{ccc}
& N & \\
Cl_2P & & PCl_2 \\
| & & || \\
N & & N \\
& P & \\
& Cl_2 &
\end{array}
\quad \text{or} \quad
\begin{array}{ccc}
& Cl_2 & \\
& N=P-N & \\
| & & || \\
Cl_2P & & PCl_2 \\
|| & & | \\
N-P=N & \\
& Cl_2 &
\end{array}
\quad \xrightarrow{250-350°}
$$

$$
\longrightarrow \cdots -\overset{\underset{|}{Cl}}{\underset{Cl}{P}}=N-\overset{\underset{|}{Cl}}{\underset{Cl}{P}}=N-\overset{\underset{|}{Cl}}{\underset{Cl}{P}}=N-\cdots
$$

According to the results of several authors, the polymer begins to depolymerize above 350° [590, 591, 594], that is, an equilibrium, which depends on the temperature, exists between low and high molecular weight polyphosphonitrilic chlorides.

$$
(PNCl_2)n \underset{\text{above } 360°}{\overset{250-350°}{\rightleftarrows}} (PNCl_2)_{n'}
$$

where $n = 3$ or 4 and n' is of the order of ten and above.

If, however, the depolymerization is not conducted *in vacuo*, then more profound changes take place in the substance. Patat and Kollinsky [606] showed that the heating of polyphosphonitrilic chloride to 600° lead to loss of elasticity and the formation of a brittle, horny material. Detailed investigations on the depolymerization of polyphosphonitrilic chloride have been made by Patat and Derst [608].

Investigations on the bulk polymerization of phosphonitrilic chloride [606] have shown that the greater part of the polymer thus formed is insoluble in organic solvents and hardly swells in some of them. The soluble part of the polyphosphonitrilic chloride was of low molecular weight, having a degree of polymerization of 3–7, and its amount (in a typical polymer) dropped with increasing temperature and degree of polymerization.

Experimental studies on the solution polymerization in a range of hydrogen-containing solvents (aromatic and aliphatic hydrocarbons) have been unsuccessful, since the phosphonitrilic chlorides react with the solvents with the formation of resinous substances and the evolution of hydrogen chloride. Further investigations have been carried out in liquids which do contain hydrogen: halogenated hydrocarbons, phosphorus trichloride, phosphoryl chloride and also concentrated sulphuric acid. In these cases the percent soluble part of the polymer varied, depending on the experimental conditions, from 18 to 50%, and at the same time its degree of polymerization reached 300, as opposed to the 3–7 found in the bulk polymerization case.

The role of oxygen in the solution polymerization of phosphonitrilic chloride is very great. In its presence neither polymerization nor the reaction with solvent (see above) is observed. As the quantity of oxygen decreases to about 1%, the rate of polymerization rapidly increases. Patat and Kollinsky [606] have suggested that the oxygen reacts with the cyclic trimeric and tetrameric phosphonitrilic chlorides by opening the rings and forming free radicals which appear at the beginning of the growing chains. Oxygen also appears to be the cause of the cutting short of the chains and of the formation of reticulated insoluble polymers (oxygen bridges can vulcanize inorganic rubber). The kinetic chain length, according to the results of Patat and Kollinsky, is about 1000 times greater than the macromolecular chain length; this simply indicates that chain transfer reactions occur during polymerization. It is interesting to note that the polymerization of pure trimeric phosphonitrilic chloride, uncontaminated by the tetramer and pentamer, leads to a product which is harder, less swollen by benzene and which crystallizes more quickly than the rubber-like substances obtained by polymerization of mixtures of low molecular weight phosphonitrilic chlorides [609]. For technical purposes the polymerization of phosphonitrilic chlorides is sometimes carried out in two stages. For this the monomer is heated for half-an-hour at 150–200°, and the partially polymerized product, which is an oil, is dissolved in an aromatic solvent. The material to be treated with the polymer is soaked in this solution and then heated when the final stage of the polymerization takes place [610]. The reactive atoms in the monomeric and polymeric phosphonitrilic chlorides are the chlorine atoms, which are, however, significantly less reactive than they are in other compounds which have a P—Cl bond. By the action of alcoholates, phenates, alcohols in the presence of organic bases, and by treatment with water, amides, amines, urea derivatives, mercaptans and other reagents, the chlorine atoms are replaced by the corresponding alkoxy-groups [599, 604, 611–614] aryloxy-groups [611, 615], hydroxyl-groups [588, 599], amino-groups [615–620], etc. If unsaturated alkoxy-groups, such as allyl, are introduced into the low molecular weight phosphonitrilic chlorides, then substances are obtained which can be easily polymerized on account of the double bonds in their molecules [604]. The introduction of a certain amount of alkoxy-groups into polyphosphonitrilic chloride is accompanied by the replacement of atoms of chlorine by oxygen and by a certain amount of depolymerization. Both these effects can be virtually avoided if the polyphosphonitrilic chloride is swollen in a suitable solvent before alcoholysis.

By heating solutions of phosphonitrilic chloride in hydrogen-containing solvents under pressure in the presence of aluminium chloride [595, 606], by irradiating such solutions with ultra-violet light in high vacuum [621], or by the action of organomagnesium compounds [622], soluble and insoluble products are formed by replacement (to a variable degree) of the chlorine atoms by the corresponding radicals. It is interesting to note that the trimeric and tetrameric phosphonitrilic phenyls $[PN(C_6H_5)_2]$ have recently been obtained by treating trichlorodiphenylphosphorane with liquid ammonia or with ammonium chloride [623]. Some results relating to the substitution of chlorine atoms in low and high molecular weight phosphonitrilic chlorides by various radicals are given in Tables 119, 120 and 121.

The low molecular weight cyclic compounds, in which the radicals are joined directly to phosphorus or through oxygen, are polymerized by the breaking of the rings by thermal treatment in an analogous manner to phosphonitrilic chloride. Other phosphonitrilic halides are known in which the chlorine

TABLE 119. SOME TRIMERIC PHOSPHONITRILIC ESTERS

R	b. p. °C (mm)	n_D^{20}	d_4^{20}	Yield (%)	Reference
CH_3—	127–218* (0·1)				[604]
C_3H_5— (allyl)	Easily polymerizes to a viscous oil				[604] [604]
C_4H_9—	170–171 (0·03)	1·4473	1·0342	56	[604]
C_6H_5—	Does not distill at 320° (several mm)				[614]
4-$CH_3C_6H_4$—	Does not distill at 360°/3 mm				[615]

* Obviously a misprint in the original paper. It should read 127—128° (0·1)

TABLE 120. THE SUBSTITUTION OF CHLORINE
IN POLYPHOSPHONITRILIC CHLORIDES BY
ALKOXY-GROUPS IN THE PRESENCE OF
PYRIDINE [612]

Alcohol	Percent replacement of chlorine in $(PNCl_2)n$	Percent alkoxy-group introduced into $(PNCl_2)n$
Ethyl	99·5	79·5
Isoamyl	98·0	63·5
2-Ethylhexyl	88·0	68·5

TABLE 121. THE REACTION OF TRIMERIC AND TETRAMERIC
PHOSPHONITRILIC CHLORIDES WITH BENZENE
AND DECAHYDRONAPHTHALENE [621]

Phosphonitrilic chloride	Reagent	Molar concentration of phosphonitrilic chloride	Time of irradiation of the system with ultra-violet light (hr)	Replacement of chlorine by the radical (%)
$(PNCl_2)_3$	Benzene	$\begin{cases}0·5\\0·1\end{cases}$	15 A* 5	30 33·3 50
	Phenylmagnesium bromide		Not irradiated [595]	100
	Decahydronaphthalene	$\begin{cases}0·5\\0·1\end{cases}$	15 5	58 75
$(PNCl_2)_4$	Benzene	0·5	15	26
	Dehydronaphthalene	0·5	15	42

A* — In the presence of aluminium chloride and not by irradiation [595].

is replaced (in various degrees) by fluorine. Such compounds are formed by treating phosphonitrilic chloride with zinc fluoride, silver fluoride or lead difluoride [600]. In this way compounds are formed with the following approximate formulae: $(PNF_2)_3$, $(PNF_2)_4$, $P_3N_3Cl_2F_4$, $P_3N_3ClF_5$ and $P_4N_4Cl_2F_6$ (the last substance was made in the pure state). Pure trimeric and tetrameric phosphonitrilic fluorides have been obtained by treating the corresponding chlorides with potassium fluorosulphite [598]:

$$PNCl_2 + 2KSO_2F \longrightarrow PNF_2 + 2KCl + 2SO_2$$

The heating of such phosphonitrilic fluorides in an autoclave at 260° brings about the processes discussed previously with the formation of rubber-like polymers.

By slow ageing in air, high molecular weight polyphosphonitrilic halides loose their capacity of being dissolved and also their elasticity, owing to cross-linking under the influence of moist air to give reticular structures:

$$
\begin{array}{cc}
\overset{\displaystyle Cl}{\underset{\displaystyle Cl}{\cdots -P=N- \cdots}} & \overset{\displaystyle Cl}{\underset{\displaystyle O}{\cdots -P=N- \cdots}} \\
+ & \underset{\displaystyle Cl}{\cdots -P=N- \cdots} \\
\overset{\displaystyle Cl}{\underset{\displaystyle Cl}{\cdots -P=N- \cdots}} &
\end{array}
+ H_2O \longrightarrow \qquad + 2HCl
$$

While inorganic rubbers are quite highly resistant to organic solvents and to acidic and alkaline reagents, their solutions are significantly less stable. Thus, for example, polyphosphonitrilic chloride in ether or dioxan solution is easily destroyed by alkali (even in the cold). Also, if the chlorine atoms are replaced by alkoxy-, aryloxy-, alkyl- or aryl-groups, then the chemical stability of the polymers is significantly increased (they decompose only in boiling toluene [612]). At the same time their solubility decreases: many high molecular weight esters of this kind dissolve only in boiling tetrachloroethane. Films from such esters adhere well to glass.

HIGH MOLECULAR WEIGHT COMPOUNDS BASED ON TETRAKIS-(HYDROXYMETHYL)PHOSPHONIUM CHLORIDE (THPC) AND TRIS-(HYDROXYMETHYL)-PHOSPHINE OXIDE (THPO)

As a result of reaction with THPC, or with the related THPO, many substances having mobile hydrogen atoms or easily broken rings in the molecules form heterochain high molecular weight products containing phosphorus in the main chains. These products can be fitted, according to their structures, into the various groups of high molecular weight compounds described previously. Since the wide knowledge of THPC which has been obtained in recent years has revealed it to be an extremely useful substance for making new and important types of high molecular weight organophosphorus compounds, this subject is most suitably discussed separately.

THPC and THPO, which have hydroxymethyl groups joined to electronegative phosphorus atoms, are very reactive compounds. They react easily with organic acids, acid anhydrides, phenols, amines, melamine, urea, etc., and are reminiscent of aqueous formaldehyde in their reactivity. The reactions, as a rule, proceed easily, often at room temperature or sometimes by slight heating.

THPC is easily converted into THPO (see p. 114) and in most reactions it reacts as a tri- and not a tetra-(hydroxymethyl)compound (except for reactions in strongly basic media). The reactions of THPC with organic acids and their anhydrides are, obviously, simple esterifications [624]:

$$
\overset{|}{\underset{|}{>}}P-CH_2OH + HO_2CR \longrightarrow \quad \overset{|}{\underset{|}{>}}P-CH_2OCOR + H_2O
$$

The reactions of THPC and THPO with phenols proceed with the evolution of water, which is formed by reaction between the hydroxyl-groups of the phosphorus-containing compounds and the active hydrogens in the *ortho*- and *para*-positions of the phenols [624, 625], probably according to the following scheme:

$$(HOCH_2)_4PCl + \underset{}{\text{[phenol]}} + \tfrac{1}{2}O_2 \longrightarrow (HOCH_2)_2PCH_2-\underset{}{\text{[phenol]}} + H_2O +$$

$$+ CH_2O + HCl$$

The initially formed linear polycondensation product only changes into a cross-linked resin if the phenol used has three reactive positions. If, however, the *para*-position or one of the *ortho*-positions is occupied by a substituent, then a fusible and soluble product is formed. This reaction is catalysed by amines and can proceed (as can the reactions of formaldehyde with phenols) in various media: from weakly basic to strongly acidic [624].

THPC and THPO easily condense (again with the evolution of water) with various substances of the amine type [626–634]. As a result of this, linear, water soluble products of the type $(HOCH_2)_2PCH_2NHR$ are formed: these are

$$\parallel$$
$$O$$

strenthened by standing in the cold for several hours, or by heating at 100–150° for several minutes, when cross-linked products are formed. The structure of a unit of the cross-linked product of the reaction of THPC with ethylenediamine is said to be [624]:

$$\left(\underset{}{\text{>}}NCH_2\right)_2 PCH_2OCH_2CH_2N<$$
$$\parallel$$
$$O$$

The reaction of salts of unsaturated acids with THPC leads to the introduction of radicals of these acids into the THPC [635]:

$$(HOCH_2)_4PCl + KO_2C—R \longrightarrow (HOCH_2)_4PO_2C—R + KCl$$

The usual result of all reactions of THPC and THPO with polyfunctional compounds is the simple and rapid formation of highly branched, cross-linked, high molecular weight phosphorus-containing compounds which are insoluble and non-flammable, as is shown in Table 122.

The naturally occurring high molecular weight organophosphorus compounds (ribonucleic acids, phosphoproteins, phosphorus-containing enzymes, etc.) and also the phosphorylation products of albumin (these substances also have heterochain structures) are related more to biochemistry than to the theme of this book, and so we will not consider them.

There is a brief description of compounds of this type in the monograph of Pletz [1].

TABLE 122. PRODUCTS OF THE REACTION OF THPC AND THPO WITH ACID ANHYDRIDES, PHENOLS AND SUBSTANCES OF THE AMINE TYPE

Components	Reaction conditions	Properties of the product	Reference
$(HOCH_2)_4PCl$ + 1,4,5,6,7,7-hexachloro-bicyclo-[2,2,1]hept-5-ene-2,3-dicarboxylic acid anhydride	Heated on a hot-plate for 10 min	Transparent hard, brittle; soluble in acetone, insoluble in water and toluene. % P = 2·5	[624]
$(HOCH_2)_4PCl$ + phenol + water	Refluxed on a hot-plate at pH 1 (after 5 min considerable heat begins to be evolved)	Brown, hard, brittle, % P = 0·7	[624]
,,	,, at pH 5 (reaction less violent)	Tan-coloured % P = 1·4	[624]
$(HOCH_2)_4PCl$ + phloroglucinol	Refluxed in aqueous media on the hot-plate until a viscous straw coloured solution was formed: then heated at 110° and treated with water	Brittle, % P = 6·01; % Cl = 5·95	[624]
,,	,, but in alcoholic media	Brittle, % P = 9·26; % Cl = 5·77	[624]
,,	,, with the addition of ammonium hydroxide (the mixture hardened in 1 min)	Brittle, % P = 9·91; % N = 3·32	[624]
$(HOCH_2)_4PCl$ + urea + water	100° for 15 min, 120° for 25 min	Hard, transparent, soluble in water	[624, 627]
,, with sodium carbonate added (pH = 5)	Refluxed until gelatinized — 55 min	Gel	[624, 627]
,,	,, (4-amino-4-methylpentan-2-ol as catalyst) for 9 min, then 110° for several min	Brittle, insoluble in water, non-flammable, % P = 14·7; % N = 21	[624, 627]
$(HOCH_2)_4PCl$ + guanidine + water	Mixed at 25°. The resulting clear solution was kept for three days	Water-insoluble syrup	[627]

TABLE 122 — (contd.)

Components	Reaction conditions	Properties of the product	Reference
$(HOCH_2)_4PCl$ + ethylenimine + water	Exothermic reaction in the cold	Water-soluble gel	[624]
$(HOCH_2)_4PCl$ + ethylenimine + water	Gel heated at 150°	Brown, hard, insoluble in water and alkali. On standing for a short time an elastic substance is formed which swells in water, $\% P = 6.2$; $\% N = 14.9$	[624]
$(HOCH_2)_4PCl$ + melamine + water + urea (sometimes) + formaldehyde (in various amounts)	The mixture of components was heated at 65–90° (15–20 min). The clear solution obtained gradually polymerized into a gel (if the HCl evolved is neutralized then the polymerization proceeds very quickly after 1–2 hr at 110°	Insoluble, infusible, non-flammable resins, containing phosphorus and nitrogen	[624, 627]
$(HOCH_2)_4PCl$ + cetylamine	The reaction was carried out in alcohol solution in the presence of sodium carbonate. The grease obtained was washed with hot ethanol	Mealy product; m. p. 70–90°. $\% P = 5.5$; $\% N = 4.36$; Yield, 78%	[624, 627]
$(HOCH_2)_4PCl$ + aminoethylcellulose + melamine (or methylamine)	The aminoethylcellulose was impregnated with the other components and dried at 100°	Phosphorus- and nitrogen-containing, non-flammable, cellulose derivative	[626, 629]
$(HOCH_2)_3PO$ + urea + water	Refluxed for 1 hr. The clear gel obtained was heated at 140° for 20 min	Infusible, non-flammable	[627]
$(HOCH_2)_3PO$ + melamine + water	Similar to above	,,	[627]
$(HOCH_2)_3PO$ + $(HOCH_2)_4PCl$ + melamine + water	,,	,,	[627]

HIGH MOLECULAR WEIGHT PHOSPHORUS-CONTAINING COMPOUNDS WITH INORGANIC SKELETONS

(BESIDES POLYAMIDES, POLYPHOSPHONITRILIC HALIDES AND THEIR DERIVATIVES)

This large and important field of the chemistry of phosphorus-containing substances does not form part of the theme of this book and it should really be the subject of an independent survey. Here we will only make an extremely brief survey of some aspects of this field.

The basic types of inorganic phosphorus-containing polymers have structures of the following form:

$$
\begin{array}{c}
\vdots \qquad \vdots \\
\cdots\!-\!\mathrm{P}\!-\!\mathrm{P}\!-\!\mathrm{P}\!-\!\cdots \\
\cdots\!-\!\mathrm{P}\!-\!\mathrm{P}\!-\!\mathrm{P}\!-\!\cdots \\
\vdots \qquad \vdots \\
\cdots\!-\!\mathrm{P}\!-\!\mathrm{P}\!-\!\cdots \\
\cdots\!-\!\mathrm{P}\!-\!\mathrm{P}\!-\!\cdots
\end{array}
$$

$$
\cdots\!-\!\mathrm{P}\!=\!\mathrm{N}\!-\!\mathrm{P}\!=\!\mathrm{N}\!-\!\mathrm{P}\!=\!\mathrm{N}\!-\!\cdots
$$

$$
\begin{array}{c}
\cdots\!-\!\mathrm{P}\!=\!\mathrm{B}\!-\!\mathrm{P}\!=\!\mathrm{B}\!-\!\mathrm{P}\!=\!\mathrm{B}\!-\!\cdots \\
\| \qquad \| \qquad \| \\
\mathrm{O} \qquad \mathrm{O} \qquad \mathrm{O}
\end{array}
$$

$$
\begin{array}{c}
\cdots\!-\!\mathrm{P}\!-\!\mathrm{O}\!-\!\mathrm{P}\!-\!\mathrm{O}\!-\!\mathrm{P}\!-\!\mathrm{O}\!-\!\cdots \\
\| \qquad \| \qquad \| \\
\mathrm{O} \qquad \mathrm{O} \qquad \mathrm{O}
\end{array}
$$

$$
\begin{array}{c}
\cdots\!-\!\mathrm{P}\!-\!\mathrm{O}\!-\!\mathrm{X}\!-\!\mathrm{O}\!-\!\mathrm{P}\!-\!\mathrm{O}\!-\!\mathrm{X}\!-\!\cdots \\
\| \qquad \vdots \qquad \| \qquad \vdots \\
\mathrm{O} \qquad \vdots \qquad \mathrm{O} \qquad \vdots
\end{array}
$$

where X = third element.

High molecular weight compounds containing only phosphorus in the main chain

D. I. Mendyeleyev [636] first suggested that red phosphorus was the product of polymerization of white phosphorus.

The investigation of the polymerization of white phosphorus produced much chemistry. It was noted that various modifications of red phosphorus could be formed, although their structures are still not completely clear.

The work of Kraft and Parini [637–640] has established that these modifications of red phosphorus are neither solid solutions nor absorbants between amorphous phosphorus and the polymerization solvent (as was previously supposed), but are true polymers of white phosphorus. The elements of solvent are joined to the macromolecular phosphorus by valency bonds and appear as end groups in these polymers.

Recently, a new type of phosphorus-containing compound has been prepared in which the phosphorus atoms are joined together in four- and five-membered rings. Treatment of trifluoromethylphosphonous di-iodide with metallic mercury gives a mixture of cyclic tetramers and pentamers [641, 642]:

$$CF_3PI_2 + Hg \longrightarrow (CF_3P)_4 + (CF_3P)_5 + HgI_2$$

These compounds are very stable and, according to the authors of this work, have the following structures:

$$CF_3-P-P-CF_3 \atop CF_3-P-P-CF_3 \quad \text{and} \quad CF_3-P \underset{CF_3-P-P-CF_3}{\overset{P-CF_3}{\diagup \diagdown}} P-CF_3$$

An analogous structure is presumably possessed by the tetraphenyl cyclotetraphosphine which is formed by the reaction of phenylphosphonous dichloride with phenylphosphine [643]:

$$2C_6H_5PCl_2 + 2C_6H_5PH_2 \longrightarrow \begin{array}{c} C_6H_5-P-P-C_6H_5 \\ C_6H_5-P-P-C_6H_5 \end{array}$$

An interesting polymer containing phosphorus in the main chain has been obtained by the treatment of thiophosphoryl bromide with magnesium [644]:

$$2PSBr_3 + 3Mg \longrightarrow \left[\begin{array}{c} -P= \\ \| \\ S \end{array} \right]_n + 3MgBr_2$$

High molecular weight compounds containing phosphorus and nitrogen in the main chain

Many inorganic phosphorus- and nitrogen-containing high molecular weight compounds are formed by the reaction of phosphoryl chloride with ammonia [645–649] or with phosphoric triamide [650]:

$$nPOCl_3 + nNH_3 \longrightarrow \left(\begin{array}{c} -P=N- \\ \| \\ O \end{array} \right)_n + 3nHCl$$

Polymers of this group are also produced by the heating of phosphorus pentachloride with ammonia [651] or ammonium chloride (in the ratio 1 : 2);

by the thermal homopolymerization of triamides of phosphoric and phosphoro-thionic acids [652]:

$$nPO(NH_2)_3 \longrightarrow NH_2\!-\!\!\left[\begin{array}{c} O \\ \| \\ -P\!-\!NH\!- \\ | \\ NH_2 \end{array}\right]\!\!-\!PO(NH_2)_2 + (n\!-\!1)NH_3$$

(cross-linked polymers then form); and by the thermal homopolymerization of pyrophosphoric tetra-amides, pyrophosphoramidic acids [653] or certain other compounds. The phosphonitrilic halides and their derivatives have been discussed previously (see p. 239–245).

High molecular weight compounds containing phosphorus, boron and (sometimes) nitrogen in the main chain

Of considerable interest and promise are the trimeric and tetrameric dimethylphosphinoborines which are obtained by the action of dimethyl-phosphine on diborane (Burg and co-workers [654]):

$$(CH_3)_2PH + B_2H_6 \longrightarrow [\text{complex}] \xrightarrow[\text{heat}]{-H_2} [(CH_3)_2P\!-\!BH_2]_n$$

where $n = 3$ or 4.

It has been shown that the isomers of these compounds — the dimethyl-borinophosphines $[PH_2\!-\!B(CH_3)_2]_n$ — are unstable substances and it has not been possible to obtain them in a pure state. The same authors also synthesized the trimer of dimethylphosphinodimethylborine [654]:

$$(CH_3)_2PH + BrB(CH_3)_2 + N(C_2H_5)_3 \longrightarrow [(CH_3)_2PB(CH_3)_2 + N(C_2H_5)_3 \cdot HBr$$

the trimer of bistrifluoromethylphosphinoborine [641]:

$$9(CF_3)_2PF + 3B_2H_6 \longrightarrow [(CF_3)_2PBH_2]_3 + 6(CF_3)_2PH + 3BF_3 + 3H_3$$

and copolymers from the reaction of (dimethylphosphino)-dimethylamine with diborane [655] $[(B_{10}H_{22})(CH_3)_2P\!-\!N(CH_3)_2]_n$.

High molecular weight compounds containing phosphorus and oxygen in the main chain
(polyphosphates, polyphosphoric acids and their derivatives)

The polycondensation of alkali metal dihydrogen phosphates leads to the evolution of water and the formation of mixtures of condensed phosphates — polyphosphates and polymetaphosphates — having linear structures:

$$nHO\!-\!\overset{\overset{\displaystyle O}{\|}}{\underset{\underset{\displaystyle OMe}{|}}{P}}\!-\!OH \longrightarrow (n\!-\!1)H_2O + H\!\!\left[\begin{array}{c} O \\ \| \\ -O\!-\!P\!- \\ | \\ OMe \end{array}\right]_n\!\!-\!OH$$

where Me = alkali metal, and $n = 1 \ldots\ldots 10^6$. Consequently, the usual formulae of polyphosphates are $Me_{n+2}P_nO_{3n+1}$ or $Me_nH_2P_nP_{3n+1}$. A large number of investigations have been made into these compounds since the time of Graham [656] 120 years ago (a number of reviews only are given in the listed references [657–660]).

Polyphosphates are glass-like substances which are very soluble in water. An important property of the polyphosphates is the capacity of the metal atoms in their macromolecules to be quite easily replaced by other cations.

Aqueous solutions of polyphosphates are quite stable at moderate temperatures. At temperatures above 60° hydrolysis begins and it is accelerated at higher temperatures. Polyphosphoric acids are usually made by desiccating orthophosphoric acid [659, 661] or by reacting it with phosphorus pentoxide. The general formulae of these compounds are:

$$H-\left[-O-\overset{\overset{O}{\|}}{\underset{\underset{OH}{|}}{P}}-\right]_n-OH \quad \text{or} \quad H_{2n+2}P_nO_{3n+1}$$

where $n = 1 \ldots\ldots\ldots 10^6$.

Polyphosphoric acids can have weakly or strongly acidic hydroxyl groups for their two end groups: they are syrups or crystalline substances.

Esters of polyphosphoric acids (usually with small numbers of repeating units) are prepared by the action of phosphoryl chloride on alcohols [662], for example:

$$4POCl_3 + 9ROH \longrightarrow RO\left[-\overset{\overset{O}{\|}}{\underset{\underset{OR}{|}}{P}}-O-\right]_4-R + 3RCl + 9HCl$$

or on trialkyl phosphates [663], from the reactions of mixtures of phosphoryl chloride and phosphorus pentoxide with alcohols [664], from dialkyl phosphoro-chloridates and trialkyl phosphates [665], from phosphorus pentoxide and ethers [666] and by certain other methods [667].

High molecular weight compounds containing phosphorus, oxygen and a third element in the main chain (silicon, nitrogen, boron, arsenic and titanium)

The methods which have been described for obtaining inorganic polymers containing atoms of phosphorus, oxygen and silicon in the main chains involve the reaction of polysiloxanes, or the products of hydrolysis of dialkyl-silicon dihalides, with phosphorus pentoxide [667–671]:

$$2 \rangle SiOH + P_2O_5 + 2HO-Si\langle \longrightarrow \rangle Si-O-\overset{\overset{O}{\|}}{\underset{\underset{O}{|}}{P}}-O-\overset{\overset{O}{\|}}{\underset{\underset{O}{|}}{P}}-O-Si\langle + 2H_2O$$
$$ \rangle Si \qquad Si\langle$$

or with meta-, pyro- or ortho-phosphoric acids [668]; the reactions of ortho-silicic esters with phosphorus pentoxide [667, 672], trialkyl phosphates [673], phosphorus trichloride or phosphoryl chloride [674]:

$$2nSi(OC_2H_5)_4 + 2nPOCl_3 \longrightarrow$$

$$\longrightarrow \left[-O-Si-O-P-O-Si-O-P-O- \right]_n + 6nC_2H_5Cl$$

and also the reactions of silicon halides with acid esters of orthophosphoric acid or alkali metal salts of this acid [675]. Some polymers of linear structure, having phosphorus, oxygen and nitrogen in the main chain, have been patented. They were obtained by reaction of the tetra-acid halides of pyrophosphoric acid with ammonia [676].

Phosphorus-, oxygen- and boron-containing polymers have been synthesized by the reaction of acid chlorides [677] or esters of phosphonic or phosphoric acids [677, 678] with boron triacetate or other boron esters:

$$nB(OCOCH_3)_3 + nPO(OC_2H_5)_3 \longrightarrow$$

$$\longrightarrow 3nCH_3COOC_2H_5 + \left(-O-B-O-P- \right)_n$$

These polymers have high softening temperatures (about 200°) but they are easily broken down hydrolytically (particularly by hot water).

Polymers have been described whose main chains consist of atoms of phosphorus, oxygen and arsenic: they were prepared by roasting mixtures of the mono-sodium salts of orthophosphoric and arsenic acids [679]:

$$nNaH_2PO_4 + nNaH_2AsO_4 \xrightarrow{\text{heat}} \left[-O-P-O-As- \right]_n$$

The reaction of titanium tetrachloride with orthophosphoric or pyrophosphoric acid is accompanied by the copious evolution of hydrogen chloride and leads to the formation of cross-linked high molecular weight compounds, the skeletons of which consist of alternate atoms of phosphorus, oxygen and titanium [680].

CHAPTER VI.

OTHER ORGANOPHOSPHORUS POLYMERS

PRODUCTS FROM TELOMERIZATION REACTIONS INVOLVING
ORGANOPHOSPHORUS COMPOUNDS

SEVERAL cases are known of the polymerization of unsaturated compounds and also lactones, in the presence of organophosphorus compounds which contain active hydrogen atoms (dialkyl hydrogen phosphites) or trivalent phosphorus (trialkyl phosphites). In this way, relatively low molecular weight compounds were obtained which had a dialkoxyphosphinyl group at one end of the chain:

$$(RO)_2P—$$
$$\underset{O}{\overset{\|}{}}$$

The reactions of ethylene [681] and tetrafluoroethylene [682] with dialkyl hydrogen phosphites under the influence of heat and pressure and in the presence of radical initiators of polymerization have been described:

$$HPO(OR)_2 + nCX_2 = CX_2 \longrightarrow H(CX_2)_{2n}PO(OR)_2$$

where X = hydrogen or fluorine.

The compounds obtained were viscous liquids with various degrees of telomerization. In other examples of telomerization, trialkyl phosphites were used as telogens. According to Kukhtin, Kamai and Sinchenko, during the reaction with lactones [683] or with methacrylic acid [684, 685] in the presence of alkaline or peroxidic reagents, an intermediate dipolar ion is first formed [684] which either changes into the usual Arbusov rearrangement product, or is stabilized either by joining to several molecules of an unsaturated compound or by opening the ring of a cyclic compound. For example:

$$(RO)_3P + CH_2 = C(CH_3)CO_2H \xrightarrow[\text{heat}]{\text{peroxide}} (RO)_3P^+CH_2CH(CH_3)CO_2^- \xrightarrow{nCH_2 = C(CH_3)CO_2H}$$

$$\longrightarrow (RO)_2P[CH_2CH(CH_3)CO_2]_nCH_2CH(CH_3)CO_2R$$
$$\underset{O}{\overset{\|}{}}$$

The compounds formed were viscous liquids or hard powdery substances.

Cases are also known of telomerization in which an unsaturated organophosphorus compound (triallyl phosphate) is the monomer and a halogenated methane the telogen [456, 686]. A wide variety of unsaturated compounds can participate in telomerization reactions: dienes, olefins, unsaturated esters and ethers, etc. The reaction is hence a very suitable, although as yet little used, method of obtaining a variety of compounds containing dialkoxyphosphinyl-groups. The properties of the products of telomerization in which di- and tri-alkyl phosphites have taken part are recorded in Table 123.

TABLE 123. PRODUCTS OF TELOMERIZATION WITH PARTICIPATION OF DI- AND TRI-ALKYL PHOSPHITES

Components (molar ratio)	Catalyst	Reaction conditions	Average degree of telomerization	Average m.w.	Properties of the telomer	Notes		Reference
						Yield (%)	% P	
$HPO(OC_2H_5)_2$ + ethylene (in excess)	Benzoyl peroxide	80–115°, 28 atm, 12 hr	1·2 and above (mixture)		Liquid, $C_2H_5PO(OC_2H_5)_2$, b.p. 98–99°/27–29 mm $C_4H_9PO(OC_2H_5)_2$, b.p. 121°/28 mm, and higher m. w. cpds.			[681]
$HPO(OC_2H_5)_2$ + tetra-fluoroethylene	,,	98°, autoclave, 8 hr, unreacted components distilled out	3 and 4, mixture		Semi-solid mass			[682]
,,	Di-$tert$.-butyl peroxide	140°, autoclave, 8 hr, same work up	3 and 4 mixture		,,			[682]
,,	Succinoyl peroxide (2 g)	60°, autoclave, 4 hr, same work up	4		,,			[682]
,,	α,α'-Azobis-isobutyronitrile	90° autoclave, 4 hr, same work up	From 1 to 12, mainly 10		,,			[682]
$P(OC_2H_5)_3$ + β-propio-lactone		150–160°, 16 hr	2		Liquid, $(C_2H_5O)_2P(O)CH_2$— —$COOCH_2CH_2COOC_2H_5$ b. p. 175–177°/1·3 mm n_D^{20} 1·4440	10		[683]
$P(OC_2H_5)_3$ + β-propio-lactone 1 : 1	Triethylamine (5%)	130°, 3 hr	3		Liquid $(C_2H_5O)_2P(O)$ $[C_2H_5COO]_3C_2H_5$, b. p. 144–151°/0·4 mm n_D^{20} 1·4493			[683]

TABLE 123 — (contd.)

Components (molar ratio)	Catalyst	Reaction conditions	Average degree of telomerization	Average m.w.	Properties of the telomer	Yield (%)	% P	Reference
1 : 4	Triethylamine (10%)	40°, 4 hr		490	Viscous light-yellow oil, n_D^{20} 1·4570			[683]
P(OC$_2$H$_5$)$_3$ + β-propiolactone 2 : 1	Sodium methoxide (0·3%)	38–40°, 6 hr		460	Oil			[683]
				1147	White powder			
P(OC$_2$H$_5$)$_3$ + methacrylic acid + butyl iodide 1 : 1 : 1	—	Room temperature	11	1190	,,		2·71	[685]
P(OC$_2$H$_5$)$_3$ + methacrylic acid 1 : 2	Sodium methoxide (0·2%)		5	558	White powder, soluble in warm methyl alcohol and acetic acid; insoluble (at room temp.) in acetone, dioxan, hexane, benzene, nitrobenzene, aniline, chloroform, carbon tetrachloride and ethyl alcohol	26·8	5·5	[684]
1 : 2	Triethylamine (0·4%)	,,	5	582	Similar to above			[684]
1 : 1	Benzoyl peroxide (0·01%)	,,	4	504	,,	47·3	6·1	[684]
1 : 5	,,	,,	7	752	,,	44·4	3·9	[684]
1 : 10	Benzoyl peroxide (0·01%)	,,	14	1410	,,	30·2	2·4	[684]
1 : 5	(0·001%)	,,	4	515	,,	14·3	5·9	[684]
1 : 5	(0·1%)	,,	23	2109	,,	89·2	1·34	[684]
1 : 4	(0·01%)	,,	6	680	,,	51·2	4·6	[684]
P(OC$_3$H$_7$)$_3$ + methacrylic acid 1 : 2	(0·2%)	,,	8	930	,,	34·5	3·4	[684]

HIGH MOLECULAR WEIGHT ORGANOPHOSPHORUS COMPOUNDS OF UNKNOWN STRUCTURE

In this group a large number of more or less high molecular weight organophosphorus compounds are listed, whose structures (and consequently the environment of the phosphorus) are unknown or unstated.

Substances of this type are formed by the polymerization of dienes in the presence of alkyl- and aryl-phosphines [687]; by the treatment of saturated hydrocarbons with phosphorus sulphides (or with phosphorus and sulphur) followed by reaction of the products with unsaturated compounds (or with polymers containing double bonds [688–690]); by the similar treatment of fats [691, 692], waxes [692, 693], unsaturated hydrocarbons [692], glycerides of fatty acids [692], high molecular weight amines or ketones [692], and olefin oxides [694]; by the reaction of amides of phosphoric acid with aldehydes [695], etc.

Detailed descriptions to illustrate the methods of obtaining these substances and their derivatives can be found in Katayama and Hagano's review [692] and in Dintses and Druzhinina's monograph [693] and so details of these substances will not be given here. There is no doubt that, as a result of the above mentioned reactions, the phosphorus actually enters into the composition of the polymers formed and its presence is not due to simple solutions or dispersions of the phosphorus sulphides in the other components. The reaction of coal with phosphorus trichloride (refluxing in the presence of aluminium chloride followed by treatment of the mixture obtained with dichloroethane and water) must be mentioned here. Coal treated in this way contains chemically linked phosphoric acid groups [173].

Before turning to an examination of the applications of organophosphorus polymers, some special properties — which have been expounded in detail in a number of books [465, 696–698] — of various high molecular weight compounds will be very briefly discussed.

Those polymers, copolymers and polycondensation products which have linear structures can be melted, dissolved in various solvents, moulded, extruded into fibres and can undergo other changes of shape under the influence of various factors (temperature, pressure, solvents, etc.).

Those high molecular weight compounds which have a three-dimensional structure, that is, they consist not of separate maromolecular chains but are one gigantic branched molecule, of course possess other properties. These compounds under the influence of heat cannot be melted but only soften (that is, they change into an elastomeric state and not a viscous one) and they can only swell in solvents but not dissolve in them. The particular structure of the three-dimensional polymers gives them, in comparison with the high molecular weight polymers of linear structure (it is only possible to compare, of course, substances of the same general type) greater mechanical strength, particularly in highly elastic structures, greater resistance to wear, chemical attack, etc.

As examples illustrative of the above statements, it is possible to compare ordinary polystyrene with the three-dimensional polystyrene obtained by the copolymerization of styrene with a small amount of divinylbenzene; linear polyesters with cross-linked, and so on.

The excellent mechanical and chemical properties of cross-linked polymers make them valuable materials for the preparation of various articles. However, the advantages of these substances may at the same time be disadvantages; their infusibility and insolubility, for example, render them difficult to work, to make varnishes from and to mould.

Recently, Kargin and his co-workers have shown that it is possible to form structural (that is, cross-linked) poly(vinyl chloride) by mechanical action [699–701]. In the main, this effect and also the preparation of block- and graft-copolymers in a similar way, can be explained mechanistically [702] (see p. 196), since in all three cases the main chain bonds of the macromolecules are broken and the high molecular weight free radicals which form recombine into the most probable shapes and least strained structures. In the cases of the block- and graft-copolymers various substances of linear structure enter into the reaction, whereas the case mentioned here only involves the reconstruction of the skeleton into a three-dimensional macromolecule.

These investigations by Kargin and his co-workers show principally that it is possible to obtain types of three-dimensional polymers which hitherto had been thought impossible to prepare.

The high molecular weight compounds of phosphorus are subject, of course, to all the effects listed above.

Representatives of phosphorus-containing polymers of linear structure are the polymers and copolymers of esters or amides of phosphorus acids, provided that the monomers have only one double bond, and also the copolymers of such organophosphorus compounds with dienes, provided that the degree of polymerization is not too great. Also possessing linear structures are the phosphorus-containing polyesters, polyamides, polyurethanes, other high molecular weight compounds formed by polycondensation of difunctional components, certain polyphosphonitrilic chlorides and their derivatives, etc.

Phosphorus-containing polymers with cross-linked structures are formed by the polymerization and copolymerization of esters and amides of phosphorus acids when the monomers (or one of them) have not less than two double bonds in the molecules; by polycondensation reactions with tri- and higher-functional phosphorus-containing compounds ($POCl_3$, unsaturated diamides of phosphonic acids, etc.); by the ageing of polyphosphonitrilic halides in air, etc.

The phosphorus atoms present in organophosphorus polymers give the latter certain special characteristics besides the previously described properties which are common to all high molecular weight compounds. It has been stated previously (see pp. 147, 154, 220) that the presence of phosphorus often reduces the reactivity of a monomeric organic compound. This same feature is also revealed in organophosphorus polymers; it gives them their well-known inert-

ness to chemical reagents as compared with "completely organic" polymers-
of analogous structure.

Certain organophosphorus high molecular weight compounds have good
thermal stabilities, that is, they can withstand comparatively high temperatures without being decomposed. The transparent phosphorus-containing
polymers as a rule have high refractive indices. Another important property
of these compounds is their great fire-resistance — which sometimes reaches
complete non-flammability. It appears that the amount of phosphorus is not
the only factor which influences fire-resistance. Independent factors are the
presence of other inorganic substituents (for example, halogens), the magnitude
of the molecular weight, the degree of branching in the polymer, the character
of the radicals joined to the phosphorus, and the nature of the phosphorus-
containing group.

CHAPTER VII.

USES OF HIGH MOLECULAR WEIGHT
PHOSPHORUS-CONTAINING COMPOUNDS

THERE is quite an extensive literature (most of it in patents) on the applications of the various high molecular weight organophosphorus compounds. From the point of view of industrial applications, however, these substances have, as yet, been little studied.

In recent years, a number of ways in which high molecular weight organophosphorus compounds can be used have been discovered. The following discussion of these uses does not include any mention of commercial manufacturing processes when these do not differ from the standard methods described in the literature.

ARTIFICIAL GLASS

In previous chapters of this book it was mentioned that the polymers and copolymers of many unsaturated esters of phosphorus acids possess good transparency, wear resistance, thermal resistance, chemical resistance and flame-resistance. These qualities render these substances very suitable for materials from which artificial glass can be made, particularly for special purposes. Many authors have described or recommended preparations of transparent laminar plastics, artificial glasses (and also armoured glass fabrics), glasses for aviation, for optical apparatus, etc., based on the polymers and copolymers of the diallyl and methallyl esters of alkyl- and aryl-phosphonic acids [101, 105, 184–186, 188, 189, 250, 274, 442–444, 448, 449, 452, 453, 473]. Occasionally the use of triallyl phosphate [472] and certain phosphorus-containing polyesters [555] for the preparation of artificial glass is encountered in the literature.

Little investigated, but probably of some value, is the possible application of the polymers and copolymers of vinyl- and isopropenyl-phosphonic esters for the preparation of artificial glass, since these polymers are known to possess good mechanical and optical properties [85, 466, 468].

Several monomers necessary for the preparation of artificial glasses, particularly the diallyl esters of chloromethyl- and phenyl-phosphonic acids, are available in industrial quantities [455, 703].

PAINTS AND LACQUERS

The chemical stability and flame-resistance of many high molecular weight organophosphorus compounds together with their good adhesion to various materials (for example, wood, metals, glass, porcelain, leather, etc.) renders these substances very suitable as raw materials for the preparation of lacquers and paints. For these purposes several classes of organophosphorus polymers have been proposed: copolymers (with various monomers) of β,γ-unsaturated esters of phosphonous, phosphonic and phosphoric acids [179, 274, 449–451, 471], of esters of α,β- and β,γ-unsaturated phosphonic acids [100, 235, 466], and also of alkyl- and aryl-phosphonous dichlorides [544, 545]. The use of phosphorus-containing polyesters [302, 549–551, 555, 556, 560, 562, 577], polyamides [56, 57], polyphosphonitrilic chloride and its esters [610, 612], 616, 617, 704], polyphosphoric amides [645, 649], etc. [705], has also been recommended.

A number of starting materials for preparing organophosphorus lacquers and paints (for example, phosphoryl chloride, chloromethylphosphonic dichloride, phenylphosphonous dichloride, phenylphosphonothionic dichloride [703, 706], polyphosphonitrilic chloride, as mixtures of the trimer and tetramer [707], triallyl phosphate [708, 709], etc.) are available in industrial quantities.

FILMS AND FIBRES

Many organophosphorus polymers of linear structure can be used for making flame-resistant and chemically resistant films and fibres. For this purpose copolymers of the following compounds have been described: esters and amides of certain α,β- and β,γ-unsaturated acids of phosphorus [235, 236, 466, 467, 471] and of polyphosphates [710], and also phosphorus-containing polyesters [579], polyamides [56, 57, 367, 579] and polyepoxides [531].

PLASTICIZERS

Patent claims have been made for the application as plasticizers of low molecular weight polymers and copolymers of certain unsaturated esters of phosphorus acids [99, 448], esters from phosphonitrilic chlorides [611, 613], and also products from the reaction of phosphorus pentoxide with glycols [566].

GLUES

Descriptions have been made of applications for a variety of requirements of glues made from phosphorus-containing polyesters — which possess considerable adhesiveness to many materials [549–551, 577, 711, 712] (see pp. 220 222) — and also of certain unsaturated phosphorus-containing polyesters having not less than two double bonds [713, 714]. With the last type the glueing is effected by polymerizing the ester monomer between the surfaces of the materials to be glued.

SUBSTANCES FOR INCREASING THE FLAME-RESISTANCE
OF FIBRES, SYNTHETIC RESINS AND PLASTICS

The production of flame-resistant materials is one of the problems which is of importance to the peoples of all nations, and it is natural, therefore, that there is a very extensive literature on this subject [504, 632, 715–718].

The application of organophosphorus polymers, either by their simple additions to the materials, or as substances chemically linked to them or absorbed on them, often permits this problem to be solved very easily and effectively. For example, textile articles can be rendered flame-proof by treating them with solutions of phosphoric acid or its salts, urea phosphates, dialkyl phosphorochloridates and other phosphorus-containing compounds [487, 504, 512, 513, 515, 543, 632, 682, 719–726]. In this way phosphates of cellulose with various structures are formed; this diminishes their burning capacity. As flame-resistant additives to textile articles the following are sometimes used: the polycondensation products of phosphoryl chloride and ammonia [645–649, 727–729], poly(vinyl phosphate) [494], polyphosphonitrilic chloride derivatives [612, 614, 730, 731], and also the copolymers of alkyl- and aryl-phosphonous dichlorides with olefins and dienes [544, 545].

In recent years a wide knowledge has been obtained of the treatment of fabrics with the telomerization products of triallyl phosphate with halogenated methanes (particularly bromoform) [628, 632, 718, 732, 733], and with the polymers or halogenated polymers of some allyl esters of phosphoric, phosphoramidic and phosphonic acids [136, 137, 474, 732, 734, 735]. Fabrics have also been treated with copolymers of esters of substituted β,γ-unsaturated phosphonic acids [235, 236, 446], and with the products of polycondensation of tetrakis-(hydroxymethyl)phosphonium chloride or tris-(hydroxymethyl)phosphine oxide with substances containing amino- or imino-groups (urea, melamine, ethylenimine, etc.) [624–632, 634, 718, 732]. Sometimes, the action of combinations of some of the aforementioned components is applied [633, 732, 736–738]; for example, triallyl phosphate, bromoform and tetrakis-(hydroxymethyl)phosphine oxide.

The fabrics are usually impregnated with solutions of the required phosphorus-containing substances, or with the partially polymerized materials, which are then completely polymerized on the fabric itself or on the article: this results in the formation of a phosphorus-containing matrix which penetrates through the whole fabric, or is linked chemically with it, and which renders it flame-proof.

In order to flame-proof polyester resins — which are usually obtained by the polycondensation of maleic or phthalic anhydrides with polyglycols — the linear polyester chains are cross-linked by utilizing mixtures of styrene with di-(2-chloroethyl) vinylphosphonate [539] or with the allyl esters of the phosphorus acids [453, 454, 475, 540, 541, 735]. The production of fire resistant films and fibres with high melting points from mixtures of solutions of poly meric di-(2-chloroethyl) vinylphosphonate with polyamides, polyurethanes or polyesters has been described [739].

The increased flame-resistance of the artificial glasses, lacquers, paints and resins prepared from high molecular weight phosphorus-containing compounds was mentioned above (see pp. 260, 261 and references [577, 740]).

Many of the phosphorus-containing substances used for flacme-proofing (phosphoric acid and its salts; triallyl phosphate [708, 709]; tetrakis-(hydroxy-methyl)-phosphonium chloride [741, 742]; a protecting emulsion, containing the triallyl phosphate-bromoform adduct, for the impregnation of textile materials [743]; etc.) are available in industrial quantities.

The flame-proofing of cotton articles (one of the methods) [631]

Two solutions are prepared: (a) crystalline tetrakis-(hydroxymethyl)-phosphonium chloride (1868 g of 95%) and triethanolamine (338 g) in water (1800 ml); and (b) tris-(hydroxymethyl)methylamine (un-methylated) (1609 g) and urea (1114 g) in water (5062 ml).

These solutions are mixed and the cotton article is immersed in the mixture and then squeezed out between rollers until its weight increase is $71 \cdot 5\%$. It is dried at 85°, and then at 142° (this hardens the resin), and washed and re-dried.

ION-EXCHANGE RESINS AND DETERGENTS

Ion-exchange resins find very wide application for the softening of water, the purification of sea water, the extraction of metals from sewer water and rivers, the separation of electrolytes, rare-earth elements, isotopes and amino acids, in the manufacture of foods, in analytical chemistry, etc.

Ion-exchange resins are cross-linked high molecular weight compounds which contain acidic or basic groups which are the active centres of these resins. An extensive literature is devoted to the preparation, investigation and application of ion-exchange resins [483, 744–753].

The phosphorus-containing cation-exchange resins are new and, as yet, little studied; their main features can, however, be briefly described here. Their advantages are their thermal stability, their highly selective ion-exchange action and their good mechanical strength.

They are three-dimensional, high molecular weight compounds which contain free phosphonic $[-PO(OH)_2]$, or phosphinic $[> PO(OH)]$ acid groups. These groups are joined with the hydrocarbon skeleton either directly (C—P bond) [469, 517, 518, 521, 524–528], or through oxygen (C—O—P link) [483, 489, 490, 494, 505, 506, 508, 516].

The phosphorus-containing cationic exchange resins are prepared by the treatment of three-dimensional polymers of unsaturated aromatic hydrocarbons with phosphorus trichloride in the presence of aluminium chloride, or by the treatment of polymers containing halogenated methyl groups with trialkyl phosphates, followed by oxidation and hydrolysis of the reaction products [517, 518, 521, 524–527] (see pp. 201, 202). For the same purpose it is also possible to utilize the reaction of hydroxyl-containing polymers (poly-(vinyl alcohol), starch, cellulose, etc.) with phosphoryl chloride, phosphoric acid or urea phosphate [483, 489, 490, 494, 505, 506, 516] (see pp. 199, 200). Preparations are also known of such ion-exchange resins by the polycondensation of aldehydes with aryloxymethylphosphonic acids [485] or with the acid esters from phosphoric acids and aromatic polyhydroxy compounds [483, 582]. Recently the preparation was described of phosphonic acid cation-exchange resins by the copolymerization of esters of vinylphosphonic acid with divinylbenzene, followed by hydrolysis of the copolymer obtained [469]; and also by the partial hydrolysis of polymers of esters of some phosphorus acids [173, 277]. Uses are known of phosphonic acid cation-exchange resins for the separation of alkali-metals [754–756], uranium [173, 528], copper [277, 757] and other metals [757], for the purification of certain plasticizers (esters of phthalic acid) from mixtures [758], etc. [759]. An obviously wide application is destined for the continuous ion-exchange processes which can be effected by endless ribbons of phosphorylated fabrics [505].

Recently several experimental types of phosphonic acid cation-exchange resins have been released in the U. S. S.R. [483, 453, 760] (RF, KF—1, KF-2, KF-3, KF-4) and in other countries [761] (Duolite S-60, S-61, S-62, S-65, Permutit XII).

The only known phosphorus-containing anion-exchange resins are those which contain quaternary phosphonium groups [547].

Unique soluble ion-exchange resins, which have found wide industrial use (for joining in building work and for preparing synthetic detergents) are the polyphosphates, the annual production of which in the United States alone runs into the hundreds of thousands of tons [762].

CATALYSTS FOR CHEMICAL REACTIONS

The release in industrial quantities of the desiccation products of orthophosphoric acid — the so-called polyphosphoric acids (708–763), PPA — has resulted in them being shown to be specific and mild catalysts for a range of chemical reactions.

With the help of these catalysts it is possible to carry out a number of cyclization reactions in significantly better yields than were obtained with the formerly used cyclization agents (aluminium chloride, ferric chloride, stannic chloride, boron trifluoride, sulphuric acid, etc.). With PPA the following conversions can be effected: 2,3-diaryl fatty acids into tetralin derivatives [764], isonitrosoacetanilide derivatives into isatin derivatives [765], carbostyril-carboxylic acid β-phenylethylamide into 4-(3,4-dihydro-1-isoquinolinyl)carbostyril [766], a range of amino-acids into diketopiperazines [767], pyridine-3-thioacetic acid into a thienopyrrole [768], etc. [769–781].

In the presence of PPA, aromatic hydrocarbons, phenol esters and alicyclic olefins are smoothly acylated by saturated and unsaturated organic acids [782, 783]. Besides such intermolecular acylations, PPA can also cause intramolecular acylation — which is of course cyclization — to occur in many cases.

The use of PPA has enabled simple and convenient methods of synthesis to be achieved for 2-alkyl(aryl) substituted benziminazoles, benzoxazoles and benzthiazoles by the condensation of aliphatic and aromatic acids, or their esters, amides or nitriles, with o-phenylenediamine, o-aminophenol and o-amino-thiophenol, respectively [784–786]. The intramolecular acylation of substituted ferrocenes has been brought about by PPA [787, 788]. The following reactions have also been achieved with this catalyst: the hydrolysis of β-ketonitriles to β-ketoamides [789] and of nitriles to amides generally [790], the reactions of nitromethane with fluorenone and benzophenone [791], the conversion of carboxylic acids into amines [792] and amides [793], anomalous Beckmann rearrangements [794–796], the Fries rearrangement [797], etc. [798–801]. Detailed descriptions of the properties and applications of PPA have been given by Popp and McEwan [802] and also by Freedman and Doak [803].

Catalytic properties of other organophosphorus compounds are also known.

There have been described, for example, the hydrolysis of ethylene oxide [804] and the reactions of 1,2-glycols with carbonyl compounds [805] under the influence of phosphorus-containing ion-exchange resins, the removal of sulphur from hydrocarbon distillates by the catalytic action of phosphorus–titanium polymers [680, 806], the heterogeneous copolymerization of sulphur dioxide with olefins in the presence of iron phosphate [807]. A stabilizing influence, that is, essentially negative catalysis, is shown by sodium polyphosphate on vinylic polymers and on metals [809; 810]; here the polyphosphate inhibits corrosion.

LUBRICANT ADDITIVES

A large number of high molecular weight compounds of unstated structure, usually containing phosphorus and sulphur, have found wide application in the industry of all nations as additives for improving the properties of lubricants [692, 693]. In this problem, practice has outstripped theory, since in most cases neither the structure nor the mode of action of these substances is known. It has also been proposed that the telomerization products of diethyl hydrogen phosphite with tetrafluoroethylene [682], poly(vinyl phosphate) [811] and the polyphosphonitrilic chlorides [611, 812, 813] be used as lubricant additives.

OTHER FIELDS OF APPLICATION OF HIGH MOLECULAR WEIGHT ORGANOPHOSPHORUS COMPOUNDS

Organophosphorus polymers (mostly the cellulose phosphates, which are formed by the action of phosphoric acid derivatives on fabrics, see p. 200) are widely used in the textile industry. The preparation of crease-resistant and unshrinkable fabrics by treatment with a mixture of phosphoric acid and urea

[511] or with phosphonitrilic chloride [814] or diammonium phosphate [815] has been described. As well as this, diammonium phosphate gives fabrics fire-resistance, as was described earlier (p. 262), water-resistance and also anti-septic properties [816].

The product of the partial esterification of the morpholine salt of phosphoric acid with lauryl alcohol improves the properties of acetate silk [817]. It has been reported that sodium tripolyphosphate can be used with success for de-gumming raw silk [818]. The polycondensation products of tetrakis-(hydroxymethyl)-phosphonium chloride give fabrics not only flame-resistant, but also water-resistant, properties [631, 633]. The use of a polyester resin, obtained by the reaction of phosphoric acid with polyethylene oxide, as an oil, emulsion, etc., is known in the textile industry [819]. There are patent claims for the use of the products of the reaction of sodium diallyl phosphite with linseed oil [820] and for the use of certain phosphonitrilic esters [611] as hydraulic fluids. It has been suggested that the transesterification products of diethyl ethylphosphonate with partially esterified glycerol can be used in the polygraphic industry [569].

The preparation of elastic and thermally-resistant polymers by the treatment of polyphosphates with solutions of compounds containing isothiouronium groups has been described [821, 822].

The introduction of phosphorus atoms into rubbers and high-molecular weight organosilicon compounds has been shown to be useful. For example, the reaction of arylphosphonous dichlorides with various rubbers can give them greater resistance to solvents and oils (532–534). The reaction of phosphonitrilic chloride, or dialkylphosphoramidous chlorides and phosphoric acid, with liquid polysiloxanes changes the polysiloxanes into elastic gels which can then be converted into rubbers [823]. The treatment of organosilicon polymers with small quantities of arylphosphonous acids, arylphosphonic acids, or phenyl phosphorodichloridate increases their thermal reisistance and their low-temperature elasticity [824–826]. The thermal resistance of polymers is also improved by the addition of phosphonitrilic esters [613, 827], or the reaction products of phosphonitrilic chloride with urea or dichloroaniline [618].

The application of phosphonitrilic chlorides as bonding agents for grinding wheels [828] and ceramic articles [830] has been described. Certain phosphonitrilic esters are insecticides [830]. Recently there was described an original, and in some cases very important, method of colouring certain synthetic fibres (nylon, Terylene, etc.) by using a film of a Phoryl resin previously dyed in the desired colour. Because of the good adhesion of these resins to the fibres the latter take the colour of the film; the resin can then be removed by hydrolysis or by other methods [831]. There are communications that deal with the re-investigation of many heterochain polymers, in particular those polymers which contain phosphorus and boron or phosphorus and nitrogen in the main chain, because of their usefulness in the field of textiles where high tempera-ture resistance is required, as, for example, in fast flight [832–834].

REFERENCES

1. V. M. PLETS, *Organicheskiye soyedineniya fosfor (Organic compounds of phosphorus)*, Oborongiz, Moscow (1940).
2. G. M. KOSOLAPOFF, *Organophosphorus Compounds*, New York (1950).
3. *Spravochnik khimika (The Chemist's Handbook)*, Vol. II, Goskhimizdat, Moscow/Leningrad (1951).
4. V. M. PLETS, *Zh. obsch. khim.* **6**, 1198 (1936).
5. E. N. WALSH, T. M. BECK and W. H. WOODSTOCK, *J. Amer. Chem. Soc.* **77**, 929 (1955).
6. R. D. STAINER, *U. S. Pat.* 2686803 and 2693482; *Chem. Abstr.* **49**, 11000, 13287 (1955).
7. M. I. KABACHNIK and T. YA. MEDVED, *Avt. svid. (U. S. S. R. Pat.)* 116882; *Byull. isobr.*, **12**, 28 (1958); *Izv. Akad. Nauk SSSR, Otdel. khim. nauk*, 2142 (1959).
8. K. SCHIMMELSCHMIDT and W. DENK, *Ger. (West) Pat.* 1023033; *Ref. zh. khim.*, ref. 2082 (1960).
9. J. E. MARSH and J. A. GARDNER, *J. Chem. Soc.* **65**, 35 (1894).
10. A. K. HARNIST, *Über die Addition von Phosphorpentachlorid an Äthylenkörper*, Dissertation, Strassburg (1910).
11. F. BULLE, *Über die Addition von Phosphorpentachlorid an Inden*, Dissertation, Berlin/Wilmersdorf (1912).
12. E. BERGMANN and A. BONDI, *Ber. dtsch. Chem. Ges.* **63**, 1158 (1930).
13. E. BERGMANN and A. BONDI, *Ber. dtsch. Chem. Ges.* **64**, 1455 (1931).
14. E. BERGMANN and A. BONDI, *Ber. dtsch. Chem. Ges.* **66**, 278 (1933).
15. E. BERGMANN and A. BONDI, *Ber. dtsch. Chem. Ges.* **66**, 286 (1933).
16. G. M. KOSOLAPOFF and W. F. HUBER, *J. Amer. Chem. Soc.* **68**, 2540 (1946).
17. J. B. CONANT and B. B. COIN, *J. Amer. Chem. Soc.* **44**, 2530 (1922).
18. J. B. CONANT, A. D. McDONALD and A. B. McKINNEY, *J. Amer. Chem. Soc.* **43**, 1928 (1921).
19. M. I. KABACHNIK, *Usp. khim.* **16**, 403 (1947).
20. M. I. KABACHNIK and YE. S. SHEPELEVA, *Dokl. Akad. nauk SSSR*, **75**, 219 (1950).
21. M. I. KABACHNIK and YE. S. SHEPELEVA, *Izv. Akad. nauk SSSR, Odtel. khim. nauk*, 39 (1950).
22. M. I. KABACHNIK and YE. S. SHEPELEVA, *Izv. Akad. nauk SSSR, Odtel. khim. nauk*, 185 (1951).
23. M. I. KABACHNIK and YE. S. SHEPELEVA, *Izv. Akad. nauk. SSSR, Otdel, khim. nauk*, 540 (1952).
24. YE. S. SHEPELEVA, Thesis, Moscow (1952).
25. J. B. CONANT, *J. Amer. Chem. Soc.* **39**, 2679 (1917).
26. J. B. CONANT, A. H. BUMP and H. S. HOLT, *J. Amer. Chem. Soc.* **43**, 1677 (1921).
27. A. MICHAELIS and A. FLEMING, *Ber. dtsch. Chem. Ges.* **34**, 1297 (1901).
28. L. N. HAMILTON, *U. S. Pat.* 2365466; *Chem. Abstr.* **39**, 4619 (1945).
29. L. N. PARFENT'EV and M. KH. SHAFIYEV, *Trud. Uzbek. gos. univ.* **15**, 87 (1939).
30. A. MICHAELIS, *Ber. dtsch. Chem. Ges.* **17**, 1273 (1884); **18**, 898 (1885).
31. L. R. DRAKE and C. S. MARVEL, *J. Org. Chem.* **2**, 387 (1937).
32. L. ANSCHUTZ, E. KLEIN and G. CERMAK, *Ber. dtsch. Chem. Ges.* **77M**, 726 (1944).
33. YU. M. ZINOV'EV, L. I. MULER and L. Z. SOBOROVSKII, *Zh. obshch. khim.* **24**, 380 (1954).

34. J. A. Gardner and G. B. Cockburn, *J. Chem. Soc.* **71**, 1157 (1897); **73**, 704 (1898).
35. K. Schimmelschmidt and W. Denk, *Ger. (West) Pat.* 1020019; *Ref. zh. khim.* ref. 39595 (1959); *Ger (West) Pat.* 1023034 (1956).
36. M. I. Kabachnik and T. Ya. Medved', *Izv. Akad. nauk SSSR, Otdel. khim. nauk,* To be published.
37. W. H. Woodstock, *U. S. Pat.* 2471472; *Chem. Abstr.* **43**, 7499 (1949).
38. K. N. Anisimov and A. N. Nesmeyanov, *Izv. Akad. nauk SSSR, Otdel. khim. nauk,* 610 (1954).
39. K. N. Anisimov, N. Ye. Kolobova and A. N. Nesmeyanov, *Izv. Akad. nauk SSSR, Otdel. khim. nauk,* 796 (1954).
40. K. N. Anisimov, N. Ye. Kolobova and A. N. Nesmeyanov, *Izv. Akad. nauk SSSR, Otdel. khim. nauk,* 799 (1954).
41. K. N. Anisimov, *Izv. Akad. nauk SSSR, Otdel. khim. nauk,* 803 (1954).
42. K. N. Anisimov, N. Ye. Kolobova and A. N. Nesmeyanov, *Izv. Akad. nauk SSSR, Otdel. khim. nauk,* 23 (1956).
43. K. N. Anisimov and N. Ye. Kolobova, *Izv. Akad. nauk SSSR, Otdel. khim. nauk,* 923 (1956).
44. K. N. Anisimov and N. Ye. Kolobova, *Izv. Akad. nauk SSSR, Otdel. khim. nauk,* 927 (1956).
45. W. N. Woodstock and E. N. Walsh, *U. S. Pat.* 2685602; *Chem. Abstr.* **49**, 10358 (1955).
46. E. N. Walsh, *U. S. Pat.* 2685603; *Chem. Abstr.* **49**, 10358 (1955).
47. J. P. Clay, *J. Org. Chem.* **16**, 892 (1951).
48. A. M. Kinnear and E. A. Perren, *J. Chem. Soc.* 3437 (1952).
49. L. Z. Soborovskii, Yu. M. Zinov'ev and M. A. Englin, *Avt. svid. (U. S. S. R. Pat.)* 117901; *Byull. isobr.* **3**, 14 (1959).
50. L. Z. Soborovskii, Yu. M. Zinov'ev and M. A. Englin, *Dokl. Akad. nauk SSSR,* **67**, 293 (1949).
51. J. O. Clayton and W. L. Jensen, *J. Amer. Chem. Soc.* **70**, 3880 (1948).
52. B. A. Vovsi, Yu. A. Sharanin, A. A. Petrov, L. K. Maslii and T. V. Yakovlev, *Nauch. dokl. Vyssh. shkol. Khim. i khim. tekhn.* 335 (1958).
53. L. A. Hamilton and N. J. Pitman, *U. S. Pat.* 2382309; *Off. Gaz.* **577**, N2, 465 (1945).
54. K. N. Anisimov, N. Ye. Kolobova and A. N. Nesmeyanov, *Izv. Akad. nauk SSSR, Otdel. khim. nauk,* 665 (1955).
55. K. N. Anisimov, N. Ye. Kolobova and A. N. Nesmeyanov, *Izv. Akad. nauk SSSR, Otdel. khim. nauk,* 834 (1955).
56. H. W. Coover, *U. S. Pat.* 2642413; *Chem. Abstr.* **47**, 9057 (1953).
57. J. B. Dickey and H. W. Coover, *U. S. Pat.* 2666750; *Chem. Abstr.* **48**, 10380 (1954).
58. K. N. Anisimov and A. N. Nesmeyanov, *Izv. Akad. nauk SSSR, Otdel. khim. nauk,* 19 (1956).
59. H. Z. Lecher and E. Kuh, *U. S. Pat.* 2654738; *Chem. Abstr.* **48**, 10053 (1954).
60. H. W. Coover and J. B. Dickey, *U. S. Pat.* 2725371; *Chem. Abstr.* **50**, 11054 (1956).
61. H. W. Coover and N. H. Shearer, *U. S. Pat.* 2856390; *Chem. Abstr.* **53**, 5131 (1959).
62. J. N. Short, *U. S. Pat.* 2818406; *Chem. Abstr.* **52**, 6407 (1958).
63. K. N. Anisimov, N. Ye. Kolobova and A. N. Nesmeyanov, *Izv. Akad. nauk SSSR, Otdel. khim. nauk,* 240 (1955).
64. K. N. Anisimov, N. Ye. Kolobova and A. N. Nesmeyanov, *Izv. Akad. nauk SSSR, Otdel. khim. nauk,* 425 (1955).
65. K. N. Anisimov, N. Ye. Kolobova and A. N. Nesmeyanov, *Izv. Akad. nauk SSSR, Otdel. khim. nauk,* 432 (1955).
66. K. N. Anisimov, N. Ye. Kolobova and A. N. Nesmeyanov, *Izv. Akad. nauk SSSR, Otdel. khim. nauk,* 669 (1955).

67. K. N. ANISIMOV, N. YE. KOLOBOVA and A. N. NESMEYANOV, *Izv. Akad. nauk SSSR, Otdel. khim. nauk*, 823 (1955).
68. K. N. ANISIMOV, N. YE. KOLOBOVA and A. N. NESMEYANOV, *Izv. Akad. nauk SSSR, Otdel. khim. nauk*, 827 (1955).
69. K. N. ANISIMOV, N. YE. KOLOBOVA and A. N. NESMEYANOV, *Izv. Akad. nauk SSSR, Otdel. khim. nauk*, 999 (1955).
70. K. N. ANISIMOV and A. N. NESMEYANOV, *Izv. Akad. nauk SSSR, Otdel. khim. nauk*, 1003 (1955).
71. K. N. ANISIMOV and A. N. NESMEYANOV, *Izv. Akad. nauk SSSR, Otdel. khim. nauk*, 1006 (1955).
72. K. N. ANISIMOV and A. N. NESMEYANOV, *Izv. Akad. nauk SSSR, Otdel. khim. nauk*, 16 (1956).
73. G. M. KOSOLAPOFF, *U. S. Pat.* 2389576; *Chem. Abstr.* **40**, 1536 (1946).
74. A. N. PUDOVIK and K. KH. YARMUKHAMETOVA, *Izv. Akad. nauk SSSR, Otdel. khim. nauk*, 636 (1954).
75. M. I. KABACHNIK, *Izv. Akad. nauk SSSR, Otdel. khim. nauk*, 233 (1947).
76. A. H. FOORD-MOORE and J. H. WILLIAMS, *J. Chem. Soc.* 1465 (1947)
77. G. M. KOSOLAPOFF, *J. Amer. Chem. Soc.* **70**, 1971 (1948).
78. G. M. KOSOLAPOFF and J. F. MCCULLOUGH, *J. Amer. Chem. Soc.* **73**, 855 (1951).
79. A. N. PUDOVIK and G. M. DYENISOVA, *Sbornik statei po obshchei khimii (Collected papers on general chemistry)*, Vol. 1, p. 338, Akad. Sci. U. S. S. R. (1953).
80. V. S. ABRAMOV and G. A. KARP, *Zh. obshch. khim.* **24**, 1823 (1954).
81. V. S. ABRAMOV and A. P. REKHMAN, *Zh. obshch. khim.* **26**, 163 (1956).
82. V. S. ABRAMOV and N. A. IL'INA, *Zh. obshch. khim.* **26**, 2014 (1956).
83. M. KH. SHAFIYEV, *Trud. Samarkand. ped. inst.* **5**, 29 (1947).
84. L. Z. SOBOROVSKII, YU. M. ZINOV'EV and L. I. MULER, *Dokl. Akad. nauk SSSR*, **109**, 98 (1956).
85. E. K. FIELDS, *U. S. Pat.* 2579810; ZBL. 2995 (1953).
86. A. YE. ARBUSOV, *Thesis*, St. Petersburg (1905).
87. A. MICHAELIS and T. BECKER, *Ber. dtsch. Chem. Ges.* **30**, 1003 (1897).
88. P. NYLEN, *Studien über organische Phosphorverbindungen*, Upsala (1930).
89. L. N. PARFENT'EV, *Uch. zap. Kazan. gos. univ.* 75 (1925).
90. A. YE. ARBUSOV and A. I. RAZUMOV, *Izv. Akad. nauk SSSR, Otdel. khim. nauk*, 714 (1951).
91. A. YE. ARBUSOV and V. M. ZOROASTROVA, *Izv. Akad. nauk SSSR, Otdel. khim. nauk*, 357 (1950).
92. G. M. KOSOLAPOFF, *J. Amer. Chem. Soc.* **73**, 4040 (1951).
93. A. N. PUDOVIK and K. A. KOVYRZINA, *Zh. obshch. khim.* **24**, 307 (1954).
94. A. N. PUDOVIK and M. M. FROLOVA, *Zh. obshch. khim.* **22**, 2052 (1952).
95. A. N. PUDOVIK, *Zh. obshch. khim.* **19**, 1179 (1949).
96. A. N. PUDOVIK and B. A. ARBUSOV, *Izv. Akad. nauk SSSR, Otdel. khim. nauk*, 522 (1949).
97. A. N. PUDOVIK and I. V. SHERGINA, *Zh. obshch. khim.* **27**, 2750 (1957).
98. A. N. PUDOVIK, *Zh. obshch. khim.* **22**, 109 (1952).
99. M. L. ERNSBERGER, *U. S. Pat.* 2491920; *Chem. Abstr.* **44**, 2547 (1950).
100. J. B. DICKEY and H. W. COOVER, *U. S. Pat.* 2559854; *Chem. Abstr.* **45**, 8810 (1951).
101. G. KAMAI and B. A. KUKHTIN, *Trud. Kazan. khim. — tekhn. inst. im. S. M. Kirova* **16**, 29 (1952).
102. H. W. COOVER, M. A. MCCALL and J. B. DICKEY, *J. Amer. Chem. Soc.* **79**, 1963 (1957).
103. A. N. PUDOVIK, *Zh. obshch. khim.* **20**, 92 (1950).
104. A. YE. ARBUSOV and A. A. DUNIN, *Zh. russk. khim. obshch.* **46**, 295 (1914).

105. G. Kamai and V. A. Kukhtin, *Dokl. Akad. nauk SSSR*, **89**, 309 (1953).
106. R. H. Wiley, *U. S. Pat.* 2478441; *Chem. Abstr.* **44**, 2010 (1950).
107. A. N. Pudovik and D. Kh. Yarmukhametova, *Izv. Akad. nauk SSSR, Otdel. khim. nauk*, 721 (1952).
108. A. N. Pudovik and Yu. P. Kitayev, *Zh. obsch. khim.* **22**, 467 (1952).
109. A. N. Pudovik and G. Zametayeva, *Izv. Akad. nauk SSSR, Otdel. khim. nauk*, 932 (1952).
110. A. N. Pudovik and B. A. Arbusov, *Zh. obshch. khim.* **21**, 382 (1951).
111. V. M. Zoroastrova, *Thesis*, Kazan (1945); A. Ye. Arbuzov. *Izbrannyye trudy (Selected works)*, p. 509, Acad. Sci. U. S. S. R. (1952).
112. M. Podladchikov, *Zh. russk. khim. obshch.* **31**, 30 (1899).
113. T. Milobendzki and A. Sachnowski, *Chem. Polski*, **15**, 34 (1917).
114. N. A. Chadayeva and G. Kamai, *Zh. obshch. khim.* **20**, 1487 (1950).
115. G. Kamai and N. A. Chadayeva, *Trud. Kazan. khim. — tekh. inst. im. S. M. Kirova*, **15**, 32 (1951).
116. K. V. Nikonorov, *Trud. Kazan. khim. — tekh. inst. im. S. M. Kirova*, **10**, 39 (1946).
117. Ye. V. Kuznetsov and R. K. Valentdinov, *Trud. Kazan. khim. — tekh. inst. im. S. M. Kirova*, **23**, 174 (1957); R. K. Valetdinov, *Thesis*, Kazan (1958).
118. J. Hechenbleikner, *U. S. Pat.* 2852551; *Chem. Abstr.* **53**, 4212 (1959).
119. R. C. Morris and J. L. Winkle, *U. S. Pat.* 2728789; *Zbl.* 8357 (1957).
120. Ye. L. Gefter and M. I. Kabachnik, *Dokl. Akad. nauk SSSR*, **114**, 541 (1957); Ye. L. Gefter, Thesis, Moscow (1954).
121. A. N. Nesmeyanov, I. F. Lutsenko, Z. S. Kraits and A. P. Bokovoi, *Dokl. Akad. nauk SSSR.* **124**, 1251 (1959).
122. G. Kamai and Ye. I. Shugurova, *Dokl. Akad. nauk SSSR*, **72**, 301 (1950).
123. Ye. I. Shugurova and G. Kamai, *Zh. obshch. khim.* **21**, 658 (1951).
124. W. E. Craig and W. F. Hester, *U. S. Pat.* 2495958; *Chem. Abstr.* **44**, 3202 (1950).
125. L. Henry, *Ber. dtsch. Chem. Ges.* **8**, 398 (1875).
126. E. D. Bergmann and D. Herrman, *J. Amer. Chem. Soc.* **73**, 4013 (1951).
127. J. Kennedy, *Brit. Pat.* 778077; *J. Appl. Chem.* **9**, 152 (1959).
128. A. N. Pudovik and N. I. Khlyupina, *Zh. obshch. khim.* **26**, 1672 (1956).
129. L. N. Whitehall and R. S. Barker, *U. S. Pat.* 2394829; *Chem. Abstr.* **40**, 2454 (1946).
130. R. M. Reinhardt, *J. Amer. Chem. Soc.* **74**, 1093 (1952).
131. A. D. F. Toy and J. R. Costello, *U. S. Pat.* 2754315; *Chem. Abstr.* **51**, 1244 (1957).
132. E. C. Britton and C. L. Moyle, *U. S. Pat.* 2176416; *Chem. Abstr.* **34**, 1035 (1940).
133. E. C. Britton and C. L. Moyle, *U. S. Pat.* 2275041; *Chem. Abstr.* **36**, 4135 (1942).
134. A. Covach, H. Jean and G. Garnier, *Chim. et Ind.* **64**, 287 (1950).
135. G. E. Walter and co-workers, *U. S. Pat.* 2574516 and 2574517; *Chem. Abstr.* **46**, 9579, 9580 (1952); *Zbl.* 4116 (1953).
136. G. L. Martin Co., *Brit. Pat.* 688372; *Zbl.* 2056 (1956).
137. G. L. Martin Co., *Brit. Pat.* 699951; *Zbl.* 5688 (1956).
138. G. M. Steinberg, *J. Org. Chem.* **15**, 637 (1950).
139. Ye. V. Kuznetsov and R. K. Valentdinov, *Zh. obshch. khim.* **29**, 2017 (1959).
140. Yu. S. Zal'kind and Ye. G. Dmitriyeva, *Avt. svid. (U. S. S. R. Pat.)* 40348; *Vestn. komiteta po isobretatel'stvu*, **12**, 107 (1934).
141. *Brit. Pat.* 737431; *Chem. Abstr.* **50**, 7410 (1956).
142. D. C. Ayres and H. N. Rydon, *J. Chem. Soc.* 1109 (1957).
143. C. B. Scott, *J. Org. Chem.* **22**, 1118 (1957).
144. K. Dimroth and R. Ploch, *Ber. dtsch. Chem. Ges.* **90**, 801 (1957).
145. *Chem. Eng. News*, **28**, 3452 (1950).
146. V. M. Plets, *Zh. obshch. khim.* **8**, 1296 (1938).

147. V. Tichy, *Chem. Zvesti,* **9**, 232 (1955).

148. J. Cavalier, *Bull. soc. chim. France,* **13**, 885 (1895).

149. J. Cavalier, *Compt. rend.* **122**, 69 (1895).

150. O. Bailly, *Bull. soc. chim. France,* **31**, 848 (1922).

151. J. Cavalier, *Bull. soc. chim. France,* **19**, 883 (1898).

152. C. Oeser, *Liebig's Ann.* **131**, 280 (1864).

153. C. F. Boehringer and U. Sohne, *Ger. Pat.* 98522; *Zbl.* II, 950 (1898).

154. K. Langheld, *Ber. dtsch. Chem. Ges.* **43**, 1857 (1910).

155. P. Karrer and H. Bendas, *Helv. Chim. Acta,* **19**, 98 (1936).

156. R. W. Upson, *U. S. Pat.* 2557805; *Chem. Abstr.* **45**, 8298 (1951); *J. Amer. Chem. Soc.* **75**, 1763 (1953).

157. J. F. Allen, S. K. Reed, O. H. Johnson and N. J. Brunsvold, *J. Amer. Chem. Soc.* **78**, 3715 (1956).

158. W. Perkow, K. Ullerich and F. Meyer, *Naturwiss.* **39**, 353 (1952).

159. W. Perkow, *Ber. dtsch. Chem. Ges.* **87**, 755 (1954).

160. W. Perkow, R. W. Krocow and K. Knoevenagel, *Ber. dtsch. Chem. Ges.* **88**, 662 (1955).

161. A. R. Stiles, *U. S. Pat.* 2685552; *Chem. Abstr.* **48**, 12365 (1954).

162. A. N. Pudovik and N. M. Lebedeva, *Dokl. Akad. nauk SSSR,* **101**, 889 (1955).

163. A. N. Pudovik, *Dokl. Akad. nauk SSSR,* **105**, 735 (1955).

164. A. N. Pudovik, *Zh. obshch. khim.* **25**, 2173 (1955).

165. A. N. Pudovik and V. P. Aver'yanova, *Zh. obshch. khim.* **26**, 1426 (1956).

166. A. N. Pudovík and L. G. Salekhova *Zh. obshhch. khim.* **26**, 1431 (1956).

167. A. N. Pudovik, *Zh. obshch. khim.* **26**, 2238 (1956).

168. A. N. Pudovik and L. G. Biktimirova, *Zh. obshch. khim.* **27**, 2104 (1957).

169. J. F. Allen and O. H. Johnson, *J. Amer. Chem. Soc.* **77**, 2871 (1955).

170. N. Kreutzkamp and H. Kayser, *Naturwiss.* **42**, 415 (1955).

171. M. S. Karasch and J. S. Bengelsdorf, *J. Org. Chem.* **20**, 1357 (1955).

172. J. S. Bengelsdorf, *J. Org. Chem.* **21**, 475 (1956).

173. J. Kennedy, E. C. Lane and B. K. Robinson, *J. Appl. Chem.* **8**, 459 (1958).

174. W. F. Bartel, B. H. Alexander, P. A. Giang and S. A. Hall, *J. Amer. Chem. Soc.* **77**, 2424 (1955).

175. W. Lorenz, A. Henglein and G. Schrader, *J. Amer. Chem. Soc.* **77**, 2554 (1955).

176. A. M. Mattson, J. T. Spillane and G. W. Pearce, *J. Agric. Food Chem.* **3**, 319 (1955).

177. R. C. Morris and J. L. Winkle, *U. S. Pat.* 2744128; *Chem. Abstr.* **52**, 1208 (1958).

178. A. Ye. Arbuzov and K. V. Nikonorov, *Zh. obshch. khim.* **18**, 2008 (1948).

179. R. C. Morris, V. W. Buls and S. A. Ballard, *U. S. Pat.* 2577796; *Chem. Abstr.* **46**, 9581 (1952).

180. G. Kamai, *Trud. Kazan. khim. — tekh. inst. im. S. M. Kirova,* **10**, 29 (1946).

181. G. Kamai, *Dokl. Akad. nauk SSSR,* **55**, 223 (1947).

182. G. Kamai and L. P. Yegorova, *Zh. obshch. khim.* **16**, 1521 (1946).

183. D. Harman and A. R. Stiles, *U. S. Pat.* 2601520; *Chem. Abstr.* **46**, 8417 (1952); *U. S. Pat.* 2659714; *Chem. Abstr.* **48**, 12168 (1954).

184. A. D. F. Toy, *J. Amer. Chem. Soc.* **70**, 186 (1948).

185. A. D. F. Toy and L. V. Brown, *Industr. Engng. Chem.* **40**, 2276 (1948).

186. A. D. F. Toy and R. S. Cooper, *J. Amer. Chem. Soc.* **76**, 2191 (1954).

187. J. Kennedy, *Chem. and Ind.* 378 (1956).

188. A. J. Castro and W. E. Elwell, *J. Amer. Chem. Soc.* **72**, 2275 (1950).

189. E. C. Shokal and L. N. Whitehill, *Brit. Pat.* 645222; *Chem. Abstr.* **45**, 4267 (1951).

190. V. S. Abramov, R. V. Dmitriyeva and A. S. Kapustina, *Zh. obshch. khim.* **23**, 257 (1953).

191. V. S. ABRAMOV and N. A. IL'INA, *Zh. obshch. khim.* **24,** 124 (1954).
192. YE. L. GEFTER and M. I. KABACHNIK, *Avt. svid (U. S. S. R. Pat.)* 104285; *Byull. isobr.* **9,** 9 (1956).
193. A. I. RAZUMOV and N. PETROV, *Trud. khim. — tekh. inst. im. S. M. Kirova,* **10,** 35 (1946).
194. B. A. ARBUZOV, B. P. LUGOVKIN and N. P. BOGONOSTSEVA, *Zh. obshch. khim.* **20,** 1468 (1950).
195. A. YE. ARBUZOV and P. I. ALIMOV, *Izv. Akad. nauk SSSR, Otdel. khim. nauk,* 530 (1951).
196. D. HARMAN and R. E. THORPE, *U. S. Pat.* 2614990; *Chem. Abstr.* **47,** 1379 (1953).
197. N. D. DAWSON and A. BURGER, *J. Amer. chem. Soc.* **74,** 5312 (1952).
198. E. C. LADD and M. P. HARVEY, *U. S. Pat.* 2597938; *Chem. Abstr.* **47,** 1182 (1953).
199. E. C. LADD and M. P. HARVEY, *U. S. Pat.* 2631162; *Chem. Abstr.* **48,** 7048 (1954).
200. M. I. KABACHNIK and P. A. ROSSIISKAYA, *Izv. Akad. nauk SSSR, Otdel. khim. nauk,* 48 (1957).
201. V. S. ABRAMOV, *Dokl. Akad. nauk SSSR,* **95,** 991 (1954).
202. G. KAMAI and V. A. KUKHTIN, *Dokl. Akad. nauk SSSR,* **102,** 283 (1955).
203. H. W. COOVER and J. B. DICKEY, *U. S. Pat.* 2652416; *Chem. Abstr.* **48,** 10053 (1954).
204. R. L. MCCONNELL and H. W. COOVER, *J. Amer. chem. Soc.* **78,** 4453 (1956).
205. H. J. JACOBSON, R. G. HARVEY and E. V. JENSEN, *J. Amer. chem. Soc.* **77,** 6064 (1955).
206. M. I. KABACHNIK and P. A. ROSSIISKAYA, *Izv. Akad. nauk SSSR, Otdel. khim. nauk,* 364 (1945).
207. F. F. FAIZULLIN and N. A. TRIFONOV, *Uch. zap. Kazan. gos. univ.* **112,** bk. 4, 131, 139, 145 (1952).
208. A. M. SLADKOV, *Thesis,* Moscow (1950); A. M. SLADKOV and G. S. PETROV, *Zh. obshch. khim.* **24,** 450 (1954).
209. A. MICHAELIS and W. LA-COSTE, *Ber. dtsch. chem. Ges.* **18,** 2109 (1885).
210. A. YE. ARBUZOV, G. KH. KAMAI and L. V. NESTEROV, *Trud. Kazan. khim. — tekh. inst. im. S. M. Kirova,* **16,** 17 (1952).
211. A. YE. ARBUZOV and L. V. NESTEROV, *Izv. Akad. nauk SSSR, Otdel. khim. nauk,* 431 (1954).
212. A. I. RAZUMOV and N. N. BANKOVSKAYA, *Dokl. Akad. nauk SSSR,* **116,** 241 (1957).
213. *Reaktsii i metody issledovaniya organicheskikh soyedinenii (Reactions and methods of investigation of organic compounds),* bk. III, pp. 7—72, Goskhimizdat, Moscow (1954).
214. L. V. NESTEROV, *Thesis* Kazan (1953).
215. B. A. ARBUZOV and B. P. LUGOVKIN, *Zh. obshch. khim.* **21,** 99 (1951).
216. G. KAMAI, *Zh. obshch. khim.* **18,** 443 (1948).
217. P. O. TAWNEY, *U. S. Pat.* 2535172 and 2535174; *Chem. Abstr.* **45,** 3408 (1951).
218. P. O. TAWNEY, *U. S. Pat.* 2570503; *Chem. Abstr.* **46,** 3556 (1952).
219. A. N. PUDOVIK and M. G. IMAYEV, *Izv. Akad. nauk. SSSR, Otdel. khim. nauk,* 916 (1952).
220. A. N. PUDOVIK, *Dokl. Akad. nauk SSSR,* **80,** 65 (1951).
221. A. N. PUDOVIK and G. M. DENISOVA, *Zh. obshch. khim.* **23,** 263 (1953).
222. A. N. PUDOVIK and O. N. GRISHINA, *Zh. obshch. khim.* **23,** 267 (1953).
223. A. N. PUDOVIK and N. G. POLOZNOVA, *Zh. obshch. khim.* **25,** 778 (1955).
224. P. O. TAWNEY, *U. S. Pat.* 2535175; *Chem. Abstr.* **45,** 3409 (1951).
225. E. C. LADD, *U. S. Pat.* 2611784 and 2622096; *Chem. Abstr.* **47,** 9355, 9344 (1953).
226. J. B. DICKEY and H. W. COOVER, *U. S. Pat.* 2550651; *Chem. Abstr.* **45,** 8029 (1951).
227. A. YA. YAKUBOVICH, L. Z. SOBOROVSKII, L. I. MULER and V. S. FAYERMARK, *Zh. obshch. khim.* **28,** 317 (1958).

228. Ye. L. Gefter, *Zh. obshch. khim.* **28,** 2500 (1958).

229. G. S. Kolesnikov and Ye. F. Rodionova, *Vysokomolekulyarnyye soyedineniya,* **1,** 641 (1959).

230. G. S. Kolesnikov, Ye. F. Rodionova and L. S. Fedorova, *Vysokomolekulyarnyye soyedineniya* **1,** 367 (1959).

231. Ye. L. Gefter, *Khim. nauka i prom.* **3,** 544 (1958).

232. J. Kennedy and G. M. Meaburn, *Chem. and Ind.* 930 (1956).

233. H. W. Coover and J. B. Dickey, *U. S. Pat.* 2652416; *Chem. Abstr.* **48,** 10053 (1954).

234. W. H. Woodstock, *U. S. Pat.* 2516168; *Chem. Abstr.* **45,** 639 (1951).

235. H. W. Coover and J. B. Dickey, *U. S. Pat.* 2636027; *Chem. Abstr.* **47,** 11808 (1953).

236. J. B. Dickey and H. W. Coover, *U. S. Pat.* 2721876; *Chem. Abstr.* **50,** 10123 (1956); *Zbl.* 808 (1957); *U. S. Pat.* 2780616; *Chem. Abstr.* **51,** 7765 (1957).

237. A. N. Pudovik and I. V. Konovalova, *Zh. obshch. khim.* **28,** 1208 (1958).

238. F. Johnston, *Brit. Pat.* 693742; *Chem. Abstr.* **48,** 10053 (1954).

239. A. R. Stiles and D. Harman, *U.S. Pat.* 2711403; *Zbl.* 6810 (1956).

240. G. Kamai and V. A. Kukhtin, *Zh. obshch. khim.* **28,** 939 (1958).

241. L. A. R. Hall and C. N. Stephens, *J. Amer. Chem. Soc.* **78,** 2565 (1956).

242. N. P. Bogonotseva, *Uch. zap. Kazan. gos. univ.* **116,** bk. 2, 71 (1956).

243. A. N. Pudovik, L. P. Shchelkina and L. A. Bashilova, *Zh. obshch. khim.* **27,** 2367 (1957).

244. C. J. Albisetti and M. J. Hogsed, *U. S. Pat.* 2671106; *Chem. Abstr.* **49,** 2482 (1955).

245. G. Kamai and O. N. Belorossova, *Izv. Akad. nauk SSSR, Otdel. khim. nauk,* 191 (1947).

246. *Dutch Pat.* 69357; *Chem. Abstr.* **47,** 143 (1953).

247. *Brit. Pat.* 660918; *Chem. Abstr.* **46,** 8145 (1952).

248. B. A. Ackerman, T. A. Jordan and D. Swern, *J. Amer. Chem. Soc.* **78,** 6025 (1956).

249. H. J. Jacobson, M. J. Griffin and S. Palis, *J. Amer. Chem. Soc.* **79,** 2608 (1957).

250. G. Kamai and V. A. Kukhtin, *Zh. obshch. khim.* **24,** 1855 (1954).

251. F. Johnston, *Brit. Pat.* 695782; *Chem. Abstr.* **48,** 10054 (1954).

252. A. N. Pudovik, *Zh. obshch. khim.* **27,** 2755 (1957).

253. D. C. Rowlands, *U.S. Pat.* 2728791; *Ref. zh. khim.* ref. 2204 (1958).

254. P. I. Alimov and I. V. Cheplanova, *Izv. Kazan. fil. Akad. nauk SSSR, ser. khim.* **4,** 43 (1957).

255. *Khimiya i primeneniye fosfororganicheskikh soyedinenii. Trud. Pervoi konf. (The Chemistry and Applications of Organophosphorus compounds. Proc. First. Conf.)* p. 248, Acad. Sci. U. S. S. R. (1957).

256. A. V. Kukhtin, *Dokl. Akad. nauk SSSR,* **121,** 466 (1958).

257. N. Kreutzkamp and H. Kayser, *Liebig's Ann.* **609,** 39 (1957).

258. A. N. Pudovik and L. G. Biktimirova, *Zh. obshch. khim.* **28,** 1496 (1958).

259. T. Yanagawa, S. Hashimoto and J. Furukawa, Cited in *Ref. zh. khim.* ref. 61026 (1958).

260. E. Plueddermann, *U. S. Pat.* 2612514; *Zbl.* 6848 (1954).

261. H. Tolkmith, *U.S. Pat.* 2693483; *Chem. Abstr.* **49,** 9867 (1955).

262. A. Einhorn and C. Frey, *Ber. dtsch. Chem. Ges.* **27,** 2455 (1894).

263. G. M. Kosolapoff, *Organophosphorus Compounds,* p. 261, New York (1950).

264. C. L. Moyle, *U. S. Pat.* 2552576; *Chem. Abstr.* **45,** 9080 (1951).

265. G. Shrader, *Usp. khim.* **22,** 712 (1953).

266. S. S. Kukalenko and N. N. Mel'nikov, *Zh. obshch. khim.* **28,** 157 (1958).

267. E. K. Fields, *J. Amer. Chem. Soc.* **78,** 5821 (1956).

268. C. L. Moyle, *U.S. Pat.* 2552575; *Chem. Abstr.* **45,** 9080 (1951).

269. N. I. Rizpolozhenskii and M. A. Zvereva, *Izv. Akad. nauk SSSR, Otdel. khim. nauk,* 358 (1959).

270. G. KAMAI and YE. A. GERASIMOVA, *Trud. Kazan. khim.* — *Izkh. inst. im. S. M. Kirova* **23**, 138 (1957).

271. J. L. WINKLE, E. R. BELL and R. C. MORRIS, *U.S. Pat.* 2712029; *Chem. Abstr.* **51**, 470 (1957).

272. A. F. McKAY, R. A. B. BANNARD, R. O. BRAUN and R. L. BENNESS, *J. Amer. Chem. Soc.* **76**, 3546 (1954).

273. H. REINHARDT, D. BIANCHI and D. MÖLLE, *Ber. dtsch. Chem. Ges.* **90**, 1656 (1957).

274. A. D. F. TOY and K. H. RATTENBURY, *U.S. Pat.* 2714100; *Chem. Abstr.* **49**, 14380 (1955).

275. D. HARMAN and A. R. STILES, *U.S. Pat.* 2632756; *Chem. Abstr.* **48**, 2760 (1954); *Zbl.* 5897 (1955).

276. K. C. KENNARD and C. S. HAMILTON, *J. Amer. Chem. Soc.* **77**, 1156 (1955).

277. J. KENNEDY and K. G. FICKEN, *J. Appl. Chem.* **8**, 465 (1958).

278. W. J. JONES, W. C. DAVIES, S. T. BOWDEN, C. EDWARDS, W. E. DAVIS and L. H. THOMAS, *J. Chem. Soc.* 1446 (1947).

279. L. MAIER, D. SEIFERTH, F. G. A. STONE and E. G. ROCHOW, *Z. Naturforsch.* **12**b, 263 (1957); *J. Amer. Chem. Soc.* **79**, 5884 (1957).

280. H. HARTMANN, C. BEERMANN and H. CREMPIK, *Angew. Chem.* **67**, 233 (1955).

281. H. HARTMANN, C. BEERMANN and H. CREMPIK, *Z. anorg. Chem.* **287**, 261 (1956).

282. D. E. WORRAL, *J. Amer. Chem. Soc.* **52**, 2933 (1930).

283. W. B. McCORMACK, *U. S. Pat.* 2663737; *Chem. Abstr.* **49**, 7601 (1955).

284. W. B. McCORMACK, *U. S. Pat.* 2663738; *Chem. Abstr.* **49**, 7602 (1955).

285. J. B. CONANT, J. B. S. BRAVERMANN and R. E. HUSSEY, *J. Amer. Chem. Soc.* **45**, 165 (1923).

286. A. HOFMANN, *Liebig's Ann. Suppl.* **1**, 275 (1861).

287. W. POPE and C. S. GIBSON, *J. Chem. Soc.* **101**, 735 (1912).

288. J. MEISENHEIMER and co-workers, *Liebig's Ann.* **449**, 213 (1926).

289. E. ROTHSTEIN, R. W. SAVILLE and P. E. HORN, *J. Chem. Soc.* 3994 (1953).

290. G. KAMAI and L. A. KHISMATULINA, *Zh. obshch. khim.* **26**, 3426 (1956).

291. F. RAMIRES and S. DERSHOWITZ, *J. Org. Chem.* **22**, 41 (1957).

292. M. M. RAUHUT *et al.*, *J. Amer. Chem. Soc.* **81**, 1103 (1959).

293. P. A. ROSSIISKAYA and M. I. KABACHNIK, *Izv. Akad. nauk SSSR, Otdel. khim. nauk*, 509 (1947).

294. R. M. CAVEN, *J. Chem. Soc.* **81**, 1368 (1902).

295. B. HOLMSTED, *Acta physiolog. Scand.* **25**, Suppl. 90 (1951).

296. J. WALCZYNSKA, *Roczniki Chem.* **6**, 110 (1926).

297. B. C. SAUNDERS, G. J. STACEY, F. WILD and J. WILDING, *J. Chem. Soc.* 699 (1948).

298. W. GERRARD, *J. Chem. Soc.* 1464 (1940).

299. H. R. GAMRATH, *U. S. Pat.* 2750399; *Chem. Abstr.* **51**, 458 (1957).

300. M. YA. KRAFT and V. V. KATYSHKINA, *Dokl. Akad. nauk SSSR*, **86**, 725 (1952).

301. V. V. KATYSHKINA and M. YA. KRAFT, *Zh. obshch. khim.* **26**, 3060 (1956).

302. V. V. KORSHAK, I. A. GRIBOVA and M. A. ANDREYEVA, *Izv. Akad. nauk SSSR, Otdel. khim. nauk*, 880 (1958).

302a. I. K. RUBTSOVA and R. D. ZHILINA, *Zh. prikl. khim.* **32**, 2604 (1959).

303. H. ZENFTMANN *et al.*, *Brit. Pat.* 644467 and 651656; *Chem. Abstr.* **45**, 3862, 9081 (1951).

304. V. AUGER and P. DUPUIS, *Compt. rend.* **146**, 1151 (1908).

305. M. GUGGENHEIM, *U.S. Pat.* 1960184; *Chem. Abstr.* **28**, 4539 (1934).

306. E. C. BRITTON. *U.S. Pat.* 2033918; *Chem. Abstr.* **30**, 2988 (1936).

307. M. RAPP, *Liebig's Ann.* **224**, 156 (1884).

308. K. W. ROSENMUND and H. VOGT, *Arch. Pharm.* **281**, 317 (1943).

309. R. ANSCHÜTZ and G. D. MOORE, *Liebig's Ann.* **239**, 314 (1887).

310. R. ANSCHÜTZ and R. ANSPACH, *Liebig's Ann.* **346**, 312 (1906).

311. R. ANSCHÜTZ and H. MEHRING, *Liebig's Ann.* **346**, 300 (1906).

312. R. ANSCHÜTZ and A. ROBITSEK, *Liebig's Ann.* **346**, 323 (1906).

313. R. ANSCHÜTZ, A ROBITSEK and F. SCHMITZ, *Liebig's Ann.* **346**, 330 (1906).

314. R. ANSCHÜTZ, E. SCHROEDER, E. WEBER and R. ANSPACH, *Liebig's Ann.* **346**, 341 (1906).

315. G. DISCALZO, *Gazz. chim. ital.* **15**, 278 (1885).

316. S. L. BASS, *U.S. Pat.* 2071017; *Zbl.* (I), 4848 (1937).

317. E. C. BRITTON and S. L. BASS, *U.S. Pat.* 2117290; *Zbl.* (II), 1312, (1938).

318. E. C. BRITTON and S. L. BASS, *U.S. Pat.* 2117291; *Zbl.* (II), 1312 (1938).

319. P. KUNZ, *Ber. dtsch. Chem. Ges.* **27**, 2559 (1894).

320. R. WOLFENSTEIN, *Ber. dtsch. Chem. Ges.* **20**, 1966 (1887).

321. F. GUICHARD, *Ber. dtsch. Chem. Ges.* **32**, 1572 (1899).

322. R. B. FOX, *J. Amer. Chem. Soc.* **72**, 4147 (1950).

323. M. S. KARASCH, E. V. JENSEN and S. WEINHOUSE, *J. Org. Chem.* **14**, 429 (1949).

324. L. I. ZAKHARKIN and O. YU. OKHLOBYSTIN, *Dokl. Akad. nauk SSSR*, **116**, 236 (1957).

325. O. YU. OKHLOBYSTIN and L. I. ZAKHARKIN, *Izv. Akad. nauk SSSR, Otdel. khim. nauk*, 1006 (1958).

326. A. SACCO, *Atti accad. naz. Lincei*, **11**, 101 (1951).

327. A. YA. YAKUBOVICH, V. A. GINSBURG and S. P. MAKAROV, *Dokl. Akad. nauk SSSR*, **71**, 303 (1950).

328. A. YA. YAKUBOVICH and V. A. GINSBURG, *Zh. obshch. khim.* **22**, 1534 (1952).

329. M. S. KARASCH, E. V. JENSEN and W. H. URRY, *J. Amer. Chem. Soc.* **67**, 1864 (1945).

330. V. A. GINSBURG and A. YA. YAKUBOVICH, *Zh. obshch. khim.* **28**, 728 (1958).

331. V. A. GINSBURG and H. F. PRIVEZENTSEVA, *Zh. obshch. khim.* **28**, 736 (1958).

332. C. WALLING, *U.S. Pat.* 2437796; *Chem. Abstr.* **42**, 4199 (1948).

333. I. P. KOMKOV, S. Z. IVIN and K. V. KARAVANOV, *Zh. obshch. khim.* **28**, 2963 (1958).

334. A. I. RAZUMOV, O. A. MUKHACHEVA and SIM-DO-KHEN, *Izv. Akad. nauk SSSR, Otdel. khim. nauk*, 894 (1952).

335. A. MICHAELIS, *Liebig's Ann.* **181**, 265 (1876).

336. A. MICHAELIS, *Liebig's Ann.* **293**, 193 (1896).

337. A. MICHAELIS, *Liebig's Ann.* **294**, 1 (1896).

338. A. YE. ARBUSOV, *Zh. russk. khim. obshch.* **42**, 398 (1910).

339. H. LECOQ, *Bull. soc. chim. Belg.* **42**, 199 (1933).

340. J. LINDNER, W. WIRTH and B. ZAUNBAUER, *Monatsh. Chem.* **70**, 1 (1937).

341. G. KAMAI, *Zh. obshch. khim.* **2**, 524 (1932).

342. W. T. DYE, *J. Amer. Chem. Soc.* **70**, 2595 (1948).

343. B. BUCHNER and L. B. LOCKHART, *J. Amer. Chem. Soc.* **73**, 755 (1951).

344. YE. L. GEFTER, *Avt. svid. (U.S.S.R. Pat.)* 107266; *Byull. isobr.* **6**, 25 (1957).

345. YE. L. GEFTER, *Z. obshch. khim.* **28**, 1338 (1958).

346. G. KAMAI, *Z. obshch. khim.* **4**, 192 (1934).

347. A. SCHENK and A. MICHAELIS, *Ber. dtsch. Chem. Ges.* **21**, 1497 (1888).

348. P. MELCHIKER, *Ber. dtsch. Chem. Ges.* **31**, 2915 (1898).

349. H. H. HATT, *J. Chem. Soc.* 776 (1933).

350. J. LINDNER and M. STRECKER, *Monatsh. Chem.* **53**, 274 (1929).

351. M. I. KABACHNIK and P. A. ROSSIISKAYA, *Izv. Akad. nauk SSSR, Otdel. khim. nauk*, 515 (1946).

352. L. Z. SOBOROVSKII and YU. M. ZINOV'EV, *Zh. obshch. khim.* **24**, 516 (1954).

353. W. FOSSEK, *Monatsh. Chem.* **7**, 20 (1886).

354. J. WELLER, *Ber. dtsch. Chem. Ges.* **21**, 1492 (1888).

355. E. ZEIBNITZ and K. NAUMANN, *Chem. Tech.* **3**, 5 (1951).

356. H. Schnell, *Angew. Chem.* **68,** 633 (1956).

357. A. Ye. Chichibabin, *Osnovnyye nachala organicheskoi khimii (The Fundamentals of Organic Chemistry)*, Vol. 1, Goskhimizdat, Moscow/Leningrad (1953).

358. A. I. Lun'yak, *Zh. russk. khim. obshch.* **36,** 301 (1904).

359. H. Pauly and W. Schans, *Ber. dtsch. Chem. Ges.* **56,** 979 (1923).

360. J. E. Johnson and D. R. Mussel, *U.S. Pat.* 2538725; *Chem. Abstr.* **45,** 4412 (1951).

361. R. P. Perkins and F. Bryner, *Ger. (West) Pat.* 905977; *Zbl.* 5410 (1954).

362. A. Dianin, *Zh. russk. khim. obshch.* **23,** 488 (1891).

363. A. Russanow, *Ber. dtsch. Chem. Ges.* **22,** 1943 (1889).

364. Th. Zinke, *Liebig's Ann.* **363,** 246 (1908).

365. A. Michaelis, *Liebig's Ann.* **315,** 92, 97 (1901).

366. P. W. Morgan and B. C. Herr, *J. Amer. Chem. Soc.* **74,** 4536 (1952).

367. B. A. Zhubanov, *Thesis*, Moscow (1953).

368. G. S. Kolesnikov, V. V. Korshak and B. A. Zhubanov, *Tez. dokl. IX konf. po obshch. vop. khim. i fiz. vysokomolekulyar. soyedinenii (Abstr. IXth Conf. on General Problems of Chem. and Phys. of High-Molecular-Weight Compounds)*, p. 12, Moscow (1956).

369. G. S. Forbes and H. H. Anderson, *J. Amer. Chem. Soc.* **62,** 761 (1940).

370. H. H. Anderson, *J. Amer. Chem. Soc.* **64,** 1757 (1942).

371. G. S. Forbes and H. H. Anderson, *J. Amer. Chem. Soc.* **65,** 2271 (1943).

372. A. C. Haven, *J. Amer. Chem. Soc.* **78,** 842 (1956).

373. A. Hofmann, *J. Amer. Chem. Soc.* **43,** 1684 (1921).

374. A. Hofmann, *J. Amer. Chem. Soc.* **52,** 2995 (1930).

375. W. A. Reeves, F. F. Flin and J. D. Guthrie, *J. Amer. Chem. Soc.* **77,** 3923 (1955).

376. H. S. Bloch, *U. S. Pat.* 2570512; *Chem. Abstr.* **46,** 3555 (1952).

377. D. H. Chadwick, *U. S. Pat.* 2582817; *Chem. Abstr.* **46,** 7581 (1952).

378. A. Ye. Arbuzov and P. I. Rakov, *Izv. Akad. nauk SSSR, Otdel. khim. nauk*, 237 (1950).

379. A. Ye. Arbuzov and N. A. Rasumova, *Izv. Akad. nauk SSSR, Otdel. khim. nauk*, 187 (1956).

380. Ye. L. Gefter and M. I. Kabachnik, *Izv. Akad. nauk SSSR, Otdel. khim. nauk*, 194 (1957).

381. A. Ye. Arbuzov and V. M. Zoroastrova, *Izv. Akad. nauk SSSR, Otdel. khim. nauk*, 779 (1952).

382. A. Ye. Arbuzov and V. M. Zoroastrova, *Izv. Akad. nauk SSSR, Otdel. khim. nauk*, 536 (1951).

383. A. Ye. Arbuzov, V. M. Zoroastrova and N. I. Rizpolozhenskii, *Izv. Akad. nauk SSSR, Otdel. khim. nauk*, 208 (1948).

384. A. Ye. Arbuzov and M. M. Azanovskaya, *Izv. Akad. nauk SSSR, Otdel. khim. nauk*, 473 (1949).

385. H. G. Cock, H. McCombie and B. C. Saunders, *J. Chem. Soc.* 873 (1945).

386. B. A. Arbuzov and V. S. Vinogradova, *Izv. Akad. nauk SSSR, Otdel. khim. nauk*, 617 (1947).

387. O. Foss, *Acta Chem. Scand.* **1,** 8 (1947).

388. B. A. Arbuzov and V. S. Vinogradova, *Dokl. Akad. nauk SSSR*, **83,** 79 (1952).

389. R. W. Yohng., *J. Amer. Chem. Soc.* **75,** 4620 (1953).

390. A. Ye. Arbuzov and M. M. Azanovskaya, *Izv. Akad. nauk SSSR, Otdel. khim. nauk*, 544 (1951).

391. A. Ye. Arbuzov and F. G. Valetova, *Izv. Akad. nauk SSSR, Otdel. khim. nauk*, 801 (1952).

392. W. Gerrard, *J. Chem. Soc.* 85 (1944).

393. F. R. Atherton, H. T. Howard and A. R. Todd, *J. Chem. Soc.* 1106 (1948).

394. A. YE. ARBUZOV, *Izv. Akad. nauk SSSR, Otdel. khim. nauk*, 226 (1946).

394. A. YE. ARBUZOV, *Izv. Akad. nauk SSSR, Otdel. khim. nauk*, 226 (1946).

395. A. YE. ARBUZOV and V. M. ZOROASTROVA, *Izv. Akad. nauk SSSR, Otdel. khim. nauk*, 770 (1952).

396. H. J. LUCAS, F. W. MITCHELL and C. N. SCULLY, *J. Amer. Chem. Soc.* **72**, 5491 (1950).

397. A. YE. ARBUZOV and V. M. ZOROASTROVA, *Izv. Akad. nauk SSSR, Otdel. khim. nauk*, 789 (1952).

398. P. A. ROSSIISKAYA and M. I. KABACHNIK, *Izv. Akad. nauk SSSR, Otdel. khim. nauk*, 509 (1947).

399. A. F. McKAY, R. O. BRAUN and G. R. VAVASOUR, *J. Amer. Chem. Soc.* **74**, 5540 (1952).

400. R. A. B. BANNARD, J. R. GILPIN, G. R. VAVASOUR and A. F. MCKAY, *Can. J. Chem.* **31**, 976 (1953).

401. V. V. KORSHAK, I. A. GRIBOVA and V. K. SHITIKOV, *Izv. Akad. nauk SSSR, Otdel. khim, nauk*, 631 (1957).

402. B. A. ARBUZOV, M. K. SAIKINA and V. M. ZOROASTROVA, *Izv. Akad. nauk*, 1046 (1957).

403. B. A. ARBUZOV, K. V. NIKONOROV, O. N. FEDOTOVA, G. M. VINOKUROVA and Z. G. SHISHOVA, *Dokl. Akad. nauk SSSR*, **91**, 817 (1953).

404. A. YE. ARBUZOV and V. M. ZOROASTROVA, *Izv. Akad. nauk SSSR, Otdel. khim. nauk*, 453 (1952).

405. B. A. ARBUZOV, K. V. NIKONOROV and Z. G. SHISHOVA, *Izv. Akad. nauk SSSR, Otdel. khim. nauk*, 823 (1954).

406. H. R. GAMRATH and R. E. HATTON, *U.S. Pat.* 2661366; *Zbl.* 8487 (1956).

407. T. YAMASAKI and T. SATO, *Zbl.* 7530 (1956).

408. A YE. ARBUZOV and N. A. RAZUMOV, *Dokl. Akad. nauk SSSR*, **97**, 445 (1954).

409. A. D. F. TOY, *U.S. Pat.* 2382622; *Chem. Abstr.* **40**, 604 (1946).

410. M. A. SOKOLOVSKII and P. M. ZAVLIN, *Avd. svid.* *(U.S.S.R. Pat.)* 116878, 119180 and 121442; *Byull. isobr.* **12**, 28 (1958); **8**, 10 (1959); **15**, 24 (1959).

411. N. P. GRECHKIN, *Izv. Akad. nauk SSSR, Otdel. khim. nauk*, 538 (1956).

412. M. GOERING and K. NIEDENZU, *Ber. dtsch. Chem. Ges.* **89**, 768 (1956).

413. G. M. KOSOLAPOFF, *Organophosphorus Compounds*, p. 310, New York (1950).

414. G. M. KOSOLAPOFF, *Organophosphorus Compounds*, p. 311, New York (1950).

415. G. M. KOSOLAPOFF, *Organophosphorus Compounds*, p. 312, New York (1950).

416. J. HEYNA and W. NOLL, *Ger. (West) Pat.* 854651; *Zbl.* 4452 (1953).

417. R. P. PARKER, D. R. SEEGER and E. KUH, *U.S. Pat.* 2606901; *Chem. Abstr.* **47**, 5424 (1953).

418. G. M. KOSOLAPOFF, *Organophosphorus Compounds*, p. 315, New York (1950).

419. G. M. KOSOLAPOFF, *Organophosphorus Compounds*, p. 314, New York (1950).

420. H. BESTIAN, *Liebig's Ann.* **566**, 210 (1950).

421. M. SEMONSKY and A. CERNY, *Chem. Listy*, **47**, 469 (1953).

422. R. P. PARKER, D. R. SEEGER and E. KUH, *U.S. Pat.* 2606900; *Chem. Abstr.* **47**, 5424 (1953).

423. K. A. KORNEV and L. D. PROTSENKO, *Ukrain. khim. zh.* **22**, 782 (1956).

424. R. P. PARKER, D. R. DEEGER and E. KUH, *U.S. Pat.* 2606902; *Chem. Abstr.* **47**, 5424 (1953).

425. R. KLEMENT and O. KOCH, *Ber. dtsch. Chem. Ges.* **87**, 333 (1954).

426. L. F. AUDRIETH and A. D. F. TOY, *J. Amer. Chem. Soc.* **64**, 1553 (1942).

427. G. M. KOSOLAPOFF, *Organophosphorus Compounds*, p. 313, New York (1950).

428. A. ABBEY, *Brit. Pat.* 673877; *Specifications of Inventions*, 5739 (1949).

429. C. L. MOYLE, *U. S. Pat.* 2552577; *Chem. Abstr.* **45**, 9080 (1951).

430. E. Kuh and D. R. Seeger, *U.S. Pat.* 2670347; *Chem. Abstr.* **49**, 2481 (1955).
431. A. C. Buck, J. D. Bartleson and H. P. Lankelma, *J. Amer. Chem. Soc.* **70**, 744 (1948).
432. G. Wise and H. P. Lankelma, *J. Amer. Chem. Soc.* **74**, 529 (1952).
433. R. Rätz, *J. Amer. Chem. Soc.* **77**, 4170 (1955).
434. G. M. Kosolapoff, *Organophosphorus Compounds*, p. 316, New York (1950).
435. G. M. Kosolapoff, *Organophosphorus Compounds*, p. 317, New York (1950).
436. D. C. Morrison, *J. Amer. Chem. Soc.* **73**, 5896 (1951).
437. M. I. Kabachnik, *Izv. Akad. nauk SSSR, Otdel. khim. nauk*, 219 (1948).
438. A. Razumov and O. Mukhacheva, *Zh. obchch. khim.* **26**, 1436 (1956).
439. W. Jones, W. Davies and W. Dyke, *J. Phys. Chem.* **37**, 583 (1933).
440. G. M. Kosolapoff and R. Watson, *J. Amer Chem. Soc.* **73**, 4101 (1951).
441. M. I. Kabachnik and Ye. S. Shepeleva, *Izv. Akad. nauk SSSR, Otdel. khim. nauk*, 862 (1953).
442. D. E. Warren, *Plastics (Chicago)*, **7**, No. 1, 39, 71 (1947).
443. A. D. F. Toy, *Chem. Eng. News*, **25**, No. 28, 2030 (1947).
444. A. D. F. Toy, *Mod. Plastics*, **24**, No. 12, 226 (1947).
445. P. D. Bartlett and R. Altschul, *J. Amer. Chem. Soc.* **67**, 816 (1945).
446. W. F. Bruksch and L. H. Howland, *U. S. Pat.* 2583356; *Chem. Abstr.* **46**, 3800 (1952).
447. H. W. Coover and J. B. Dickey, *U. S. Pat.* 2636027; *Chem. Abstr.* **47**, 11808 (1953).
448. A. D. F. Toy, *U. S. Pat.* 2485677; *Chem. Abstr.* **44**, 2284 (1950).
449. A. D. F. Toy, *U. S. Pat.* 2497637; *Chem. Abstr.* **44**, 4287 (1950).
450. A. D. F. Toy, *U. S. Pat.* 2497638; *Chem. Abstr.* **44**, 4287 (1950).
451. A. D. F. Toy, *U. S. Pat.* 2538810; *Chem. Abstr.* **45**, 3654 (1951).
452. A. D. F. Toy and L. Brown, *U. S. Pat.* 2586884; *Chem. Abstr.* **46**, 4278 (1952).
453. A. D. F. Toy and L. Brown, *U. S. Pat.* 2586885; *Chem. Abstr.* **46**, 5888 (1952).
454. T. C. Baker, *U. S. Pat.* 2680105; *Chem. Abstr.* **48**, 11110 (1954).
455. *Chem. Week*, **77**, No. 12 (pt. II), 355 (1955).
456. J. G. Frick, J. W. Weaver, R. L. Arceneaux and M. F. Stanbury, *J. Polymer Sci.* **20**, No. 95, 307 (1956).
457. A. A. Berlin and A. M. Sladkov, *Vysokomolekulyarnyye soyedineniya*, **12**, 63 (1952).
458. Sh. A. Karapetyan, *Priroda*, **46**, No. 8, 65 (1957).
459. R. Kh. Freidlina and Ye. I. Vasil'eva, *Khim. nauka i prom.* **2**, No. 1, 2 (1957).
460. D. A. Kardashev, *Vysokomolekulyarnyye soyedineniya*, **5**, 9 (1946).
461. D. A. Kardashev, N. S. Leznov and V. P. Nuzhdina, *Khim. prom.* **2**, 5 (1945).
462. M. M. Koton, P. A. Mulyar and N. M. Kamenetskaya, *Zh. prikl. khim.* **29**, 311 (1956).
463. V. P. Golendeyev, *Uch. zap. Stalingrad. gos. ped. inst.* 1, 128 (1948).
464. *Metody vysokomolekulyarnoi organicheskoi khimii (Methods of high-molecular-weight organic chemistry)*, Vol. 1; V. V. Korshak, *Obshchiye metody sinteza vysokomolekuly-arnykh soyedinenii (Common methods of synthesis of high-molecular-weight-compounds)*, Moscow (1953).
465. V. V. Korshak, *Khimiya vysokomolekulyarnykh soyedinenii (The chemistry of high-molecular-weight compounds)*, Acad. Sci. SSSR, Moscow/Leningrad (1950).
466. R. W. Lindsey, *U. S. Pat.* 2439214; *Chem. Abstr.* **42**, 4795 (1948).
467. H. W. Coover and J. B. Dickey, *U.S. Pat.* 2743261; *Ref. zh. khim.*, ref. 62874 (1958).
468. C. S. Marvel and J. C. Wright, *J. Polymer Sci.* **8**, 255 (1952).
469. Ye. L. Gefter, A. B. Pashkov and Ye. I. Lyustgarten, *Khim. nauka i prom.* **3**, 825 (1958).

470. C. L. ARCUS and R. J. S. MATTHEWS, *J. Chem. Soc.* 4607 (1956).

471. E. C. BRITTON, H. B. MARSHALL and W. J. LE FEVRE, *U.S. Pat.* 2186360; *Chem. Abstr.* **34**, 3405 (1940).

472. J. W. HAWORTH, *Brit. Pat.* 675783; *Chem. Abstr.* **46**, 11778 (1952).

473. G. KAMAI and V. A. KUKHTIN, *Zh. obshch. khim.* **25**, 1932 (1955).

474. A. D. F. TOY and K. H. RATTENBURY, *U.S. Pat.* 2735789; *Chem. Abstr.* **50**, 9034 (1956).

475. *Chem. Week*, **79**, No. 24, 46 (1956).

476. R. HART, *Ind. chim. belge*, **21**, 1053, 1193, 1309 (1956); **22**, 39 (1957).

477. M. IMOTO, *J. Soc. org. synth. chem. Japan*, **14**, 10 (1956); *Khim. i tekh. polimer.* **2**, 119 (1957).

478. F. EIRICH and H. MARK, *J. Colloid Sci.* **11**, 748 (1956).

479. E. H. IMMERGUT and H. MARK, *Makromol. Chem.* **18—19**, 322 (1956).

480. G. NATTA et al., *Angew. Chem.* **68**, 393 (1956); *Chim. e Ind.* **38**, 751 (1956); **39**, 275 (1957) and others; *Khim. i tekh. polimer.* **5**, 139 (1957).

481. A. N. PRAVEDNIKOV and YU. S. LIPATOV, *Metody polucheniya i svoistva privitykh i blok-polimerov (The methods of obtaining and the properties of graft and block copolymers)*, Moscow (1958).

482. G. NATTA et al., *Chim. e Ind.* **40**, 813 (1958).

483. YE. B. TROSTYANSKAYA, I. P. LOSEV and A. S. TEVLINA, *Zh. anal. khim.* **11**, 578 (1956).

484. I. P. LOSEV, YE. B. TROSTYANSKAYA and A. S. TEVLINA, *Avt. svid. (U.S.S.R. Pat.)* 118207; *Byull. isobr.* **4**, 37 (1959).

485. E. N. WALSH, T. M. BECK and A. D. F. TOY, *J. Amer Chem. Soc.* **78**, 4455 (1956).

486. G. M. KOSOLAPOFF. *U. S. Pat.* 2495108; *Chem. Abstr.* **44**, 7091 (1950).

487. D. E. KVALNES and N. O. BRACE, *U.S. Pat.* 2691567; *Chem. Abstr.* **49**, 2090 (1955).

488. ASIDA, Cited in *Ref. zh. khim.*, ref. 76357 (1956).

489. V. MOTOZATO et al., *J. Chem. Soc. Japan (Ind. Chem. Sect.)* **59**, 479 (1956).

490. G. C. DAUL, J. D. REID and R. M. REINHARDT, *Industr. Engng. Chem.* **46**, 1042 (1954).

491. I. JONES, *Brit. Plastics*, **16**, 77 (1944).

492. A. KATCHALSKI and H. EISENBERG, *Nature (London)*, **166**, 267 (1950).

493. R. E. FERREL, H. S. OLKOTT and H. FRAENKEL—CONRAT, *J. Amer Chem. Soc.* **70**, 2101 (1948).

494. G. C. DAUL and J. D. REID, *U. S. Pat.* 2609360; *Chem. Abstr.* **47**, 920 (1953).

495. R. LOHMAR, J. W. SLOAN and C. E. RIST, *J. Amer. Chem. Soc.* **72**, 5717 (1950).

496. H. VOGEL, *Ber. dtsch. Chem. Ges.* **72**, 2052 (1939).

497. P. KARRER, H. KOENIG and E. USTERI, *Helv. Chim. Acta*, **26**, 1296 (1943).

498. H. K. BARRENSCHEEN and J. PANY, *Biochem. Z.* **21**, 364 (1930).

499. J. KERB, *Biochem. Z.* **100**, 3 (1919).

500. H. PRINGSHEIM and K. GOLDSTEIN, *Ber. dtsch. Chem. Ges.* **56**, 1520 (1923).

501. P. KOETS, *Proc. Acad. Sci. Amsterdam*, **38**, 63 (1935).

502. P. KOETS, *Kolloid-Beihefte*, **47**, 100 (1937); *Chem. Abstr.* **32**, 1543 (1938).

503. A. B. FOSTER and W. G. OVEREND, *Usp. khim.* **27**, 891 (1958).

504. R. W. LITTLE, *Flameproofing Textile Fabrics*, New York (1947).

505. C. H. MUENDEL and W. A. SELKE, *Industr. Engng. Chem.* **47**, 374 (1955).

506. J. D. REID and L. W. MAZZENO, *Industr. Engng. Chem.* **41**, 2828 (1949).

507. J. D. GUTHRIE, *Industr. Engng. Chem.* **44**, 2187 (1952).

508. J. D. REID, L. W. MAZZENO and E. M. BURAS, *Industr. Engng. Chem.* **41**, 2831 (1949).

509. A. C. NUESSLE, F. M. FORD, W. P. HALL and H. L. LIPPERT, *Textile Res. J.* **26**, 32 (1956).

510. J. F. JURGENS, J. D. REID and J. D. GUTHRIE, *Textile Res. J.* **18**, 42 (1948).
511. R. S. BABIARZ and W. P. HALL, *Can. Pat.* 517317; *Ref. zh. khim.* ref. 55640 (1947).
512. M. ORZEL *Polish Pat.* 35682; *Ref. zh. khim.* ref. 45849 (1957).
513. M. ORZEL and L. WIERZBOWSKA, Cited in *Ref. zh. khim.* ref. 55604 (1957).
514. C. S. MARVEL and B. R. BLUESTEIN, *J. Polymer Sci.* **6**, 351 (1951).
515. R. F. SCHWENKER and E. PASCU, *Industr. Engng. Chem.* **50**, 91 (1958).
516. G. C. DAUL and J. R. REID, *U. S. Pat.* 2583549; *Zbl.* 2496 (1954); *U.S. Pat.* 2592544; *Chem. Abstr.* **46**, 7768 (1952).
517. *Austral. Pat.* 164917; *Ref. zh. khim.* ref. 59784 (1956).
518. T. KRESSMANN and F. TYE, *Brit. Pat.* 726925; *Zbl.* 4578 (1956).
519. M. BAER, *U. S. Pat.* 2750351; *Ref. zh. khim.* ref. 41604 (1958).
520. W. FOSSEK, *Monatsh. Chem.* **5**, 121, 627 (1884); **7**, 20 (1886).
521. R. W. UPSON, *U. S. Pat.* 2599501; *Chem. Abstr.* **46**, 8416 (1952).
522. C. S. MARVEL and J. C. WRIGHT, *J. Polymer Sci.* **8**, 495 (1952).
523. S. YOLLES, *U. S. Pat.* 2829137; *Chem. Abstr.* **52**, 13606 (1958).
524. J. SCHUBERT, *Ann. Rev. Phys. Chem.* **5**, 413 (1954).
525. W. WOOD, *Ger. (West) Pat.* 930415; *Ref. zh. khim.* ref. 66676 (1956).
526. T. KRESSMAN and F. TYE, *Brit. Pat.* 726918; *Zbl.* 4291 (1956); *Ger. (West) Pat.* 947206; *Ref. zh. khim.* ref. 64829 (1957).
527. A. B. PASHKOV, M. A. SOKOLINSKII, V. S. TITOV, M. I. ITKINA and YE L. GEFTER, *Avt. svid. (U. S. S. R. Pat.)* 113041; *Byull. isobr.* **5**, 100 (1958).
528. J. KENNEDY and R. V. DAVIES, *Chem. and Ind.* 378 (1956).
529. M. E. KUPERY, *U. S. Pat.* 2692876; *Chem. Abstr.* **49**, 2119 (1955).
530. M. E. KUPERY, *U. S. Pat.* 2723971; *Zbl.* 1308 (1957).
531. E. C. SHOKAL, *U. S. Pat.* 2732367; *Ref. zh. khim.* ref. 3110 (1958).
532. G. D. MARTIN, *U. S. Pat.* 2375572; *Chem. Abstr.* **40**, 6875 (1946).
533. G. D. MARTIN, *U. S. Pat.* 2382497; *Chem. Abstr.* **39**, 5548 (1945).
534. G. D. MARTIN, *U. S. Pat.* 2387521; *Chem. Abstr.* **40**, 5595 (1946).
535. W. H. SMYERS and D. W. YOUNG, *U.S. Pat.* 2494592; *Chem. Abstr.* **44**, 3741 (1950).
536. E. C. HUGHES, H. E. ALFORD and J. D. BARTESON, *U.S. Pat.* 2695271; *Ref. zh. khim.* ref. 51993 (1956).
537. J. M. MUSSELMAN, *Can. Pat.* 511892; *Ref. zh. khim.*, ref. 79158 (1956).
538. S. A. MILLER and M. KAUFMAN, *Brit. Pat.* 706577; *Specifications of Inventions* 6066 (1954).
539. *Chem. Eng. News*, **35**, No. 37, 6 (1957).
540. *Brit. Pat.* 720566; *Ref. zh. khim.* ref. 13014 (1958).
541. B. W. LEW. *U. S. Pat.* 2726177; *Chem. Abstr.* **50**, 5330 (1956).
542. YE. L. GEFTER and L. A. RODIVILOVA, *Avt. svid. (U.S.S.R. Pat.)* 114022; *Byull. isobr.* **7**, 48 (1958); *Plastich. massy*, **2**, 35 (1959).
543. D. E. KVALNES and N. O. BRACE, *U. S. Pat.* 2691566; *Chem. Abstr.* **49**, 2090 (1955).
544. W. B. McCORMACK, *U. S. Pat.* 2671077; *Chem. Abstr.* **48**, 6737 (1954).
545. W. B. McCORMACK, *U. S. Pat.* 2671079; *Chem. Abstr.* **48**, 6738 (1954).
546. G. M. KOSOLAPOFF, *J. Amer. Chem. Soc.* **77**, 6658 (1955).
547. STAMICARBON, *Dutch Pat.* 75705; *Chem. Abstr.* **49**, 7154 (1955).
548. V. V. KORSHAK, G. S. KOLESNIKOV and B. A. ZHUBANOV, *Izv. Akad. nauk SSSR, Otdel. khim. nauk*, 618 (1958).
549. R. TUNTELER. *Plastica*, **6**, 156 (1953).
550. H. ZENFTMAN and H. R. WRIGHT, *Brit. Plastics*, **25**, 374 (1952).
551. H. R. WRIGHT and H. ZENFTMAN, *Angew. Chem.* **64**, 285 (1952).
552. H. ZENTFMAN, *Brit. Pat.* 679834; *Chem. Abstr.* **47**, 12422 (1953).
553. W. E. CASS, *U. S. Pat.* 2616873; *Chem. Abstr.* **47**, 1977 (1953).
554. H. ZENFTMAN and A. McLEAN, *U. S. Pat.* 2636876; *Ref. zh. khim.* ref. 31686 (1954).

555. A. D. F. Toy, *U. S. Pat.* 2435252; *Chem. Abstr.* **42**, 2817 (1948).

556. A. D. F. Toy, *U. S. Pat.* 2572076; *Chem. Abstr.* **46**, 775 (1952).

557. H. Zenftman and R. McGillivray, *Brit. Pat.* 653489; *Chem. Abstr.* **45**, 8808 (1951); *U. S. Pat.* 2636020; *Zbl.* 9168 (1954); *Ref. zh. khim.* ref. 33433 (1954).

558. Furakava and Oda, Cited in *Ref. zh. khim.* ref. 19109 (1957).

559. H. Tolkmith, *J. Amer. Chem. Soc.* **75**, 5270, 5273 (1953).

560. J. A. Arvin, *U. S. Pat.* 2058394; *Chem. Abstr.* **31**, 180 (1937).

561. Metallgesellschaft, *Brit. Pat.* 706410; *Chem. Abstr.* **49**, 6988 (1955).

562. B. Helferich and H. G. Schmidt, *Ger. (West) Pat.* 905318; *Zbl.* 9168 (1954).

563. H. W. Coover, *U. S. Pat.* 2682521; *Chem. Abstr.* **48**, 11111 (1954).

564. H. W. Coover and M. A. McCall, *U.S. Pat.* 2716101; *Ref. zh. khim.* ref. 44981 (1956).

565. *French. Pat.* 1172892 (1957).

566. H. Hönel, *U. S. Pat.* 2272668; *Chem. Abstr.* **36**, 3585 (1942).

567. H. Newby, *Brit. Pat.* 772486; *Chem. Abstr.* **51**, 13919 (1957).

568. H. W. Coover and M. A. McCall, *U.S. Pat.* 2682522; *Chem. Abstr.* **48**, 11112 (1954).

569. A. A. Vorontsova, *Thesis,* Moscow (1953).

570. V. V. Korshak, I. A. Gribova and V. K. Shitikov, *Tez. dokl. IX konf. po obsch. vop. khim i fiz. vysokomolekulyar. soyedinenii (Abstr. papers read at IXth Conf. on general problems of chem. and phys. of high-molecular-weigth compounds),* p. 9, Moscow (1956).

571. V. V. Korshak, I. A. Gribova and V. K. Shitikov, *Izv. Akad. nauk SSSR, Otdel. khim. nauk,* 210 (1958).

572. L. Acker, *Ber. dtsch. Chem. Ges.* **88**, 376 (1955).

573. *Angew. Chem.* **70**, 350 (1958).

574. M. I. Kabachnik and P. A. Rossiiskaya, *Izv. Akad. nauk SSSR, Otdel. khim. nauk,* 403, 515 (1946).

575. Ye. L. Gefter and M. I. Kabachnik, *Izv. Akad. nauk SSSR, Otdel. khim. nauk,* 194 (1957).

576. Ye. L. Gefter and I. K. Rubtsova, *Avt. svid. (U.S.S.R. Pat.)* 111889; *Byull. isobr.* **3**, 100 (1958).

577. *Brit. Pat.* 524510; *Chem. Abstr.* **35**, 6353 (1941).

578. V. V. Korshak, *J. Polymer Sci.* **31**, 319 (1958).

579. P. W. Morgan, *U.S. Pat.* 2646420; *Chem. Abstr.* **47**, 10276 (1953).

580. *Austral. Pat.* 200947; *Ref. zh. khim.* ref. 32546 (1957).

581. H. Z. Lecher, R. A. Greenwood, K. C. Whitehouse and T. H. Chao, *J. Amer. Chem. Soc.* **78**, 5018 (1956).

582. H. Quitman *et al., French Pat.* 1083835; *Chim. et Ind.* **75**, 96 (1956).

583. H. W. Coover and M. A. McCall, *U. S. Pat* 2716100; *Ref. zh. khim.* ref.48804 (1956).

584. A. C. Haven, *U. S. Pat.* 2716639; *Ref. zh. khim.,* ref. 52593 (1956).

585. T. M. Frunze, V. V. Korshak, V. V. Kurashev, G. S. Kolesnikov and B. A. Zhubanov, *Izv. Akad. nauk SSSR, Otdel. khim. nauk,* 783 (1958).

586. J. Liebig and F. Wöhler, *Liebig's Ann.* **11**, 9 (1834).

587. H. N. Stokes, *Amer. Chem. J.* **17**, 275 (1895); **18**, 629 (1896); **19**, 782 (1897).

588. R. Schenk and G. Römer, *Ber. dtsch. Chem. Ges.* **57**, 1343 (1924).

589. F. M. Jaeger and J. Beintema, *Proc. Acad. Sci. Amsterdam,* **35**, 756 (1932).

590. A. M. Ficquelmont, *Compt. rend.* **202**, 423 (1936).

591. A. M. Ficquelmont, *Compt. rend.* **204**, 689, 867 (1937).

592. H. Schmitz—Dumont and O. Kulkens, *Z. anorg. Chem.* **238**, 189 (1938).

593. O. Schmitz—Dumont and A. Braschos, *Z. anorg. Chem.* **243**, 113 (1939).

594. O. Schmitz—Dumont, Z. Electrochem. 45, 651 (1939).

595. H. Bode and H. Bach, Ber. dtsch. Chem. Ges. 75, 215 (1942).

596. H. Bode, Angew. Chem. 60, 67 (1948); 61, 438 (1949).

597. H. Bode, Z. anorg. Chem. 252, 113 (1943).

598. F. Seel and J. Langer, Angew. Chem. 68, 461 (1956).

599. L. F. Audrieth, R. Steinmann and A. D. F. Toy, Chem. Rev. 32, 109 (1943).

600. O. Schmitz—Dumont, Angew. Chem. 50, 415 (1937).

601. A. M. Ficquelmont, Ann. chim. 12, 169 (1939).

602. R. Steinman, B. Schirmer and L. F. Audrieth, J. Amer. Chem. Soc. 64, 2377 (1942).

603. J. Remond, Rev. prod. chim. 60, No. 1236, 145; No. 1237, 195 (1957).

604. B. Dishon, J. Amer. Chem. Soc. 71, 2251 (1949).

605. K. H. Meyer, W. Lotmar and G. W. Pankow, Helv. chim. Acta, 19, 930 (1936).

606. F. Patat and F. Kollinsky, Macromol. Chem. 6, 292 (1951).

607. F. Patat and K. Frömbling, Monathsh. Chem. 86, 718 (1955).

608. F. Patat and P. Derst, Angew. Chem. 71, 105 (1959).

609. J. A. Brydson, Plastics, 22, 384 (1957).

610. H. J. Kauth, U. S. Pat. 2382423; Chem. Abstr. 39, 4706 (1945).

611. D. Lipkin, U. S. Pat. 2192921; Chem. Abstr. 34, 4836 (1940).

612. F. Goldschmidt and B. Dishon, J. Polymer Sci. 3, 481 (1948).

613. B. Dishon and F. Goldschmidt, U. S. Pat. 2586312; Chem. Abstr. 46, 5361 (1952).

614. C. Hamalainen, U. S. Pat. 2681295; Chem. Abstr. 48, 12419 (1954).

615. C. J. Brown, J. Polymer Sci. 5, 465 (1950).

616. C. J. Brown, U. S. Pat. 2374646; Chem. Abstr. 40, 6885 (1946).

617. Brit. Pat. 568594; Chem. Abstr. 41, 4332 (1947).

618. F. R. Hurley, U. S. Pat. 2637704; Chem. Abstr. 47, 8292 (1953).

619. D. Lipkin, U. S. Pat. 2214769; Chem. Abstr. 35, 825 (1941).

620. R. J. A. Otto, J. Amer. Chem. Soc. 80, 5894 (1958).

621. B. Dishon and Y. Hirshberg, J. Polymer Sci. 4, 75 (1949).

622. H. Rosset, Compt. rend. 180, 750 (1925); Bull soc. chim. France, (4), 37, 518 (1925).

623. C. P. Haber, D. L. Herring and E. A. Lawton, J. Amer. Chem. Soc. 80, 2116 (1958).

624. W. A. Reeves and J. D. Guthrie, Industr. Engng. Chem. 48, 64 (1956).

625. H. Mark, Kunststoffe, 44, 541 (1954).

626. W. A. Reeves. O. J. McMillan and J. D. Guthrie, Textile Res. J. 23, 527 (1953).

627. W. A. Reeves and J. D. Guthrie, U. S. Pat. 2809941 and 2810701; Chem Abstr. 52, 2421, 10602 (1958).

628. J. D. Reid, Textile Res. J. 26, 136 (1956).

629. W. A. Reeves and J. D. Guthrie, U. S. Pat. 2668096; Chem. Abstr. 48, 6710 (1954).

630. Albright and Wilson Ltd. Brit. Pat. 740269 and 764313; Chem. Abstr. 50, 17533 (1956); 51, 9216 (1957).

631. J. D. Guthrie, G. L. Drake and W. A. Reeves, Amer. Dyestuff Reporter, 44, 328 (1955).

632. H. A. Schuyten, J. W. Weaver and J. D. Reid, Industr. Engng. Chem. 47, 1433 (1955).

633. W. A. Reeves, G. L. Drake, L. H. Chance and J. D. Guthrie, Textile Res. J. 27, 260 (1957).

634. French Pat. 1109922; Ref. zh. khim. ref. 45144 (1958).

635. F. Fekete, U. S. Pat. 2831838; Chem. Abstr. 52, 13314 (1958).

636. D. I. Mendeleyev, Osnovy khimii (The fundamentals of chemistry), Vol. II, p. 168 (1947).

637. M. Ya. Kraft and V. P. Parini, Dokl. Akad. nauk SSSR, 77, 57 (1951).

638. M. YA. KRAFT and V. P. PARINI *Sb. statei po obshchei khimii (Collected papers on general chemistry)*, Vol. I, p. 716, Acad. Sci. U.S.S.R. (1953).

639. M. YA. KRAFT and V. P. PARINI, *Sb. statei po obshchei khimii (collected papers on general chemistry)*, Vol. 1, p. 723, Acad. Sci. U.S.S.R. (1953).

640. M. YA. KRAFT and V. P. PARINI, *Sb. statei po obshchei khimii (Collected papers on general chemistry)*, Vol. 1, p. 729, Acad. Sci. U.S.S.R. (1953).

641. *Chem. Eng. News*, **35**, No. 21, 28 (1957).

642. W. MAHLER and A. B. BURG, *J. Amer. Chem. Soc.* **79**, 251 (1957).

643. W. KUCHEN and H. BUCHWALD, *Angew. Chem.* **68**, 791 (1956).

644. W. KUCHEN and H. G. BECKERS, *Angew. Chem.* **71**, 163 (1959).

645. J. E. MALOVAN and F. R. HURLEY, *U.S. Pat.* 2596935; *Chem. Abstr.* **46**, 9232 (1952).

646. M. L. NIELSEN, *U.S. Pat.* 2642405 and 2648597; *Chem. Abstr.* **47**, 8943, 11750 (1953).

647. J. E. MALOVAN, *U.S. Pat.* 2661263, 2661364 and 2661342; *Chem. Abstr.* **48**, 2386 (1954).

648. H. K. NASON and M. L. NIELSEN, *U.S. Pat.* 2661341; *Chem. Abstr.* **48**, 2412 (1954).

649. *Brit. Pat.* 683560; *Specifications of Inventions*, 5836 (1952).

650. M. GOERING and R. NIEDENZU, *Ber. dtsch. Chem. Ges.* **89**, 1774 (1956).

651. B. V. NEKRASOV, *Kurs obshchei khimii (A course of general chemistry)*, p. 398, Goskhimizdat (1955).

652. R. KLEMENT and O. KOCH, *Ber. dtsch. Chem. Ges.* **87**, 333 (1954).

653. M. GEORING and K. NIEDENZU, *Ber. dtsch. Chem. Ges.* **89**, 1771 (1956).

654. A. B. BURG and R. I. WAGNER, *J. Amer. Chem. Soc.* **75**, 3872 (1953).

655. *Chem. Eng. News*, **35**, No. 15, 32 (1957).

656. T. GRAHAM, *Pogg. Ann.* **32**, 33 (1834).

657. B. TOPLEY, *Quart. Rev.* **3**, 345 (1949).

658. ALBRIGHT AND WILSON LTD., *Lab. Practice*, **5**, 23 (1956).

659. E. THILO, *Zh. prikl. khim.* **29**, 1621 (1956).

660. E. THILO, *Chem. Tech.* **2**, 70 (1958).

661. M. A. RAKUZINA and A. A. ARSEN'EVA, *Zh. russk. khim. obshch.* **53**, 376 (1921).

662. E. P. PLUEDDERMANN, *U.S. Pat.* 2558380; *Chem. Abstr.* **46**, 1024 (1952).

663. G. M. KOSOLAPOFF, *Science*, **108**, No. 2809, 485 (1948).

664. L. P. KYRIDES, *U.S. Pat.* 2510033; *Chem. Abstr.* **44**, 8361 (1950).

665. G. M. KOSOLAPOFF, *U.S. Pat.* 2486658; *Chem. Abstr.* **44**, 1644 (1950).

666. D. C. HULL and J. R. SNODGRASS, *U. S. Pat.* 2492153; *Chem. Abstr.* **44**, 3005 (1950).

667. A. CLOSSE, *Chemiker-Ztg.* **81**, 72, 103, 141 (1957).

668. J. F. HIDE, *U.S. Pat.* 2571039; *Chem. Abstr.* **46**, 2837 (1952).

669. *Brit. Pat.* 687759; *Ref. zh. khim.* ref. 22524 (1955).

670. F. FEHER et al., *Ber. dtsch. Chem. Ges.* **90**, 134 (1957).

671. F. ALFREY, F. HONN and H. MARK, *J. Polymer Sci.* **1**, 102 (1946).

672. A. P. KRESHKOV and D. A. KARATEYEV, *Zh. prikl. khim.* **30**, 1416 (1957).

673. *Brit. Pat.* 706781; *Ref. zh. khim.* ref. 8243 (1956).

674. A. P. KRESHKOV and D. A. KATATEYEV, *Zh. obshch. khim.* **27**, 2715 (1957).

675. C. E. TRAUTMAN, *U.S. Pat.* 2488449; *Chem. Abstr.* **44**, 2287 (1950).

676. J. A. BENCKISER, *Ger. (West) Pat.* 1025840 (1956).

677. W. MOSCHEL, H. JONES and W. NOLL, *Ger. Pat.* 832499; *Zbl.* 6774 (1952).

678. F. A. HENGLEIN, R. LANG and L. SCHMACK, *Macromol. Chem.* **22**, 103 (1957).

679. E. THILO and J. PLÄTSCHKE, *Z. anorg. Chem.* **260**, 297 (1949).

680. W. ZIMMERSCHIED, *U.S. Pat.* 2727010; *Ref. zh khim.* ref. 79129 (1956).

681. W. E. HANFORD and R. M. JOYCE, *U.S. Pat.* 2478390; *Chem. Abstr.* **44**, 1126 (1950).

682. J. A. BITTLES and R. M. JOYCE, *U.S. Pat.* 2559754; *Chem. Abstr.* **46**, 1026 (1952).

683. R. L. McCONNEL and H. W. COOVER, *J. Amer. Chem. Soc.* **78**, 4453 (1956).

684. V. A. KUKHTIN, G. KAMAI and L. A. SINCHENKO, *Dokl. Akad. nauk SSSR,* **118,** 505 (1958).

685. V. A. KUKHTIN and G. KAMAI, *Zh. obshch. khim.* **28,** 1196 (1958).

686. J. WEAVER, *U.S. Pat.* 2778747; *Ref. zh. khim.* ref. 25904 (1959).

687. J. L. PARKER, *U.S. Pat.* 2382812; *Chem. Abstr.* **39,** 5121 (1945).

688. M. W. HILL and R. H. JONES, *U.S. Pat.* 2640053; *Chem. Abstr.* **47,** 7773 (1953.)

689. M. W. HILL and R. H. JONES, *U.S. Pat.* 2712528; *Chem. Abstr.* **49,** 16420 (1955).

690. H. C. H. JENSEN and W. LOWENSTEIN, *French Pat.* 1080492; *Ref. zh. khim.* ref. 24400 (1957).

691. J. M. MUSSELMAN and R. E. KNOWLTON, *U.S. Pat.* 2698296; *Ref. zh. khim.* ref. 66115 (1956).

692. YU. KATAYAMA and M. HAGANO, *J. Soc. org. synth. Chem. Japan.* **11,** No. 10, 11 (1953).

693. A. I. DINTSES and A. I. DRUZHININA, *Sinteticheskiye smazochnyye masla (Synthetic lubricants),* Gostoptekhizdat, Moscow (1958).

694. W. H. WOODSTOCK, *U. S. Pat.* 2568784; *Chem. Abstr.* **46,** 3066 (1952).

695. L. ORTHNER and M. REUTER, *Ger. (West) Pat.* 1009629; *Ref. zh. khim.* ref. 68358 (1958).

696. G. S. PETROV, B. N. RUTOVSKII and I. P. LOSEV, *Tekhnologiya sinteticheskikh smol i plasticheskikh mass (The technology of synthetic resins and plastics),* Goskhimizdat, Moscow—Leningrad (1946).

697. E. I. BARG, *Technologiya sinteticheskikh plasticheskikh mass (The technology of synthetic plastics),* Goskhimizdat, Leningrad (1954).

698. Z. A. ROGOVIN, *Osnovy khimii i tekhnologii proizvodstva sinteticheskikh volokon (The fundamentals of the chemistry and technology of production of synthetic fibres),* Gizlegprom, Moscow (1957).

699. V. A. KARGIN and T. I. SOGOLOVA, *Dokl. Akad. nauk SSSR,* **108,** 662 (1956).

700. V. A. KARGIN, T. I. SOGOLOVA, G. L. SLONIMSKII and YE. V. REZTSOVA, *Zh. fiz. khim.* **30,** 1903 (1956).

701. V. A. KARGIN and T. I. SOGOLOVA, *Zh. fiz. khim.* **31,** 1328 (1957).

702. A. A. BERLIN, *Usp. khim.* **27,** 94 (1958).

703. *Chem. Week,* **81,** No. 12, pt. I, 86 (1957).

704. J. H. KAUTH, *U.S. Pat.* 2334710; *Chem. Abstr.* **38,** 2768 (1944).

705. P. DUVAL, *Corros. et anti-corros.* **5,** 189 (1957).

706. *Chem. Week,* **81,** No. 12, pt. II, 237 (1957).

707. *Chem. Week,* **81,** No. 12, pt. I, 54 (1957).

708. *British Chemicals and their Manufacturers,* London (1957).

709. *Chem. Week,* **81,** No. 12, pt. II, 557 (1957).

710. *Umschau Forshr. Wiss. Tech.* **53,** 279 (1953).

711. J. D. BRANDNER, *Can. Pat.* 509645; *Ref. zh. khim.* ref. 2574 (1957).

712. G. D. JEFFERSON and E. K. STIGGER, *Can. Pat.* 509646; *Ref. zh. khim.* ref. 13058 (1958).

713. *Danish Pat.* 78543; *Ref. zh. khim.* ref. 28629 (1957).

714. J. PUIG, *Rev. Plasticos (Madrid),* **8,** 329 (1957) ; *Ref. zh. khim.* ref. 101310 (1959).

715. J. M. GOTTLIEB, *Textile Res. J.* **26,** 156 (1956).

716. S. KHASIMOTO and I. FURUKAVA, *Khim. i tekh. polimer.* **2,** No. 5, 92 (1958).

717. P. A. SIMIGIN, M. N. ZUSMAN and F. I. RAIKHLIN, *Zashchitnyye propitki tekstil'nykh materialov (Protective coatings for textile materials),* Gizlegprom, Moscow (1957).

718. *Rubber and Plastics Age,* **37,** 98, 103, 289, 375 (1956); **38,** 877 (1957); *Kunststoffe,* **46,** 148 (1956).

719. R. A. PINGREE and R. C. ACKERMAN, *U.S. Pat.* 2488034; *Chem. Abstr.* **44,** 2280 (1950).

720. *Brit. Pat.* 690291; *Ref. zh. khim.* ref. 36911 (1954).

721. G. JONES and S. SOLL, *U.S. Pat.* 2452054; *Chem. Abstr.* **43**, 1126 (1949).

722. G. JONES, W. JUDA and S. SOLL, *U.S. Pat.* 2452055; *Chem. Abstr.* **43**, 1126 (1949).

723. B. LEHMAN, J. LINTVER and P. WILLIAME, *French Pat.* 1100929. *Ref. zh. khim.* ref. 24509 (1957).

724. A. R. SCHROTD, *French Pat.* 1059731; *Zbl.* 3524 (1955).

725. M. R. BURNELL and J. E. FLINN, *U.S. Pat.* 2582961; *Chem. Abstr.* **46**, 3291 (1952).

726. *Vestnik TEI* No. 1, 52 (1958).

727. A. E. MALOWAN, *Can. Pat.* 515267; *Ref. zh. khim.* ref. 79380 (1956).

728. M. L. NIELSEN, *Textile Res. J.* **27**, 603 (1957).

729. M. L. NIELSEN *et al.*, *U.S. Pat.* 2596936—2596939; *Chem. Abstr.* **46**, 9233 (1952).

730. C. HAMALAINEN and J. D. GUTHRIE, *Textile Res. J.* **26**, 141 (1956).

731. R. F. W. RATZ and C. J. GRUNDMANN, *U.S. Pat.* 2858306 (1957); C. A. REDFARN and H. COATES, *U.S. Pat.* 788785; *Chem. Abstr.* **52**, 9624 (1958).

732. A. J. McQUADI, *Amer. Dyestuff Reporter*, **44**, 749 (1955).

733. J. G. FRICK, J. W. WEAVER and J. D. REID, *Textile Res. J.* **25**, 100 (1955).

734. G. E. WALTER, *U.S. Pat.* 2660542 and 2660543; *Chem. Abstr.* **48**, 1700 (1954).

735. *Brit. Pat.* 721341; *Ref. zh. khim.* ref. 6440 (1958).

736. *Sci. News Letter*, 12. 11. 56.

737. J. D. REID, J. G. FRICK and R. L. ARCENAUX, *Textile Res. J.* **26**, 137 (1956).

738. C. HAMALAINEN, W. A. REEVES and J. D. GUTHRIE, *Textile Res. J.* **26**, 145 (1956).

739. R. G. BEAMAN, *U.S. Pat.* 2854434; *Chem. Abstr.* **53**, 1825 (1959).

740. E. SIMON and F. W. THOMAS, *U.S. Pat.* 2577279; *Chem. Abstr.* **46**, 3324 (1952).

741. *Chem. Week*, **81**, No. 12, pt. II. 549 (1957).

742. *Fibres, Engng. and Chem* **13**, 400 (1957).

743. *Chem. Week*, **79**, No. 24, 60 (1956).

744. R. KUNIN and R. MAYERS, *Ionoobmennyye smoly. Foreign Literature Publishing House, Moscow* (1952).

745. G. H. OSBORN, *Synthetic Ion-Exchangers*, London (1955).

746. A. DE KAT, *Ind. chim. belge*, **21**, 457 (1956); *Khim. i tekh. polimer.* **3**, 106 (1957).

747. J. M. HUTCHEON, *Chem. and Process Engng.* **35**, 12, 379 (1954); **36**, 5 (1956).

748. R. KUNIN, *Industr. Engng. Chem.* **44**, 79 (1952).

749. G. NAUMANN, *Chem. Tech.* **7**, 255 (1955).

750. V. S. TITOV, *Vestnik TEI* **1**, 44 (1957).

751. R. KUNIN *et al.*, *Liebig's Ann.* **28**, 729 (1956).

752. R. KUNIN, *Industr. Engng. Chem.* **44**, 79 (1952).

753. A. B. PASHKOV and V. S. TITOV, *Khim. prom.* 270 (1958).

754. J. I. BREGMAN and J. MURATA, *J. Amer. Chem. Soc.* **74**, 1867 (1952).

755. E. TOOPER, J. D. AMICE and J. I. BREGMAN, *Drug and Allied Ind.* **39**, 9 (1953).

756. N. K. SHCHIPAKINA, YE. M. NEMIROVSKAYA and M. M. SENYAVIN, *Zh. anal. khim.* **12**, 70 (1957).

757. N. F. KEMBER and R. A. WELLS, *Nature (London)*, **175**, 512 (1955).

758. A. F. FINELLI, *U.S. Pat.* 2748159; *Ref. zh. khim.* ref. 23303 (1958).

759. KHE BIN-LIN' and TSYAN' LUN-ZUI, Cited in *Ref. zh. khim.* ref. 62849 (1958).

760. YE. B. TROSTYANSKAYA, I. P. LOSEV and A. C. TEVLINA, *Usp. khim.* **24**, 69 (1955).

761. W. BUSER *et al.*, *Chimia*, **9**, No. 4, 73 (1955).

762. *Chem. Ind. (Düsseldorf)*, **8**, 422 (1956).

763. R. N. BELL, *Industr. Engng. Chem.* **40**, 1464 (1948).

764. J. CYMERMAN-CRAIG, D. MARTIN, M. MOYLE and P. C. WAILES, *Austral. J. Chem.* **9**, 373 (1956).

765. F. PIORRI and G. FAVINE, Cited in *Ref. zh. khim.* ref. 41128 (1957).

766. J. THESING and F. H. FUNK *Ber. dtsch. Chem. Ges.* **89**, 2498 (1956).

767. A. M. GALINSKY, J. E. GEARIN and E. E. SMISSMAN Cited in *Ref. Zh. khim.* ref. 14518 (1958).
768. D. S. MATTESON and H. SNYDER, *J. Amer. Chem. Soc.* **79**, 3610 (1957).
769. C. T. ELSTON, Thesis; *Chem. Abstr.* **49**, 2997 (1955).
770. A. BERTHO, *Ber. dtsch. Chem. Ges.* **90**, 29 (1957).
771. H. J. SCHMID, A. HUNGER and K. HOFFMAN, *Helv. Chim. Acta*, **39**, 607 (1956).
772. J. E. BANFIELD, W. DAVIES, B. C. ENNIS, S. MUDDLETON and Q. N. PORTER, *J. Chem. Soc.* 2603 (1956).
773. IKEDA, KANAKHARA and NISIKAVA, Cited in *Ref. zh. khim.* ref. 17973 (1958).
774. G. TRAVERSO, *Gazz. chim. ital.* **87**, 76 (1957).
775. N. MOSBY, *J. Amer. Chem. Soc.* **74**, 2564 (1952).
776. F. UHLIG, *Angew. Chem.* **66**, 435 (1954).
777. C. R. HAUSER and C. J. EBY, *J. Amer. Chem. Soc.* **79**, 728 (1957).
778. W. DAVIES and S. MIDDLETON, *Chem. and Ind.* 599 (1957.)
779. C. DJERASSI and G. PETTIT, *J. Org. Chem.* **22**, 393 (1957).
780. M. S. NEWMAN and R. M. WISE, *J. Amer. Chem. Soc.* **78**, 450 (1956).
781. J. THESING, H. REMBOCH, S. WILLERSINN and F. FUNK, *Angew. Chem.* **68**, 387 (1956).
782. S. DEV, *J. Indian Chem. Soc.* **33**, 703 (1956); **34**, 169 (1957).
783. S. DEV, *Chem. and Ind.* 1071 (1954).
784. P. D. GARDNER, *J. Amer. Chem. Soc.* **76**, 4550 (1954).
785. NAKADZAVA *et al.*, Cited in *Ref. zh. khim.* ref. 74884 and 78106 (1956); *Chem. Abstr.* **49**, 1631 (1955).
786. H. R. SNYDER and C. T. ELSTON, *J. Amer. Chem. Soc.* **77**, 364 (1955).
787. A. N. NESMEYANOV, N. A. VOL'KENAU and V. D. VIL'CHEVSKAYA, *Dokl. Akad. nauk SSSR*, **111**, 362 (1956).
788. A. N. NESMEYANOV, N. A. VOL'KENAU and V. D. VIL'CHEVSKAYA, *Dokl. Akad. nauk SSSR*, **118**, 512 (1958).
789. C. R. HAUSER and C. J. EBY, *J. Amer. Chem Soc.* **79**, 725 (1957).
790. H. R. SYNDER and C. T. ELSTON, *J. Amer. Chem. Soc.* **76**, 3039 (1954).
791. F. A. L. ANET, P. M. G. BAVIN and M. J. S. DEWAR, *Can. J. Chem.* **35**, 180 (1957).
792. H. R. SNYDER, C. T. ELSTON and D. B. KELLOM. *J. Amer. Chem. Soc.* **75**, 2014 (1953).
793. H. R. SNYDER and C. T. ELSTON, *J. Amer. Chem. Soc.* **76**, 3039 (1954).
794. W. E. TRUCE and J. A. SIMMS, *J. Org. Chem.* **22**, 617 (1957).
795. R. K. HILL and R. T. CONLEY, *Chem. and Ind.* 1314 (1956).
796. E. C. HORNING, V. L. STROMBERG and H. A. LLOYD, *J. Amer. Chem. Soc.* **74**, 5153 (1952).
797. P. D. GARDNER, *J. Amer. Chem. Soc.* **77**, 4674 (1955).
798. D. W. HEIN, R. J. ALHEIM and J. J. LEAVITT, *J. Amer. Chem. Soc.* **79**, 427 (1957).
799. H. R. SNYDER and R. W. ROESKE, *J. Amer. Chem. Soc.* **74**, 5820 (1952).
800. H. R. SNYDER and F. X. WEBER, *J. Amer. Chem. Soc.* **72**, 2962, 2965 (1950).
801. J. P. KISPERSKY and K. KLAGER, *J. Amer. Chem. Soc.* **77**, 5433 (1955).
802. F. D. POPP and W. E. MCEWAN, *Chem. Rev.* **58**, 321 (1958).
803. L. D. FREEDMAN and G. O. DOAK, *Chem. Rev.* **57**, 479 (1957).
804. L. M. REED, L. A. WENTZEL and J. B. O'HARA, *Industr. Engng. Chem.* **48**, 205 (1956).
805. *Brit. Pat.* 739022; *Ref. zh. khim.* ref. 16858 (1957).
806. W. ZIMMERSCHIED and H. SHALIT, *U.S. Pat.* 2726991; *Ref. zh. khim.* ref. 79130 (1956).
807. W. W. CROUCH and J. F. HOWE, *Can. Pat.* 514619; *Ref. zh. khim.* ref. 24798 (1957).
808. H. V. SMITH, *Brit. Plastics.* **27**, 213 (1954).
809. A. INDELLI, *Metallurgia ital.* **49**, 333 (1957).

810. G. B. HATCH, *U.S. Pat.* 2742369; *Chem. Abstr.* **50**, 11224 (1956).

811. K. ASBOTH, *French Pat.* 1042639; *Ref. zh. khim.* ref. 48164 (1956).

812. D. LIPKIN, *U.S. Pat.* 2109490; *Chem. Abstr.* **32**, 3144 (1938).

813. O. BEECH, J. W. GIVENS and E. C. WILLIAMS, *Proc. Roy. Soc.* A. **177**, 103 (1940).

814. A. GEIGER, *Textil-Rundschau*, **12**, 560 (1957).

815. FUDZITA and IMAI, Cited in *Ref. zh. khim.* ref. 23595 (1958).

816. KHIGASI and TONAMI, *Japanese Pat.* 8896 (1955); *Ref. zh. khim.* ref. 34803 (1958).

817. R. E. DONALDSON and C. C. WHITE, *U.S. Pat.* 2743193; *Ref. zh. khim.* ref. 34784 (1958).

818. KHIRATA and KOBAYASI, Cited in *Ref. zh. khim.* ref. 10063 and 66276 (1958).

819. W. LINKE, Cited in *Ref. zh. khim.* ref. 28319 (1957).

820. J. L. WINTLE and R. C. MORRIS, *U.S. Pat.* 2681920; *Chem. Abstr.* **49**, 6989 (1955).

821. P. W. B. SEMMENS and G. E. PENKETH, *Ger. (West) Pat.* 946011; *Ref. zh. khim.* ref. 52855 (1958).

822. *French Pat.* 1108660; *Ref. zh. khim.* ref. 46199 (1958).

823. S. NITZSCHE and M. WICK, *Ger. (West) Pat.* 930481; *Ref. zh. khim.* ref. 76387 (1956); *Brit. Pat.* 765744; *Chem. Abstr.* **51**, 9202 (1957).

824. H. ELLERHORST, *U.S. Pat.* 2553643; *Chem. Abstr.* **45**, 7818 (1951).

825. M. M. SPRUNG, *U.S. Pat.* 2472629; *Chem. Abstr.* **43**, 6464 (1949).

826. M. M. SPRUNG, *U.S. Pat.* 2484595; *Chem. Abstr.* **44**, 1741 (1950).

827. *Belgian Pat.* 539823 (1954).

828. C. A. REDFARN, *U.S. Pat.* 2822255 (1954).

829. *Brit. Pat.* 801929; *Ref. zh. khim.* ref. 76822 (1959).

830. G. F. LUDVUK and G. C. KECKER, *J. Econ. Entomol.* **40**, 97 (1947).

831. *Rubber and Plastics Age*, **39**, 3, 211 (1958).

832. M. G. CHURCH, *Brit. Plastics*, **28**, 495 (1955).

833. M. M. POSTELNEK, *Rubber World*, **136**, 543 (1957).

834. *Chem. Eng. News*, **35**, No. 46, 49 (1957).

LIST OF TABLES

UNSATURATED ORGANOPHOSPHORUS ACIDS AND THEIR DERIVATIVE
Unsaturated Organophosphorus Acids

Acid chlorides of unsaturated organophosphorus acids

Amides of unsaturated organophosphorus acids

Esters of Unsaturated Organophosphorus Acids and Saturated Alcohols

Esters of α,β-unsaturated phosphonic acids

Esters of β,γ-unsaturated phosphonic acids

19 Organophosphorus

Some Compounds Containing Two Hydroxyl-groups

Di- and Tri-carboxylic Acids (and their esters) Containing Phosphinyl Groups

Phosphorus-containing Di- and Tri-isocyanates

Dialkyl Hydrogen Phosphites

Cyclic Esters of Acids of Phosphorus

Di- and Tri-amides of Acids of Phosphorus. Mono-, Di- and Tri-ethylenimides of Acids of Phosphorus

Polymers and copolymers of esters of β,γ-unsaturated phosphonic acids, phosphonic acids with two unsaturated links, and alkoxycarbonylalkylphosphonic acids of the type $RO_2C—R'—PO(OR'')_2$, where $R =$ unsaturated radical

Polymers and copolymers of unsaturated esters of inorganic acids of phosphorus (phosphorous, phosphoric and phosphoramidic)

Polymers and copolymers of esters of saturated organophosphonous (phosphonous, phosphonic, phosphinic, alkoxycarbonyalkylphosphinic) acids with unsaturated alcohols

Polymers and copolymers of esters of phosphonous acids

Polymers and copolymers of esters of phosphonic and phosphinic acids

SUBJECT INDEX

In this index, individual compounds are not listed when they are only mentioned in the Tables.

Polymers derived from individual compounds and classes of compounds are listed under headings; "Polyesters containing phosphorus, prepared by the polycondensation of . . ."; "Copolymers containing phosphorus, from . . . .", etc. They are *not* listed under the names of the compounds or their classes".